Penguin Education

Quick Statistics

Peter Sprent

Quick Statistics

An Introduction to
Non-parametric Methods

Penguin Books

Penguin Books Ltd, Harmondsworth, Middlesex, England
Penguin Books, 625 Madison Avenue, New York, New York 10022, U.S.A.
Penguin Books Australia Ltd, Ringwood, Victoria, Australia
Penguin Books Canada Ltd, 2801 John Street, Markham, Ontario, Canada L3R 1B4
Penguin Books (N.Z.) Ltd, 182–190 Wairau Road, Auckland 10, New Zealand

First published 1981
Copyright © Peter Sprent, 1981
All rights reserved

Set, printed and bound in Great Britain by
Cox & Wyman Ltd, Reading
Filmset in Linotype Times

Contents

To E. J. G. Pitman

Preface

This book starts from scratch and is self-contained. It assumes that some readers may have no formal statistical training but that they may want to know how to use simple methods to deal with real problems.

Despite the rather daunting name, *non-parametric statistics* is an ideal way to do just this. It is easy to explain the rationale of what one is doing. Many of the calculations can be done with a pencil on the back of an envelope, or even in one's head; others are just a matter of pressing the right keys on a pocket calculator.

Non-parametric methods are only part of the whole subject of statistics; perhaps not the most important, but certainly a very straightforward one. This makes them an ideal introduction for the student. Essential mathematical demands are modest. Only the basic notions of probability are needed, without the subtleties required to establish the elaborate framework of distribution theory that is an essential background to the rest of the subject. Non-parametric methods, more than any other in statistics, allow the data to speak for themselves.

The book is divided into two parts. Part I introduces the basic notions not only essential to non-parametric methods but relevant to much wider aspects of the subject as well.

Part II is devoted to applications; I have attempted to explain the rationale of tests without too much theoretical detail. Full use is made of examples to illustrate the various techniques. In the early stages of development of a technique, arguments are set out in considerable detail; later on, the reader is encouraged to work through examples with a little less prompting, but cross-references are given where appropriate.

At the end of each chapter there is a collection of exercises, and in the final chapter there are notes on the solution of these.

By illustrating techniques with examples from a wide range of disciplines, it is hoped that the reader who wishes to apply these techniques in any particular field will appreciate the versatility of many of them. I have concentrated on the major ones; the reader who wishes to learn something of the many techniques we have not had space to discuss will find references to several detailed treatises in the bibliography.

I am grateful to the literary executors of the late Sir Ronald A. Fisher, F.R.S., to Dr Frank Yates, F.R.S., and to the Longman Group Ltd, for permission to reproduce part of Table IV from their book *Statistical Tables for Biological, Agricultural and Medical Research* (6th edition, 1974) and to Dr M.G. Kendall, F.R.S., and Messrs Charles Griffin and Co. Ltd, for permission to base Table A10 in the Appendix on tables in the book *Rank Correlation Methods* (4th edition, 1970). My thanks are also due to the *Biometrika* trustees, the American Statistical Association, the American Cyanamid Company, the Institute of Mathematical Statistics and the publishers of *Statistica Neerlandica* for permission to base tables on material published by them; more detailed acknowledgements are given as footnotes to the relevant tables in the Appendix.

Finally, my thanks are due to my colleague Giles Thomas for helpful suggestions on matters of detail.

Dundee, 1980   P.S.

Part I

Basic Concepts

1.   Observations and Inferences

The Different Kinds of Numbers

Before we can explain what we mean by non-parametric methods, we must look at some of the jobs numbers do. Table 1 shows how the top players finished in the British Open Golf Championship, 1979.

Table 1   British Open Golf Championship, 1979

Contestants	Placing	Score	Prize money
S. Ballesteros	1	283	£15,000
J. Nicklaus	equal 2	286	£11,250
B. Crenshaw	equal 2	286	£11,250
M. James	4	287	£7,500
R. Davis	5	288	£6,500
H. Irwin	6	289	£6,000

When the prize money is handed out, it is the numbers in the column headed 'Placing' that tell us who gets what; they give the *ranking* of the players. It is true that they are based on the 'scores' in the next column, but had these been, respectively, 276, 282, 282, 284, 285 and 289, the rankings would have remained the same.

Let us look more closely at the different kinds of numbers; a broad division is into *categorizing numbers* and *measurements*. These names are almost self-explanatory, measurements being very familiar, while categorizing numbers have either an ordering or a labelling role. Further subdivision is desirable. The ranks in Table 1 are categorizing numbers called *ordinals* because they imply order. A *number label* carries no implied order; a good example is the town map in a tourist brochure where certain facilities are numbered on a map and a key is provided in the margin: (1) Town Hall, (2)

Cathedral, (3) Botanical Gardens, (4) Public Conveniences and (5) John Smith's Birthplace. Whether one would rank 2, 4 or 5 highest depends on whether one's needs or interests on reaching the town are spiritual, physical or historical. By convention, categorizing numbers are almost always positive whole numbers, or *integers*, if we prefer a name used by mathematicians. If they are ordinal we usually write the numbers 1, 2, 3, 4, . . . to indicate either ascending or descending order. If we rank two items equally, we must give them the same rank number. In Table 1 we ranked Nicklaus and Crenshaw equal second; since the next person, James, was fourth in order of scores, he gets the rank four. In statistical work, if there is a tie for second and third, it is more usual to give each a rank of 2·5. If there were a triple tie for fifth, sixth and seventh place, we would average these ranks and allocate the rank of six to each; but more about this in later chapters.

Measurements may be integers or fractions, and can also be divided into sub-classes. The first of these is a *count*; we might have counts of the number of people in a village professing each of several religions – Anglican, Presbyterian, Catholic, Methodist, etc. The golf scores in Table 1 are counts of the number of strokes each player made to complete 72 holes. Counts are usually integers, but there are exceptions; I might happen to have four and a half biscuits, or if some electors are allowed only half-votes, a candidate might receive 19½ votes.

The second sub-class of measurements are those made on an *interval scale*. Temperature is a good example. A characteristic of these scales is an arbitrary choice of zero; on the centigrade scale it is the freezing point of water, but zero on this scale corresponds to 32 on the Fahrenheit scale. The concept of a ratio is meaningless on such a scale. If Bill is lying on a sunny beach where the temperature is 20°C., while brother Tom is on a windswept mountain at temperature 10°C., we cannot rationally say it is twice as hot where Bill is, for if we convert both temperatures to Fahrenheit, they become 68°F. and 50°F. and the first is no longer twice the second.

The third type of measurement uses a *ratio scale* where a fixed zero results in meaningful ratios; if Tom weighs 7 stone and brother Bill 3·5 stone, then Tom *is* twice the weight of Bill, their weights being in the ratio two to one if we measure them in stones, ounces, kilograms, tons or any other units.

Measurements on interval or ratio scales are more sophisticated concepts than counts; an important feature of observations on either of these scales is that they provide a basis for ordering or ranking; if we know the precise weights of Tom, Dick, Harry, Joe and Ben, we can rank them in decreasing order of weight, numbering the heaviest as 1 and the lightest as 5.

Ranks and counts play a key role in non-parametric methods. Generally speaking, in this book we shall be little concerned with implications arising from whether we use an interval or a ratio scale. We shall often use measurements on these scales simply as a basis for ranking.

Figure 1 summarizes the sub-divisions we have been discussing.

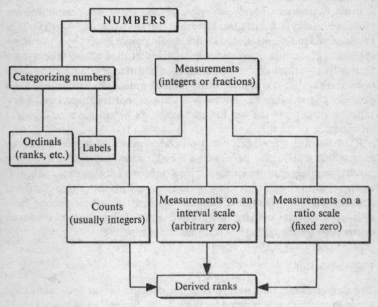

Figure 1 A useful classification of number types

Ranks

While ranks can be assigned on the basis of measurements, we may also rank objects without these. If we have specimens of several metals we may rank them in order of hardness by taking them in pairs and attempting to scratch each with a jagged specimen of the other; the harder will make a deeper scratch on the softer, if indeed the softer scratches the harder at all. By such tests a collection of metals may be objectively ranked in order of hardness.

By visual comparisons an artist may rank a series of blue pigments in order of intensity, or an experienced examiner may rank candidates in order of their ability to converse in French without being able to give a score that indicates in any meaningful way precisely *how much* better or worse one candidate is than another.

Some rankings are purely subjective. In beauty contests the prizewinners are usually selected by a panel of judges; whilst, hopefully, the judges will agree broadly on who are the more worthy contestants, they will almost certainly have to get their heads together and make a few compromises before announcing the final placings.

In market research, purely subjective rankings are of considerable interest. Housewives may be asked to rank five different kinds of apple – Cox's Orange Pippin, Golden Delicious, Red Delicious, Egremont Russet and Jonathan – in order of preference. It is extremely unlikely that all of a group of 20 or more housewives would each give the same order, and of course there is no *correct* order in a case like this as there was in arranging metals by hardness. What is of interest is whether the housewives show concordance: do one or two varieties come near the top for all housewives or are there no clear-cut favourites?

Rankings are sometimes based on combinations of measurements or judgements without the person who is making the rankings being able to specify precisely how he combines his evidence to obtain each rank. For example, a psychiatrist may be able to rank patients for degree of mental stress by taking a few simple clinical measurements and supplementing these by interviews, but would be hard pressed to explain how he combined such evidence to get the ranks; it is just a matter of expertise.

Types of Statistics

The statistical methods we are going to describe in this book are called *non-parametric*; another name for them is *distribution-free*. A pedant could with some justification claim that neither name is quite appropriate.

To explain these terms we must say a little more about what statisticians do and how they do it.

Let us start with the word 'statistics' itself. It has two meanings. First, it refers to data and the way we present and summarize them. The number of births in each UK city in a given year, records of daily passenger traffic at Heathrow or Kennedy airport, the number of trees felled each month in the State of Oregon and the number of convictions for drunken driving in Hong Kong are all statistics in this sense. The Penguin *Facts in Focus* (5th ed., 1980) is a whole book of such statistics.

Second, the word 'statistics' is used to describe the craft of making inferences that have a wider applicability than just to the observations (often very few) we have taken. If we are told, for example, that out of 83 Londoners interviewed 47 were smokers, what could we conclude about the proportion of Londoners who smoke? In what follows the word 'statistics' in this second sense is important, for *non-parametric* methods are a way of making such inferences. The inferences infer from a sample (the 83 interviewed) to a population (the people of London).

Populations and Samples

Suppose a sergeant-major is given a motley batch of 15 recruits of all different shapes and sizes for initiation into army life. To the sergeant-major this will be just another batch like hundreds of others that have passed through his hands – they will be a sample from a large population of recruits. The statistician may be prepared to regard them as a *random sample*, a term we explain more carefully on p. 52, and if so, we may use information about them to make inferences relevant to the population of all army recruits.

We may for example be interested in the heights of recruits. Before our 15 recruits even reach the sergeant-major, their heights will have been recorded during a medical examination. These, together with certain assumptions about the distribution of heights in the population, are the raw material for making inferences about the pattern of heights among army recruits as a whole. For example, we might wish to infer something about the proportion of recruits less than 175 cm. tall.

Parametric methods of inference generally make a number of fairly specific mathematical assumptions about the pattern of heights in the population; some of these may be based on little more than hunches. Non-parametric methods make fewer assumptions about the population, and very often need less detailed measurements on the sample. Even if we had no record of the heights of individual recruits in the sample, these latter methods could be used with information easily obtained very early in the training programme. One of the sergeant-major's first commands will be: 'Fall in, tallest on the right, shortest on the left.' In this way the troops are ranked in order of height. How such information is used non-parametrically we shall see in later chapters.

Distributions

Before we can be more explicit about non-parametric methods we need to say a little about parametric methods. Let us turn again to the distribution of heights of army recruits. The word *distribution* is used in a technical sense in statistics as a mathematical description of patterns of variation like those associated with heights of recruits, lengths of sentences in an essay or daily rainfall figures for some town.

Our sample of 15 may come from a population of many thousands of army recruits. The statistician often finds it theoretically convenient and very little strain on his credulity to extend the concept of a population of many thousands to a theoretically limitless group of all army recruits there ever have been or might be in future; in this concept of an infinite population he may build in a tacit (and in practice fairly reasonable) assumption that general height patterns of recruits will not change noticeably in the relevant time span.

If he wants to make inferences, he next asks himself what he can say about height patterns in such a population on the basis of general experience. From his general knowledge about heights of young men who might join the army, he will know that a fairly high proportion will be near average height and rather fewer either well above or well below it. He will also know that there will be reasonable symmetry in a large population in the sense that if we consider, say, the proportion between 5 cm. and 10 cm. *above* average height, then there will be almost the same proportion between 5 cm. and 10 cm. *below* average; similar statements can be made for other height ranges symmetrically placed about the mean or average.

Indeed, the proportion of a population of young adult males with heights in any given range is well described by a rather complicated mathematical formula, providing we know the value of two constants called *parameters*. The formula describes what is called a *normal* or *Gaussian* distribution and we shall look at its properties in Chapter 4. All we need say at the moment is that parametric or distribution-dependent inference is concerned with telling us how to *estimate* or *test* hypotheses when the parameters are unknown and we have only a *sample* of values of, in this example, heights of 15 recruits.

In a normal distribution one of the parameters tells us where the mean or average of the population lies and the other gives a measure of spread. The statistician has well-tried techniques for assessing the accuracy of estimates of these, providing he can justify certain assumptions; a key one for applying parametric methods to our example is that there exists some normal distribution which reasonably describes the variation found in a population of heights of army recruits. With parametric methods, our first task is to 'find' or estimate the parameters in that distribution.

Unfortunately the term *normal* distribution carries an application that other distributions are in some way abnormal. This is not so, for there are many situations in which the normal distribution is inappropriate. The lives of machine-made articles, for instance, often have a distribution that is by no means symmetric about their average life. A complex electronic component may have an average working life of about 1,000 hours, but in a large batch a few will have serious faults and will fail in a matter of minutes or even seconds; a majority may function for between 800 and 1,300 hours; and a few may have appreciably longer lives, some extra good ones lasting perhaps 4,000 to 5,000 hours. We can again find an appropriate mathematical formula to describe this distribution and it too will involve constants known as parameters.

There are, however, many situations when we have insufficient information or theoretical knowledge to specify a population distribution mathematically, but we may still make useful inferences about the nature of the population from sample values. The methods we then use are called distribution-free or non-parametric because we do not use a mathematical specification of population variation; if we wished to make such a specification it would involve a distribution and parameters.

While this very brief account explains the origin of the terms 'distribution-free' and 'non-parametric', they are not entirely satisfactory, for we shall see in later chapters, where we use the methods, that we are freed from assumptions about distributions and parameters only in the population; we still need the concept of a distribution in connection with samples of observations.

Problems of Inference

Parametric inferences can be very misleading if we have made wrong assumptions about a population distribution. Non-parametric methods are less likely to mislead; more importantly they can be used also when we have less sample information than that usually required for parametric methods; the latter usually need measurements whereas many non-parametric methods are based simply on ranks.

In many of the examples in Part II, even if we have actual measurements, we shall be ignoring them after using them as a basis for ranking. This, in a sense, is throwing away information, but often the amount discarded is of little value in that we get much the same answer as we would have got, had we retained it. On the other hand, we may easily be led astray using the original measurements in association with, say, a false assumption of normality, the assumption most commonly used for parametric inferences.

Non-parametric methods often require less calculation than their parametric counterparts – something that is perhaps less important in the age of cheap pocket calculators and powerful computers, but still not to be despised. More importantly from the point of view of anyone meeting statistical inference for the first time, it is often easier to explain the rationale of what one is doing without resorting to complicated mathematics; it is no bad thing to get rid of some of the mystique that surrounds mathematical and statistical concepts.

This is not to say that non-parametric methods solve all problems or dodge all statistical difficulties. We must still master basic concepts. We must know something about the way samples should be taken to ensure that they reflect population characteristics; let us again emphasize that what we avoid are the problems of postulating specific (and sometimes dubious) mathematical forms for population distributions.

The sort of questions that non-parametric methods are ideal for answering are ones like these:

Is it reasonable to assume that this sample of observations came from a symmetric distribution having a mean value of 25?

Given two samples, is it reasonable to conclude they are from populations having the same distribution?

Are rankings given by two judges reasonably consistent?

Given the success rates of two drugs on small groups of patients in a clinical trial, is it reasonable to conclude that in the long run one drug will almost certainly give more cures than the other?

Non-parametric methods are not so good at coping with very complex statistical problems involving many measurements on each of a number of units.

Historical Note

Non-parametric methods date back to at least 1710 when John Arbuthnot, son of an Aberdeenshire parson who was deposed by the Presbyterians for his Episcopalian beliefs and settled in London, published a paper in the *Philosophical Transactions of the Royal Society* entitled 'An argument for Divine Providence, taken from the constant Regularity observ'd in the Births of Both Sexes'. A strange title indeed for a statistical paper!

In it Arbuthnot observes that in each year from 1629 to 1710 the number of males christened in London exceeded the number of females christened. Suppose, he argued, there is an equal probability in any one year that the greater number of births is male or that it is female; then the probability that there are more males than females for 82 years in succession is $(\frac{1}{2})^{82}$ (we shall see why on p. 35), a very small number, from which he concluded: 'From hence it follows that it is Art, not Chance, that governs.' Quaint language indeed to describe what we would today call a statistical hypothesis test.

His paper was criticized by some of the eminent mathematicians of his time, and as R.L. Plackett (1979) has said in an interesting account of Arbuthnot's life and work: 'But let us not fool ourselves that Arbuthnot was concerned with advances in statistical methodology. As the title of his short paper clearly indicates, he was presenting an argument for the existence of God.'

Despite this early start it was not until the twentieth century that non-parametric inference developed rapidly alongside other statistical methods. The eminent statistician and geneticist, R.A. Fisher, father of modern experimental design and the analysis of experimental data, in fact justified many parametric methods based on the normal distribution not in their own right so much as upon their being sensible practical approximations to non-parametric procedures known as *randomization tests*. These tests are widely associated with the names of Fisher, Pitman and Welch, who pioneered them in the 1930s. In their most general form they are certainly cumbersome to use, and it was left largely to others to develop simple tests and estimation procedures that retained nearly all the desirable properties of general randomization tests coupled with ease of application. Also in the 1930s M.G. Kendall and others were developing tests of association in a field known as rank correlation, something pioneered by C. Spearman in psychological research at the beginning of this century.

The Pattern of this Book

My aim is to show where non-parametric methods are useful; but just as the farmer must clear virgin soil and fertilize it before he plants his crops, there are some statistical preliminaries we must understand to appreciate the methods.

Part I gives these preliminaries. Part II deals, a chapter at a time, with various situations where non-parametric methods are appropriate; each time we explain the rationale in simple terms and illustrate the various techniques with examples, giving, we hope, enough guidance to enable the reader to follow the argument.

The reader familiar with counts and the binomial distribution, samples and summary statistics, elements of probability and the normal distribution may wish just to skim through the next three chapters or even pass directly to Part II, where we come to grips with applications.

At the start of the remaining chapters we outline what is covered in each. Where possible, the account of both rationale and technique is integrated with examples; those in Part II are broken down where appropriate into sections headed: (i) 'The Problem', (ii) 'Statistical Formulation', (iii) 'Procedure', (iv) 'Conclusion' and (v) 'Comments'.

To separate a particular example from the main text, three asterisks in a row appear at the end of each example.

At the end of each chapter there are exercises for the reader, and some hints and solutions for these are given in Chapter 12.

Equations and formulae are numbered consecutively throughout the book (Eq. 1), (Eq. 2), etc.

Throughout Part II, sections headed 'Fields of Application' illustrate areas in which the main techniques are commonly used.

Exercises

1. In examples (a), (b), (c) below, classify the types of numbers involved into the appropriate sub-class among those in Figure 1:

   (a) the order of preference a smoker indicates for six different brands of tobacco,

   (b) times of sunset in G.M.T. on a given date for various cities throughout Europe,

   (c) data on percentage of flowers that set fruit on each of a number of apple trees.

2. We pointed out on p. 13 that metals may be ranked in order of hardness by scratching tests. If for three metals A, B and C we find B scratches A, B scratches C and C scratches A, rank them in ascending order of hardness. Do we need all three pieces of information to rank them in order?

2. Counting, Probabilities and the Binomial Distribution

Scope

In this chapter we look first at systematic methods of counting, a process less trivial than some people think; we use our results in discussing basic concepts of probability, then explain how we combine simple probabilities to help us deal with complicated situations. Next the binomial distribution, one of the more important in non-parametric statistics, is introduced, and finally we meet our first example of a non-parametric test. To carry it out we need to learn something of the principles of hypothesis testing.

Counting

Counting was simple for the now extinct Tasmanian aborigine. His number system was: 'one, two, plenty', and he found it perfectly adequate since his hunting implements were primitive and his possessions few. He was indeed lucky to slay more than one or two animals per day to roast on his fire and anything in excess was a bonus to be described as plenty.

Modern society requires us to count in a more sophisticated way, and because non-parametric methods make extensive use of the counting process, we need to be able to count before we use them.

One important type of count is to find the number of groups and arrangements that can be obtained using some or all of a collection of items; this is part of a branch of mathematics called *combinatorics*. Many aspects of counting are tedious – a botanist, for example, may have to count large numbers of plants of each of several dozen species growing on a plot of ground. A problem in combinatorics may be more subtle, but it is often less tedious.

Permutations and Combinations

Let us look at some ideas in combinatorics that are relevant to statistics. One common problem is to count the number of different groups with certain properties that can be formed from a collection of items; it is essential here to distinguish between situations where order *is* and where it *is not* important. If there are twelve horses in a race and prizes of £1,000, £100 and £5 for first, second and third, the finishing order is important. If three girls are to be selected from twelve to sing at a concert and all are to receive the same fee, they compete only for the honour of selection and equal financial reward, so order of selection is unimportant.

Finding how many groups of a given size – with or without regard to order – can be obtained from a larger collection would be very tedious if we had to specify all possible groups; fortunately this proves unnecessary if all we seek is the total number of groups and not the composition of each; but writing down all such groups for one simple example does give an insight into the mathematics of counting.

Example 1

Suppose we have 5 distinguishable items – *A, B, C, D, E* – and we wish to know how many groups of 3 we can get when order is important. The five items may be racehorses, beauty contestants, different brands of canned peaches, goods donated to a jumble sale or anything else that consists of distinguishable items. We introduce the notation *DEB*, etc., to indicate the group of 3 in which *D* is placed first, *E* second and *B* third. In Table 2 we list *all* possible ordered selections of 3 items from 5.

Counting the entries, we find there are 60 different ways of selecting the items when order matters. But note that each column of Table 2 has the same three letters in every entry; it is only the order that differs. In column four, for example, the letters are always *A, C* and *D*. Thus if we only want to know the number of selections *without* regard to order, the answer is *ten*, one corresponding to each column, and we may specify these by the ten triplets of letters in the first row (or any other row for that matter) of Table 2.

Table 2   Ordered selections of 3 items from 5

ABC	ABD	ABE	ACD	ACE	ADE	BCD	BCE	BDE	CDE
ACB	ADB	AEB	ADC	AEC	AED	BDC	BEC	BED	CED
BCA	BDA	BEA	CDA	CEA	DEA	CDB	CEB	DEB	DEC
BAC	BAD	BAE	CAD	CAE	DAE	CBD	CBE	DBE	DCE
CAB	DAB	EAB	DAC	EAC	EAD	DBC	EBC	EBD	ECD
CBA	DBA	EBA	DCA	ECA	EDA	DCB	ECB	EDB	EDC

*   *   *

Clearly it is tedious to write down all cases even when selecting only three items from five, and unless one is systematic it is easy to miss some. A careful inspection of Table 2 will show that it is compiled in a systematic way (e.g. each entry in the second row is obtained from the one in the first row immediately above it by reversing the second and third letters). When the number of items is larger, what was just tedious for small numbers rapidly approaches the impossible.

Example 2

Suppose 51 people apply for 5 jobs, each carrying a different salary so that order of selection is important. In how many ways can the five jobs be allocated among the 51 applicants?

We shall find that the answer is a staggering total of 281,887,200. It would be quite a tight squeeze to list more than 400 of these on one page of this book, so the complete list would require a book of some 700,000 pages!

Let us see how we get the total without this listing. We call each group of 5 out of 51 a *permutation* (of 5 from 51). To work out the number of these we note that *any* of the 51 may be selected for the first job. Once this person is selected, there *remain* 50 contenders for the second job; since any of the 50 second choices may be associated with any of the 51 first choices there are $51 \times 50 = 2,550$ ways of filling the first two jobs. This leaves 49 candidates for the third job; each choice may be combined with any of the 2,550 choices for the first two jobs giving $2,550 \times 49 = 124,950$ ways of allocating the first three jobs. Since there remain 48 candidates for the fourth job, similar arguments show that there are $124,950 \times 48 = 5,997,600$ ways of filling the first four jobs; each of these may be combined with the 47 ways of filling the final post, giving, as we asserted, $5,997,600 \times 47 = 281,887,200$ ways of filling all five posts. We could calculate this number in one step as

$$51 \times 50 \times 49 \times 48 \times 47 = 281,887,200 \qquad \text{(Eq. 1)}$$

* * *

We move now from arithmetic to algebra. This enables us to generalize results from 51 objects to any number n from which we select not 5 but r. Clearly we then have n choices for the first, $n - 1$ for the second, $n - 2$ for the third and these can be combined to give $n \times (n - 1) \times (n - 2)$ choices for the first three. A little thought is needed about the number of ways of selecting the rth or final item. When we are ready to select this we have already removed $r - 1$ items in our earlier choices, so we are left with

$$n - (r - 1) = n - r + 1$$

choices for the rth selection.

Generalizing the argument used in Example 2 we see there are

$$n \times (n - 1) \times (n - 2) \times \ldots \times (n - r + 1) \qquad \text{(Eq. 2)}$$

selections of r items from n when order is important; our notation with the three dots between $(n - 2)$ and $(n - r + 1)$ means, take the product of all integers between n and $(n - r + 1)$ inclusive. Checking in Example 2 we have $n = 51, r = 5$ so that

$$n - r + 1 = 51 - 5 + 1 = 47$$

giving the value in (Eq. 1). In Example 1 we had $n = 5$ and $r = 3$, so the number of permutations is $5 \times 4 \times 3 = 60$, agreeing with the complete listing in Table 2.

A special case is that in which $r = n$. The number of permutations is then the number of ways n different things can be arranged in order. If we put $r = n$ in (Eq. 2), then $n - r + 1 = n - n + 1 = 1$ and so the number of permutations is the product of all integers between n and 1, e.g. if $n = 7$ the product is

$$7 \times 6 \times 5 \times 4 \times 3 \times 2 \times 1 = 5,040.$$

The product is called *factorial* n and is printed $n!$ (n followed by an exclamation mark). The concept is also relevant to the number of orderings within a group of r once we have selected the particular r items that form that group, for the number of different orderings of these r items among themselves is clearly $r!$.

Looking at Table 2 we see that each column consists of all permutations of the three letters in the top entry in that column and that the six entries in any column are the $3! = 3 \times 2 \times 1 = 6$ permutations of that group of 3.

Mathematicians have a convenient shorthand for the number of permutations of r items from n, writing it ^nP_r; n is the number of items, P stands for permutation and r indicates the group size being selected. Thus (Eq. 2) may be written

$$^nP_r = n \times (n - 1) \times (n - 2) \times \ldots \times (n - r + 1).$$

When we only want to know the number of groups of size r that represent a different sub-set from the n items and are not interested in the order of selection we call the number of different sub-sets the number of *combinations* of r items from n and denote it by ^nC_r. We have seen that each combination gives rise to $r!$ orderings or permutations, so ^nP_r must equal ^nC_r multiplied by $r!$. Symbolically

$$^nC_r \times (r!) = \, ^nP_r, \text{ or equivalently } ^nC_r = \, ^nP_r \, / \, (r!).$$

Thus in Example 1 where $n = 5$ and $r = 3$ we get

$$^5C_3 = {^5P_3} / (3!) = \frac{5 \times 4 \times 3}{3 \times 2 \times 1} = 10$$

confirming what we learnt by inspecting Table 2. It is not difficult to show, although the mathematical detail need not worry us, that

$$^nC_r = \frac{n!}{r!(n-r)!}$$ (Eq. 3)

and if we replace r by $n - r$, then $n - r$ is replaced by r and the right-hand side of (Eq. 3) is unaltered, whence

$$^nC_r = {^nC_{n-r}}.$$ (Eq. 4)

In words, the number of combinations of r items from n is the same as the number of combinations of $n - r$ items from n. We can also see this directly from an argument based on logic, since every time we select a *different* set of r items we leave behind (or reject) a *different* set of $n - r$ items so there are exactly the same number of combinations of $n - r$ items from n as there are of r items from n.

In the special case $r = n$, there is clearly only *one* combination of n items from n – obtained by taking the lot. Also when $r = 0$ there is only one way of selecting no items from n, by ignoring them all. Thus

$$^nC_0 = {^nC_n} = 1.$$ (Eq. 5)

and this accords with (Eq. 4) when $r = n$. If we put $r = 0$ or $r = n$ in (Eq. 3) we get a term 0! to which we have not yet assigned a meaning. Mathematicians assign the value 1 to 0!, so that (Eq. 3) has a meaning when $r = 0$ or $r = n$ and takes the value 1 in accord with (Eq. 5). Some books use the notation $\binom{n}{r}$ instead of ^nC_r. Some calculators give values of $n!$ or of ^nC_r, a useful facility.

Counting and Probability

Permutations and combinations are important when we wish to calculate probabilities. Not all probabilities can be calculated *ab initio* using them, but many of those relevant to non-parametric methods can; we can often combine probabilities found in this way with the aid of two simple laws.

The concept of probability is closely associated with that of odds in a gambling game. We shall first turn our attention to what are called equally likely events where an *event* is simply the outcome of some experiment. If the experiment consists of tossing a coin there are two possible outcomes – the events 'heads' or 'tails' – and each is equally likely; if a die is cast there are six possible and equally likely outcomes corresponding to the number of spots (1, 2, 3, 4, 5 or 6) on the uppermost face. If a three is the outcome when a die is cast we say the event 'three' has occurred in the experiment 'casting a die'. When all outcomes of an experiment are equally likely, the probability associated with any group of these is the ratio of the number of equally likely outcomes forming the group (usually called the *favourable* cases) to the total number of equally likely outcomes.

Many of the situations we meet in this book will be equivalent to an experiment in which we place n tickets numbered 1 to n in a hat and draw a certain number of tickets out in such a way that every ticket has an equal chance of selection; we shall then be interested in *probabilities* of certain outcomes of the draw, e.g. that each of three tickets drawn shall bear odd numbers, that each bears a number less than $\frac{1}{2}n$, and so on.

Example 3

Suppose we have seven tickets in a hat numbered 1, 2, 3, 4, 5, 6, 7. What is the probability that if we draw one ticket from the hat it bears the number 4? What is the probability that the number drawn is odd?

Clearly there are 7 possible and equally likely outcomes of the experiment 'draw a ticket from the hat and note its number'. If only one, the outcome 4, is favourable, then, as is virtually self-evident, the probability of getting a 4 is 1/7. Similarly, the probability of getting an odd-numbered ticket is 4/7, since four of the equally likely outcomes, viz. drawing 1, 3, 5 or 7, are favourable to the event 'number drawn is odd'.

*　　*　　*

Example 4

Again suppose we have tickets numbered 1 to 7 in a hat, but now suppose we draw two tickets, one after the other, without replacing the first before we draw the second. What is the probability that both are odd?

Here order does not matter, so we calculate the number of ways of selecting two odd tickets from the four (1, 3, 5, 7) in the hat; this is a combinations exercise with $n = 4$ and $r = 2$. Thus, there are

$$^4C_2 = \frac{4 \times 3}{2 \times 1} = 6$$

equally likely ways of drawing two from the four odd-numbered tickets present. This is the number of equally likely favourable cases.

The total number of equally likely possible outcomes is the number of combinations of 2 items from 7, i.e.

$$^7C_2 = \frac{7 \times 6}{2 \times 1} = 21.$$

It is convenient to write the probability of an event in the form Pr(name of event); thus for this example

$$Pr(2 \text{ odds}) = {}^4C_2 \,/\, {}^7C_2 = {}^6/_{21} = {}^2/_7. \qquad \text{(Eq. 6)}$$

* * *

What other possibilities are there besides *two odds* when we draw two tickets? They could both be even, or one odd and one even.

Example 5

What are the probabilities that both are even *or* one is odd and the other even when we draw two tickets without replacement from seven numbered 1 to 7?

Since there are three even-numbered tickets we can select 2 in $^3C_2 = 3$ ways; so the probability both are even is

$$Pr(2 \text{ even}) = {}^3C_2 \,/\, {}^7C_2 = {}^3/_{21} = {}^1/_7 \qquad \text{(Eq. 7)}$$

A word now about intuition. Comparing (Eq. 6) and (Eq. 7) we see we are only half as likely to get two evens as we are to get two odds. Is this surprising? We have 4 odd- and 3 even-numbered tickets; intuition may give you the feeling that if *two odds* is twice as likely as *two evens* then the number of odds in the hat should be double the number of evens. The warning here is that intuition can easily lead one astray, a fate that has befallen many a gambler when he has tried to work out the odds on an intuitive basis.

What about one even and one odd? We might argue that since 2 cases out of 7 favour two odds and 1 case out of 7 favours two evens, then the remaining 4 cases out of 7 must favour one odd and one even, so that

$$Pr(1 \text{ odd}, 1 \text{ even}) = {}^4/_7.$$

Having been warned of the dangers of intuition, the reader may feel the above is too intuitive; we may note that we can select the odd number in $^4C_1 = 4$ ways and the even number in $^3C_1 = 3$ ways and combine each of these in pairs to give $4 \times 3 = 12$ ways, each equally likely, of getting one odd and one even, whence

$$Pr(1 \text{ odd}, 1 \text{ even}) = \frac{{}^4C_1 \times {}^3C_1}{{}^7C_2} = \frac{12}{21} = \frac{4}{7} \qquad \text{(Eq. 8)}$$

as we asserted.

* * *

In passing it is worth noticing that for *any* n, ${}^nC_1 = n$; this is obvious, since there are exactly n ways of selecting one item from n.

Mutually Exclusive Events

When we toss a coin it cannot fall both heads and tails at the same toss; if a girl can win only one prize in a beauty contest she cannot win both first prize and third prize; however, if she enters two different contests and may collect prizes in either, she can win first prize in one and third prize in the other.

When two events cannot *both* occur at one performance of an experiment we say they are *mutually exclusive* (some writers prefer the word *disjoint*).

Example 6

In Examples 4 and 5 the events 'both even', 'both odd' and 'one even and one odd' are three mutually exclusive events. The events 'both even' and 'at least one even' would clearly *not* be mutually exclusive; if the former has happened, so certainly has the latter; if the latter has happened, the former might or might not have happened.

* * *

Probabilities associated with mutually exclusive events have a very useful property; the probability that one or the other will happen is the *sum* of the probabilities that each will happen. Notationally, if we designate two *mutually exclusive* events by A and B, then

$$Pr(A \text{ or } B \text{ occurs}) = Pr(A \text{ occurs}) + Pr(B \text{ occurs}).$$

This rule is useful if we want the probability of a relatively complicated event and can break it down into two mutually exclusive events for each of which we know the probabilities. In Example 6 we considered the event 'at least one even'. This can be broken down into the two mutually exclusive events 'both even' and 'one even and one odd'.

Example 7

If two tickets are drawn without replacement from seven numbered 1 to 7, what is the probability that at least one bears an even number?

The addition rule tells us

$$Pr(\text{at least one even}) = Pr(\text{both even}) + Pr(\text{one even, one odd}),$$

whence from Examples 4 and 5 we immediately get

$$Pr(\text{at least one even}) = \frac{1}{7} + \frac{4}{7} = \frac{5}{7}.$$

* * *

When events are not mutually exclusive we cannot add probabilities in this simple way.

An interesting special case of mutually exclusive events is that in which one or the other must happen, e.g. either heads or tails must be the outcome when a coin is tossed. Between them, these events are the only possible outcomes, and it is *certain* one of them will happen. The probability of an event that is certain to happen (sometimes referred to as a *sure* event) is clearly 1. In these circumstances the events are said to be mutually exclusive *and* exhaustive.

Example 8

In Examples 4, 5 and 7 the events 'at least one even' and 'both odd' appeared. These are mutually exclusive and exhaustive. Thus

$$Pr(\text{at least one even}) + Pr(\text{both odd}) = 1,$$

whence

$$Pr(\text{at least one even}) = 1 - Pr(\text{both odd})$$

$$= 1 - \frac{2}{7} = \frac{5}{7},$$

the same result as we got in Example 7.

* * *

When two events are mutually exclusive and exhaustive they are known as *opposite* events since in any experiment one but not both will occur.

30 QUICK STATISTICS

Independent Events

Another property of events that is important when calculating probabilities is that of *independence*. When we cast a pair of dice the score on one is independent of that on the other; the two events 'score on first die' and 'score on second die' are called independent events.

On the other hand, if I have nine batteries in a box and three are flat, and I select two (without replacing the first before I take the second), then the events 'first battery is flat' and 'second battery is flat' are *not* independent.

More formally, we say that two events are independent if the probability of each happening is not influenced by whether or not the other has occurred. In casting a true die the probability of a six is always 1/6 irrespective of what happens at any other cast or with any other die that is cast at the same time.

But when we select 2 batteries from a box of 9, 3 of which are flat, the probability that the first is flat is $3/9 = 1/3$, since there are three outcomes out of nine equally likely that give rise to the event 'first battery flat'. Now the second battery is selected from the eight remaining. There are two cases:

Case *A*. *First battery flat*: there are now 2 flat and 6 good in the remaining 8. Thus

$$Pr(\text{second flat}) = {}^2/_8 = {}^1/_4. \tag{Eq. 9}$$

Case *B*. *First battery good*: there are now 3 flat and 5 good in the remaining 8. Thus

$$Pr(\text{second flat}) = {}^3/_8. \tag{Eq. 10}$$

Since the probability of 'second flat' depends upon whether or not the first is flat we say the two events are *not* independent. The probabilities in (Eq. 9) and (Eq. 10) are respectively conditional upon whether or not the first battery is flat. We call them *conditional probabilities* and to distinguish the cases write

$$Pr(\text{second flat} \mid \text{first flat}) = {}^1/_4$$

and

$$Pr(\text{second flat} \mid \text{first good}) = {}^3/_8.$$

When events are independent we have a rule that tells us that the probability that *both* occur is the *product* of the probabilities that each occur, i.e. if two events A and B are independent, then

$$Pr(A, B \text{ both occur}) = Pr(A \text{ occurs}) \times Pr(B \text{ occurs}).$$

Conversely, if the probability that both events occur is the product of the probabilities that each occur, then the events are independent.

Example 9

I toss a coin and cast a die. What is the probability that the coin lands heads and the score on the die is either 5 or 6?

Clearly the events are independent. Considering the ratio of favourable cases to the total number of equally likely cases, for the coin we have

$$Pr(\text{heads}) = \tfrac{1}{2}$$

and for the die

$$Pr(5 \text{ or } 6) = \tfrac{2}{6} = \tfrac{1}{3}$$

whence, by the multiplication rule,

$$Pr(\text{heads } and \text{ 5 or 6}) = Pr(\text{heads}) \times Pr(5 \text{ or } 6)$$

$$= \frac{1}{2} \times \frac{1}{3} = \frac{1}{6}.$$

*   *   *

Extending the Rules

The addition rule extends immediately to more than two events providing all are mutually exclusive; then the probability that one of them occurs is the sum of the probabilities of each occurring. For example, if the events A, B, C, D are mutually exclusive,

$$Pr(A \text{ or } B \text{ or } C \text{ or } D) = Pr(A) + Pr(B) + Pr(C) + Pr(D).$$

Similarly the multiplication rule extends to more than two events providing all are independent. Thus, if A, B, C are all independent,

$$Pr(A \text{ and } B \text{ and } C) = Pr(A) \times Pr(B) \times Pr(C).$$

Example 10

A fruit machine has 3 reels; the probability of a particular fruit appearing on the win line of any reel does not depend on what appears on other reels. If the probability of a plum appearing on reel 1 is 1/12, on reel 2 is 1/4 and on reel 3 is 1/24, what is the probability that a plum will appear on all three reels at one play of the machine?

The independence condition tells us that the probability required is the product of the probabilities for each reel, i.e.

$$Pr(3 \text{ plums}) = \frac{1}{12} \times \frac{1}{4} \times \frac{1}{24} = \frac{1}{1,152}.$$

Anyone playing a machine with the above characteristics could expect a win with three plums about once in every 1,152 plays in the long run.

* * *

A Word of Warning

In evaluating probabilities using the concept of the ratio of the number of favourable to the total number of equally likely cases, the *equally likely* requirement is essential.

If, for example, two coins are tossed and one is interested in the probability of two heads, it is tempting to argue that, since there are three outcomes (viz. two heads, a head and a tail, two tails) and only one of these is favourable, it follows that

$$Pr(2 \text{ heads}) = \frac{1}{3}.$$

Any gambler reasoning thus would soon find himself in trouble. There are in fact *four* equally likely outcomes. Writing that for the first coin first and denoting heads by H and tails by T, they are HH, HT, TH, TT. Only the first of these corresponds to the favourable event two heads, so the correct probability is 1/4. We may verify this by the multiplication rule, since the outcomes for each coin are independent and for each $Pr(\text{heads}) = \frac{1}{2}$. Thus,

$$Pr(2 \text{ heads}) = Pr(\text{first heads } and \text{ second heads})$$
$$= Pr(\text{first heads}) \times Pr(\text{second heads})$$
$$= \frac{1}{2} \times \frac{1}{2} = \frac{1}{4}.$$

More complicated addition and multiplication rules for probabilities hold if events are not mutually exclusive or independent, but we shall not need them in this book.

The Binomial Distribution

We now establish a result widely used in non-parametric methods. Perhaps ironically, it involves parameters and specifies a distribution, but in the applications we make it is relevant to properties of a sample. On p. 25 we explained the terms *experiment* and *event*; we shall be considering now a complete experiment that consists of a series of repeated sub-experiments; it is convenient to use the name *trial* for an individual sub-experiment in these circumstances and to keep the word experiment for the series of trials.

We shall be concerned with series of trials at each of which there are only two possible outcomes: the sex of a child may be male or female, a candidate may pass or fail an examination, a manufactured item may be marketable or defective, an elector may vote *yes* or *no* at a referendum, a man may be a smoker or a non-smoker, a player may win or lose a game of tennis, a citizen may be native-born or an immigrant, a person may be employed or unemployed. We shall be interested in how many times one of two possible outcomes occurs in a series of n trials, subject to certain conditions.

To develop the statistical theory it is convenient to arbitrarily label the two possible outcomes of a trial *success* and *failure* – denoted by S and F respectively – even though this association may not be apt in a particular example; it seems unfair to call a male birth a success and a female birth a failure, except perhaps for parents particularly desirous to have a son.

We consider a series of n trials each of which may result in S or F, these being *mutually exclusive*. The outcomes at successive trials are independent and at each the probability of S is p and that of F is q. Since S and F are the only possible outcomes, they are exhaustive (i.e. opposite events), so $p + q = 1$ or $q = 1 - p$.

We shall be interested in the probability that in our experiment consisting of n such trials we observe exactly r successes, where r is any number between 0 and n. The number of successes, r, is an example of what is called a *random variable*; this is a quantity whose value is determined by some chance or probabilistic mechanism; we cannot say with certainty in advance of a particular experiment *exactly* what value r will take in that experiment. For example, if a couple decide to have five children and the probability is one half that any child will be a boy, we cannot say in advance that there will be exactly 2 or exactly 3 boys in that family. We can, however, calculate the probabilities that in a family of given size there will be each possible number of boys between zero and the total family size.

In the experimental set-up we have described, n and p are supposed fixed. These are the constants known in statistical jargon as *parameters*.

Example 11

Assuming that each child born to a couple is equally likely to be male or female and that the sex of any child is independent of that of any children born previously to the couple, what is the probability that there will be more boys than girls in a family of six children?

This problem can be solved by repeated applications of the addition and multiplication rules for probabilitites, and we shall use this approach as an introduction to a more general formula for problems of this type.

There are more boys than girls if there are 4, 5 or 6 boys. These three outcomes are mutually exclusive, so if we obtain the probability of each we need only add them to solve our problem.

Consider first the probability of 4 boys (4 successes, S) in 6 trials when $Pr(S) = p = \frac{1}{2}$. Since $q = 1 - p$, $q = \frac{1}{2}$ also. Clearly there are various ordered sequences of births that result in 4 boys and 2 girls, e.g. the sequence 'boy, boy, girl, girl, boy, boy' or the sequence 'girl, boy, boy, boy, girl, boy'. Different sequences are clearly *mutually exclusive*. We shall make the assumption that there are no multiple births giving rise to 'ties' in the order of births.

Equating a boy to S, the first of the above sequences may be written S, S, F, F, S, S, and in view of independence the multiplication rule gives

$$Pr(\text{sequence } S, S, F, F, S, S) = Pr(S) \times Pr(S) \times Pr(F) \times Pr(F) \times Pr(S) \times Pr(S)$$

$$= \frac{1}{2} \times \frac{1}{2} \times \frac{1}{2} \times \frac{1}{2} \times \frac{1}{2} \times \frac{1}{2} = \frac{1}{64}.$$

A moment's reflection shows that if we work out the probability for any other sequence giving 4 boys and 2 girls, it will again be 1/64. Since all are mutually exclusive, the addition rule tells us that the probability of 4 boys and 2 girls is simply 1/64 multiplied by the number of different orderings.

This is a combinations problem. Look at it this way: we have *six* positions – first-born, second-born, third-born, fourth-born, fifth-born and sixth-born. From these six we have to select four and allocate to each of them a boy. The remaining two positions are then *automatically* filled by girls to satisfy the condition that there are 4 boys and 2 girls in the family. The number of ways of selecting 4 different positions from 6 is $^6C_4$. Hence the probability of exactly four boys is

$$^6C_4 \times \frac{1}{64} = \frac{15}{64}.$$

(Check for yourself that $^6C_4 = {}^6C_2 = 15$.)

Following through a similar argument you will find that the probability of 5 boys and 1 girl in a specified order is also 1/64, and a combinations argument shows there are $^6C_5 = {}^6C_1 = 6$ possible orderings, so the probability of exactly 5 boys and 1 girl is 6/64. Clearly there is only one possible ordering giving 6 boys and this again has probability 1/64. Since the probability of more boys than girls is equivalent to that of 4, 5 or 6 boys and these are mutually exclusive events

$$Pr(4, 5 \text{ or } 6 \text{ boys}) = Pr(4 \text{ boys}) + Pr(5 \text{ boys}) + Pr(6 \text{ boys})$$

$$= \frac{15}{64} + \frac{6}{64} + \frac{1}{64} = \frac{11}{32}.$$

*　　　*　　　*

The arithmetic of Example 11 was fairly simple because we had $p = q = \frac{1}{2}$. Note that J. Arbuthnot's finding (p. 18) throws some doubt on the assumption that $p = q = \frac{1}{2}$ for the sexes. In practice, records show a slightly higher probability for male births, but the difference is so small it would hardly affect calculations for family sizes of six; Arbuthnot had to look at London records over many years to establish the difference!

We now extend the ideas in Example 11 to general values of p, n and r. We have n trials that are independent; the outcomes at each are S or F with probabilities p and q ($= 1 - p$), respectively. Our objective is to attach a probability to each value of r between 0 and n.

As in Example 11, consider first a sequence of n trials with r successes (and by implication $n - r$ failures) which occur in a particular order. The ordered sequence for the case $n = 10$, $r = 7$ might be

$$S, S, F, S, F, S, S, S, F, S$$

and the probability of such a sequence, using the multiplication rule for independent events, would be

$$Pr(S,S,F,S,F,S,S,S,F,S) = p \times p \times q \times p \times q \times p \times p \times p \times q \times p = p^7 q^3.$$

Generalizing this argument to any value of n and r, it is easily seen that if we have exactly r successes, the remaining trials, of which there are $n - r$, must result in failure and for a sequence with successes and failures in a *specified order* subject to the constraint r successes and $n - r$ failures we have:

$$Pr(r \text{ successes}, n - r \text{ failures in specified order}) = p^r q^{n-r}. \quad \text{(Eq. 11)}$$

Since each *different* ordering of exactly r successes has the same probability and all such orderings are mutually exclusive (only *one* can occur at any given performance of the experiment), we need to know the number of such orderings to get the probability of exactly r successes without any restrictions on order. This is a generalization of the combinations exercise in Example 11.

We now have n distinct positions (the numbered trials from 1 to n) from which we have to select r for allocation of the symbol S for success. This can be done in ^nC_r ways with each of which is associated the probability given in (Eq. 11). The addition rule now gives:

$$Pr(\text{exactly } r \text{ successes}) = {}^nC_r p^r q^{n-r} \qquad \text{(Eq. 12)}$$

This is a formula we use perhaps more than any other in this book.

In applications, given n and p we know immediately that $q = 1 - p$, and by plugging these and the values $r = 0, 1, 2, \ldots, n$ in turn in (Eq. 12) we can evaluate the probabilities of any specified numbers of successes.

When we know the probabilities associated with each possible outcome of an experiment, we say we know the *distribution* of the outcomes. Experiments satisfying the conditions leading to (Eq. 12) give a distribution of numbers of successes following what is called the *binomial distribution*. This is our first specific example of representing a pattern of variation by a mathematical function, a concept mentioned on p. 15. Here the function is given by (Eq. 12).

If you happen to know an algebraic theorem called the *binomial theorem* you will see special relevance in the name binomial distribution, but do not worry if you have not met this theorem. What the theorem tells us is that (Eq. 12) gives the terms in the expansion of $(p + q)^n$ for any p and q. In our particular case $p + q = 1$, so the sum of the values given by (Eq. 12) taken over all values of r is 1. This is consistent with the fact that $0, 1, 2, \ldots, n$ successes are a mutually exclusive and exhaustive set of outcomes for our experiment (see p. 29).

We could have worked Example 11 by applying (Eq. 12) with $n = 6$, $p = q = \frac{1}{2}$ for $r = 4, 5$ and 6 and adding the results. The reader should check this gives the same answer.

When, and only when, $p = \frac{1}{2}$ does the binomial distribution have a property of symmetry in the sense that

$Pr(r \text{ successes and } n - r \text{ failures}) = Pr(n - r \text{ successes and } r \text{ failures})$.

Thus in Example 11 the probability of 4 or more girls equals the probability of 4 or more boys. More generally, for families of any size, if we assume that the probability of a birth of either sex is $\frac{1}{2}$, then symmetry means

$Pr(\text{more boys than girls}) = Pr(\text{more girls than boys})$.

If there are an odd number of children in a family, these outcomes are mutually exclusive and exhaustive, so the probability of each is $\frac{1}{2}$. We cannot argue this way for families containing an even number of children, because there is a further possible outcome – equal numbers of children of each sex. This was the situation in Example 11.

Example 12

Bill Smith and I play a game in which a die is cast four times. At any one cast, if a 5 or 6 is scored we call this a success, otherwise the result is a failure. The rules of the game are that I pay Bill Smith £1 if there are 1 or 3 successes in the four casts, but he pays me £1 if there are 0, 2 or 4 successes. Am I sensible to play this game?

With an even money bet I am only sensible to play if the probability of my winning exceeds one half (and consequently that the probability of the opposite event, my opponent winning, is less than one half). In this example we have a binomial distribution in which the probability of scoring a 5 or 6 (success) at each cast is 1/3. (Why?)

We calculate the probability of each number of successes between 0 and 4 by plugging $n = 4$, $p = \frac{1}{3}$ and $r = 0, 1, 2, 3, 4$ in turn into formula (Eq. 12). Thus

$$Pr(\text{no successes}) = {}^4C_0(\tfrac{1}{3})^0(\tfrac{2}{3})^4 = \frac{16}{81}$$

$$Pr(\text{one success}) = {}^4C_1(\tfrac{1}{3})^1(\tfrac{2}{3})^3 = \frac{32}{81}$$

$$Pr(\text{two successes}) = {}^4C_2(\tfrac{1}{3})^2(\tfrac{2}{3})^2 = \frac{24}{81}$$

$$Pr(\text{three successes}) = {}^4C_3(\tfrac{1}{3})^3(\tfrac{2}{3})^1 = \frac{8}{81}$$

$$Pr(\text{four successes}) = {}^4C_4(\tfrac{1}{3})^4(\tfrac{2}{3})^0 = \frac{1}{81}$$

I win if any of the three mutually exclusive outcomes 0, 2 or 4 successes occurs, and the total associated probability is

$$\frac{16}{81} + \frac{24}{81} + \frac{1}{81} = \frac{41}{81}.$$

This probability is just greater than one half; so, at each play I may expect to win one pound with probability 41/81 and lose one pound with probability 40/81; this means that in the long run I expect to show a £1 gain for every 81 games played – hardly a recipe for getting rich quickly. Whether you would play such a game in practice depends on whether the time you waste in playing 81 games is worth more or less than £1 to you.

Note that since they form a mutually exclusive and exhaustive set of outcomes, the probabilities associated with each number of successes from 0 to 4 should sum to unity; they do, and this provides a useful check on our arithmetic.

*   *   *

Probabilities are usually measured on a scale 0 to 1, but they are sometimes expressed as percentages by multiplying by 100; a probability of 0·5 corresponds to a percentage probability of 50 and that of 1 to 100 per cent.

An Application to Non-Parametric Methods

With our first example of a non-parametric test we see one way the binomial distribution is used in this field.

Example 13

A public health inspector does routine tests to determine the level of bacteria in the cream in cakes sold by local shops. The regulations require him to divide each sample he takes into two portions and to send each portion to a different laboratory for analysis. One portion goes to laboratory A, the other to laboratory B. When the reports come back he is a little worried, because they never quite agree. He does not, of course, expect complete agreement. He realizes that bacteria will not be spread exactly evenly throughout the cream, and however exact the counts are, they may differ between the two portions of a sample; he also appreciates the difficulty of getting exact counts of bacteria. Thus, he would not be surprised if there were relatively small differences with sometimes one laboratory getting the higher count and sometimes the other for the two portions of the same sample. What would worry him would be evidence of any tendency for one laboratory fairly consistently to get higher or lower counts than the other, due to differences in technique or faulty equipment in one of the labs.

He invokes the aid of a statistician to see if there is any evidence of *consistent* differences between the laboratories over and above 'random' variation of the type mentioned above. To do this he provides him with results for ten samples divided in the way we have described. These are given in Table 3.

Table 3   Bacterial counts in cream samples (thousands/ml.)

Sample	A	B	C	D	E	F	G	H	I	J
Lab. A	11·7	12·1	13·3	15·1	15·9	15·3	11·9	16·2	15·1	13·6
Lab. B	10·9	11·9	13·4	15·4	14·8	14·8	12·3	15·0	14·2	13·1

Having an inquiring nature, the health inspector asks the statistician to explain to him, in not too technical terms, what he is doing.

Liking to keep things simple, the statistician decides on a non-parametric test, and a very easy one at that. In Chapter 6 we shall look at a more sophisticated one he might have used (Example 37, p. 121). If he had wanted to, and was prepared to make the necessary assumptions, he could have used instead a parametric test; an appropriate one would have been the t-test described in most elementary statistical texts, including the author's *Statistics in Action*.

The test he actually uses for the inspector's data is called the *sign test*. As the statistician explains, he mentally subtracts the reading for laboratory B from that for laboratory A for each sample. He does not record the actual result of the subtraction, but only whether the result is positive or negative. For the first sample it is positive since $11·7 - 10·9 = 0·8$, and so on, giving the sign sequence

$$+ + - - + + - + + +.$$

We can think of these signs as allocating the data into categories analogous to the '*successes*' and '*failures*' in the binomial situation.

Our sequence contains 7 plus and 3 minus signs.

The statistician explains to the inspector that if there were no systematic tendency for one laboratory to get higher results than the other, then which one did so for a particular sample would be a matter of chance – in the long run, laboratory A would give the higher reading for about one half. The situation is analogous to tossing a fair coin, if we associate the plus sign with heads and the minus sign with tails. If we toss a fair coin a large number of times we expect to get *about* the same number of heads and tails; a marked preponderance of one outcome or the other suggests a biased coin.

For a true coin the number of heads in n tosses has a binomial distribution with $p = \frac{1}{2}$. By analogy, if there really is no systematic difference between laboratories the plus signs for the differences

Lab. A − Lab. B

will have a binomial distribution with, in our case, $n = 10$ (the number of samples) and $p = q = \frac{1}{2}$, as in tossing a fair coin.

(Eq. 12) enables us to work out the probability of getting each number of plus signs between 0 and 10. Thus the probability of getting 7 plus signs (as we had with the Table 3 data) is

$$Pr(7 \text{ plus}) = {}^{10}C_7(\tfrac{1}{2})^7(\tfrac{1}{2})^3 = \frac{10 \times 9 \times 8}{1 \times 2 \times 3} \times (\tfrac{1}{2})^{10}$$

$$= \frac{120}{1,024} = \frac{15}{128} \approx 0 \cdot 12.$$

(The symbol $\approx$ means *is approximately equal to*.)

The implication is that if we carried out this experiment a large number of times we would expect to get 7 plus signs with 10 samples about 12 times in 100, i.e. about 12 per cent of the time, *if* our hypothesis of no systematic difference were correct.

Table 4 gives the probabilities of each number of plus signs from 0 to 10 under this hypothesis. These are binomial distribution probabilities calculated from (Eq. 12) with $p = q = \tfrac{1}{2}$ and $n = 10$. You should check that you can work these out. The bottom row expresses the probabilities as percentages correct to one decimal place; these are obtained by multiplying the probabilities in the row above by 100.

Table 4   Plus signs and their probabilities ($p = \tfrac{1}{2}$)

Number of plus signs	0	1	2	3	4	5	6	7	8	9	10
Probability	$\frac{1}{1,024}$	$\frac{10}{1,024}$	$\frac{45}{1,024}$	$\frac{120}{1,024}$	$\frac{210}{1,024}$	$\frac{252}{1,024}$	$\frac{210}{1,024}$	$\frac{120}{1,024}$	$\frac{45}{1,024}$	$\frac{10}{1,024}$	$\frac{1}{1,024}$
Percentage	0·1	1·0	4·4	11·7	20·5	24·6	20·5	11·7	4·4	1·0	0·1

Hypothesis Testing

How does the statistician use the information in Table 4? The following features give us some clues. First, the probabilities of 3 and 7 plus signs are equal, as are those of 4 and 6, etc.; this is the symmetry we noted on p. 36 for the case $p = q = \tfrac{1}{2}$. Second, the result with highest probability (the most likely result) is 5 plus signs, but the probability of this is only 252/1,024 or slightly less than $\tfrac{1}{4}$; i.e. it can only be expected to occur in the long run about 24·6 per cent of the time. The combined probabilities of the two mutually exclusive but symmetric results 6 plus signs or 4 plus signs is

$$\frac{210}{1,024} + \frac{210}{1,024} = \frac{420}{1,024} \approx 0 \cdot 41.$$

Thus, we may expect in the long run plus and minus signs in the 6 to 4 or 4 to 6 ratio about 41 per cent of the time; the coin-tossing analogy would be the expected frequency of either 6 or 4 heads in 10 tosses.

Four, five or six plus signs are the more common results; at the other extreme, while it is possible to get 10 plus or 10 minus signs, Table 4 shows that each of these extreme results has a probability of less than 1 in 1,000 (precisely 1 in 1,024).

If we did get such a result in a single experiment, it would surely make us very suspicious of the hypothesis that there is no systematic difference between laboratories; for clearly, if there were such a systematic difference, one of these extreme results would be much more probable. In an extreme analogy we could compare the situation to that of tossing a double-headed coin; with this the probability of 10 heads in 10 tosses is *one* since the outcome is certain. Surely most of us getting 10 heads in 10 successive tosses of a coin would look to see if it were double-headed before concluding we had got a rather improbable result with a fair coin! A double-headed coin is an extreme example. Suppose one had a weighted coin for which the probability of heads was ¾. In that case (Eq. 12) gives

$$Pr(10 \text{ heads}) = {}^{10}C_{10}(0 \cdot 75)^{10}(0 \cdot 25)^{0}$$

$$= 0.0563$$

(a pocket calculator helps here), compared with less than 0.001 for a true coin.

These ideas are formalized in what the statistician calls *hypothesis testing*. The hypothesis on which Table 4 is based is the simple one that there is an equal probability – one half – of getting a plus or minus sign at each trial. This simple hypothesis is called the *null hypothesis*; this is usually a precise hypothesis that we are prepared to believe until we accumulate enough evidence to make us prefer some (perhaps any one of a great many) possible *alternative hypotheses*. In our example something *fairly close* to equal numbers of plus and minus signs clearly supports the null hypothesis; it is the sort of thing we expect to happen fairly often when the null hypothesis is true; a *large preponderance* of plus signs would indicate laboratory *A* was tending to give higher readings than laboratory *B*; the converse would be implied by a large preponderance of negative signs. To make this more meaningful we need more precise explanations of phrases like 'fairly close to' and 'a large preponderance'.

Since the probabilities in Table 4 have been calculated on the assumption that the null hypothesis is true, let us look more closely at the less likely outcomes and their associated probabilities. Zero or ten plus signs are the extremes. Figure 2 may help in thinking about these. Here the probabilities are represented graphically by the heights of the vertical lines corresponding to 0 to 10 plus signs represented on the horizontal or X scale.

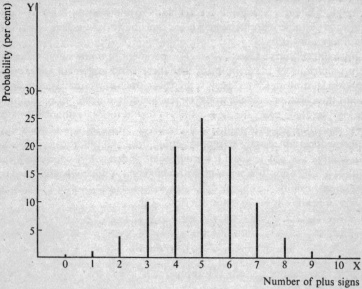

Figure 2 Graphical representation of probabilities in Table 4

In the diagram we can barely detect the probabilities for 0 or 10 when the same scale is used for all probabilities. The probability that *one or the other occurs* is only

$$\frac{1}{1,024} + \frac{1}{1,024} = \frac{1}{512}$$

so that when the null hypothesis holds, the odds against such an extreme result are greater than 500 to 1. The next most unlikely outcomes, 1 or 9 plus signs, each have associated probabilities 10/1,024, just discernible in Figure 2.

If we consider now the set of mutually exclusive and unlikely outcomes 0, 1, 9 or 10 plus signs, the addition rule tells us that the probability that one of these will occur is

$$\frac{1}{1,024} + \frac{1}{1,024} + \frac{10}{1,024} + \frac{10}{1,024} = \frac{11}{512} \approx 0.022 \qquad \text{(Eq. 13)}$$

equivalent to about 2·2 per cent (as we can check by adding the relevant percentages in Table 4).

If we introduce the next most unlikely outcomes, 2 or 8 plus signs, then the probability of 0, 1, 2, 8, 9 or 10 plus signs will be

$$\frac{1}{1,024} + \frac{1}{1,024} + \frac{10}{1,024} + \frac{10}{1,024} + \frac{45}{1,024} + \frac{45}{1,024} = \frac{56}{512} \approx 0 \cdot 11 \quad \text{(Eq. 14)}$$

equivalent to about 11 per cent.

While it is clear that occurrences of extreme events with low probabilities make us suspicious of the null hypothesis and more inclined to believe that some unspecified but different hypothesis is true, just where do we draw the line?

If the probability of getting a result as or more extreme than one we observe is less than about 0·01 (1 per cent in percentage terms), most of us would feel intuitively that we should think in terms of some alternative hypothesis rather than believe that something with a 1 in 100 chance has just 'come up' in our particular experiment. The evidence against the null hypothesis is strong.

If, on the other hand, there were a probability of 0·5 (a 50 per cent chance) of getting a result as or more extreme than the one we observe, then we would feel intuitively that we lack reasonable evidence to reject the null hypothesis, for we might equally well decide whether or not to reject it without doing any experiment but by simply tossing a coin and accepting the hypothesis if it fell heads, while rejecting it if it fell tails – since there is a 50 per cent chance of either outcome.

Where we finally draw the line is essentially a matter of convention. We usually accept the evidence against the null hypothesis as sufficiently convincing to *reject* the null hypothesis if the probability of getting a result as or more unlikely than that observed (but which would be more likely under some alternative hypothesis) is less than 0·05 (or 5 per cent). Rejection in this sense does not mean that we have *proved* the hypothesis is wrong in the sense that we prove a theorem in geometry or modern algebra; it simply means that we have assigned a measure, i.e. a probability less than 5 per cent, to getting a result in a class that includes the one we observed, when the null hypothesis is true.

Let us formalize these ideas even further, at the price of a little more statistical jargon. We make the rule that we reject the null hypothesis if we observe an outcome *in the set* for which the total probability of any equally or less likely outcome than that observed is less than 0·05 (or 5 per cent). This means we reject the null hypothesis, $p = \frac{1}{2}$, on which Table 4 is based, if we get 0, 1, 9 or 10 plus signs, because we have shown that the associated probability is 0·022 or 2·2 per cent; this is less than 5 per cent. If we have observed 2 or 8 positive signs, we have shown that the corresponding probability is 0·11 or 11 per cent; so using our convention we would *not* reject the null hypothesis for 2 or 8 plus signs; even less would we reject it for 7 plus signs, the number for the data given in Table 3.

Implicit in what we have been describing is the division of the set of all possible outcomes of an experiment – called the *sample space* – into two regions. If our observed result (in our case the number of plus signs) falls into one of these regions, we reject the null hypothesis. Otherwise we accept it. The region of rejection is known as the *critical region*. When the total probability associated with a critical region is less than 0·05 (or 5 per cent) and no larger region exists with an associated probability less than 0·05, we say the critical region has a *nominal* size of 5 per cent – more briefly that it is a *5 per cent critical region*. A result falling in this region is said to be *significant* at the 5 per cent level; some writers use the expression 'significant at the 0·05 probability level', and this means the same thing.

In this example the critical region of nominal size 5 per cent had an associated probability of only 2·2 per cent, and this is sometimes referred to as the *actual* size of the region. In many practical applications the difference between nominal and actual size is less marked.

The choice of a nominal size of 5 per cent is arbitrary, but it is a standard that has been widely adopted for published tables and has stood the test of time as a convenient practical yardstick.

We should of course be even more impressed by our evidence against the null hypothesis if an event occurs such that the probability of an equally or less likely event is lower still. We may generalize our concept of a critical region of size 0·05 or 5 per cent to one with associated probability α or 100α per cent. If in this example we were to reject the null hypothesis only when we observed 0 or 10 plus signs, the size would be

$$\frac{1}{1,024} + \frac{1}{1,024} = \frac{1}{512} \approx 0.002,$$

which is a 0·2 per cent critical region. Results in a critical region of any specified size 100α per cent (where α is a small probability) are said to be *significant* at the 100α per cent level. 'Significant' implies that they provide significant evidence *against* the null hypothesis.

Three nominal significance levels are widely used – the 5 per cent, 1 per cent and 0·1 per cent. It is common jargon to refer to a result significant at the 5 per cent but not at the 1 per cent level as *significant*, to a result significant at the 1 per cent but not at the 0·1 per cent level as *highly significant* and to one significant at the 0·1 per cent level as *very highly significant*.

These are the points the statistician put to the health inspector when he assured him there was no firm evidence for rejecting the hypothesis that there was no systematic difference between the laboratories. In Chapter 6 we shall be a bit more explicit about how to interpret this phrase.

*   *   *

One- and Two-tail Tests

Before ending a long chapter that contains quite a few subtle ideas, there is one more important point. In Example 13 the alternatives to the null hypothesis that the health inspector was prepared to entertain covered two broad possibilities:

(i) that laboratory *A* tended to return higher counts than laboratory *B*;

(ii) that laboratory *B* tended to return higher counts than laboratory *A*.

A preponderance of plus signs in the results of

Laboratory *A* − Laboratory *B*

would support the first of these, a preponderance of negative signs the second. In our choice of critical region we allowed for either possibility.

Situations may arise where on the basis of *a priori* information we would only entertain one of the above possibilities. We may know, for example, that laboratory *A* has more sophisticated counting equipment that will not miss any bacteria in the count, whereas laboratory *B* has older equipment that will certainly not overestimate the numbers, but which it is suspected may miss some of the bacteria out of the count. We may still proceed with the null hypothesis that there is no systematic difference, but, on the basis of knowledge of the equipment, accept only (i) above as a possible alternative. In this case only a large excess of plus signs would favour the alternative hypothesis. If, in the actual experiment, we did in fact observe 9 or 10 minus signs these would have a higher probability under the null hypothesis than under any alternative we are prepared to entertain; we would therefore accept the null hypothesis, concluding that we had in our single experiment observed an event of low probability. (Events of low probability do occur in real life – somebody always wins a lottery.)

When we are certain we have a 'one-sided' alternative to the null hypothesis, we may choose the critical region accordingly; in our example this means rejecting the null hypothesis only for a large number of plus signs. From Table 4 we see that a critical region consisting of 9 or 10 plus signs has actual size 1·1 per cent; it is in fact the critical region of size 5 per cent since inclusion of 8 plus signs in addition to 9 or 10 would give a region of actual size 5·5 per cent. In practice anyone carrying out this test and observing 8 plus signs would be wise to draw attention to the fact that the result *almost* reached significance at the nominal 5 per cent level. Remember 5 per cent is a conventional level not a rigid boundary.

It is the extreme or 'tail' results (see Table 4 or Figure 2) that determine whether we have significance; we speak of tests that include values from both tails in the critical region as *two-tail tests*; if only one tail is involved we speak of a *one-tail test*.

Which is appropriate depends upon the logic of the problem. Generally speaking there must be arguments based on sound reasoning to justify one-tail tests; they should not be based on prior hopes or hunches of the experimenter on the likely direction of departures from the null hypothesis. We return to this point in later examples; see in particular Chapter 5, p. 85.

In this book we adopt the convention that the actual size of the critical region must not exceed the nominal size. Some writers adopt the convention that the region of a given nominal size is the region whose actual size is nearest to that nominal size. Thus, in the example we have been discussing for a one-tail test, they would take the nominal 5 per cent region as 8, 9 or 10 plus signs with actual size 5·5 per cent since this is nearer to 5 per cent than the region we took (actual size 1·1 per cent). While the differences in this example are rather extreme, let us emphasize that it is not a question of either convention being right or wrong; it is simply a matter of preference, and no problems arise, provided that one states one's convention from the start and sticks to it.

Although hypothesis testing is not the only aspect of statistical inference, it introduces many of the basic ideas. An alternative account of the concepts is given in Chapter 2 of *Statistics in Action*, and this may be of interest to readers who feel that they have not yet come to grips with the main ideas.

Exercises

This chapter has covered a good deal of material, and the exercises below cover topics in roughly the order they were introduced. Answers and hints are given in Chapter 12.

1. Two people have to be selected from a group of nine to carry out certain unpleasant duties. Order of selection is important because the first one selected will be given the less pleasant duties. Draw up a list analogous to Table 2 to show all possible ordered selections of 2 from 9. Verify the calculated values of (i) $^9P_2$ and (ii) $^9C_2$ by counting the appropriate entries in the table.

2. Seven different cars enter a street in which there are twelve available parking meters. In how many different ways can they be parked at the meters? If two of the meters are removed, which of the following statements is true?

  (i) the number of ways is reduced by between 10 and 20 per cent;
 (ii) the number of ways is reduced by between 45 and 55 per cent;
(iii) the number of ways is reduced by over 80 per cent.

3. A card is dealt from a well-shuffled pack. Find the probabilities of each of the following events:
   (i) the card is a heart;
  (ii) the card is a red card;
 (iii) the card is a spade;
 (iv) the card is an ace;
  (v) the card is a court card (knave, queen, king);
 (vi) the card has a face value less than five (ace counts as 1);
(vii) the card is the 9 of diamonds.

List all possible sets of three of the above events that are mutually exclusive. Are there any sets of more than three of the above events that are mutually exclusive? If so, name them.

4. How many four-digit numbers can be formed using only the odd digits 1, 3, 5, 7 and 9, if no digit is to be used more than once in each number? What is the probability that the sum of the digits in a number so formed will be 20? You may assume all digits have an equal probability of selection in any position.

5. Jack and Jill take turns at shooting at a target, Jack shooting first. Results at each shot are independent. The probability Jack will hit the target with any shot is 1/3; for Jill it is 1/2. What is the probability that Jill's second shot is the first to hit the target?

6. There are fifteen identical envelopes in a box; five of them contain £1 notes, the remainder are empty. I draw two at random without replacement between draws. What is the probability that the second one I draw contains a £1 note (i) given that the first one contains a £1 note; (ii) given that the first contains nothing?

7. In the same experiment as in Question 6, what is the probability that the two I draw (i) both contain £1 notes, (ii) give me a total of £1, (iii) are both empty?

8. A fruit machine has 4 reels; the jackpot is won if 4 bells appear on the winning line; the probability of a particular symbol appearing on a reel does not depend on what appears on the other reels. If the probabilities of bells on each of the four reels are respectively 1/24, 1/12, 1/24 and 1/24, what is the probability of winning the jackpot at any one play? If I play the machine twice, what is the probability of winning (i) two jackpots and (ii) at least one jackpot?

9. A cricket correspondent of a newspaper claims that in each match of an England v. Australia test series England has a probability of 0·4 of winning. If there are 5 games in the series, calculate the probability that England wins 0, 1, 2, 3, 4 or 5 games, assuming the correspondent's assertion is correct. State for which of these

results, if any, you would reject the correspondent's hypothesis. Comment on the likely validity of the assumptions implicit in the correspondent's assertion.

10. We may carry out a sign test without actual measurements like those we had in Table 3. For example, a factory manager may be interested in observing whether a team of eight girls consistently works faster with popular or classical music as a background. So that the girls are not influenced by knowing they are experimental guinea-pigs, he might, without warning them, watch their production rates during periods with each type of music, simply noting for each girl whether she works faster with classical music than she does with 'pop', recording a *plus* if she does, otherwise a *minus*. If he records 7 plus and 1 minus for the eight girls, can he reject the null hypothesis that, so far as production is concerned, it doesn't matter which type of music is provided?

3. Samples and Populations

Scope

The aim of statistical inference is to use information from samples to infer something about a population. In this chapter we study the links between sample and population. We consider broad aspects of a population that might be expected to reflect themselves in a sample; by looking at probability from a different viewpoint from that in the previous chapter, we build a bridge between samples and populations.

We consider certain summarizing values obtained from samples which are useful indicators of population characteristics.

Although we develop these ideas firstly in relation to data in the form of counts, we generalize them to measurements on interval and ratio scales.

Another Look at Probability

In Chapter 2 we looked at probability in terms of equally likely outcomes. Another common approach is by way of the 'relative frequency' concept seen at its simplest in coin-tossing experiments. Toss a coin 100 times and you are surprised if you do not get something like 50 heads – maybe 52 or 47 or 49. None of these would surprise you – but 75 heads in 100 tosses certainly would. We call the ratio of the number of heads to the total number of tosses the *relative frequency* of heads. By experience we know that the larger the number of tosses, the closer this ratio settles down to one half – the value we assigned to the probability of heads in Chapter 2. We say more formally that the *limit* of the relative frequency when the number of tosses is large is equal to the probability of heads.

Similarly, if we cast a die, say 600 times, we expect to score a six about 100 times; it will seldom be exactly 100 times in 600 casts, but perhaps 102 or 97 or 105; the longer the die is cast, the closer the relative frequency will approach the probability.

Now let us turn to a slightly more complicated situation. Suppose we perform an experiment of tossing a coin 12 times repeatedly, perhaps 1,000 or more times. We may be interested in the proportion of cases when we get each number of heads between 0 and 12. Now in Chapter 2 we looked at situations rather like this. The probability of each number of heads can be worked out from the binomial distribution using (Eq. 12) with $p = \frac{1}{2}$ and $n = 12$.

The probabilities are given in Table 5. We can also represent these graphically on a chart similar to Figure 2, but, for reasons that will become clearer later, we use an alternative form in Figure 3. In this figure each of the rectangles has a breadth of 1 unit and is centred at one of the integers between 0 and 12 inclusive. The height of each rectangle is proportional to the probability given for the corresponding integer in Table 5.

Table 5   Probabilities of 0 to 12 heads in 12 coin tosses

Number of heads	0	1	2	3	4	5	6
Probability	$\frac{1}{4,096}$	$\frac{12}{4,096}$	$\frac{66}{4,096}$	$\frac{220}{4,096}$	$\frac{495}{4,096}$	$\frac{792}{4,096}$	$\frac{924}{4,096}$

Number of heads	7	8	9	10	11	12
Probability	$\frac{792}{4,096}$	$\frac{495}{4,096}$	$\frac{220}{4,096}$	$\frac{66}{4,096}$	$\frac{12}{4,096}$	$\frac{1}{4,096}$

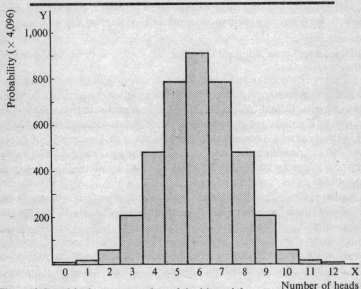

Figure 3 Graphical representation of the binomial
distribution, $p = \frac{1}{2}$, $n = 12$

We associate the probabilities in Table 5 with relative frequencies by visualizing many thousands of performances of the experiment 'tossing a coin 12 times'. At each performance we note the number of heads; what Table 5 tells us is that *in the long run* in about 1 in every 4,096 experiments we will get no heads; at the middle of the range we may expect six heads about 924 times in every 4,096 experiments.

In this sense the relative frequency of each possible number of heads from 0 to 12 approaches these probabilities if we continue doing the experiment of tossing a coin 12 times indefinitely and look upon this as a *population* of experiments.

In practice nobody is likely to spend very long actually performing experiments of this type; but as a way of filling a long winter evening you might, if probabilities fascinate you, do the experiment of tossing a coin 12 times for half an hour or so and see what pattern of results you get for numbers of heads. For 15 such experiments the numbers of heads observed in each case were:

$$4, 8, 8, 5, 3, 6, 7, 3, 6, 3, 9, 8, 6, 7, 5.$$

The relative frequencies for 5 and 8 heads observed here are respectively 2/15 and 3/15; in this small-sample experiment these and the relative frequencies for other numbers of heads do not look very like the probabilities in Table 5, but this need not alarm us. We do not expect relative frequencies in small experiments to be very close to their limiting values. However, we shall see later in the chapter that this small sample of 15 experiments mirrors certain features of the population quite well.

Realistic Samples

Most of the information we are interested in in real-life statistical situations is rather different from the sort we get by doing things like repeatedly tossing a coin 12 times. In more realistic problems we have a sample of observations; they might be the number of mistakes per thousand words made by a typist. We may have counted these in 15 specimens of her work and noted that she made, respectively, 2, 7, 0, 1, 3, 5, 1, 2, 9, 0, 2, 0, 1, 1, 2 mistakes.

Now in this situation we have no background population like that in the coin-tossing situations, where we arrived at the binomial distribution model by assuming reasonable properties for a true coin and applying the probability rules.

We do not know if the probability that the typist will make a mistake is the same from word to word, or from passage to passage; it may depend on the difficulty of the work she is asked to type; it may depend upon the time of day she does a particular piece of work. Does she make more mistakes in the late afternoon when she is tired or in the early morning when she is still dreaming of the wonderful evening she had with her boy friend? Is she accident-prone in the sense that if she makes one mistake, that tends to rattle her so that more soon follow?

In problems of statistical inference that we tackle in Part II we shall often be faced with a set of data like this and want to make inferences about the sort of population it might have come from.

Our samples will not always be counts. In Chapter 1 we mentioned our hope that a sample of 15 army recruits could reasonably be regarded as a typical sample of all potential recruits in so far as their heights (measured on a ratio scale) were concerned. Of course, there are circumstances when a sample may clearly not be typical of the population we are interested in. The heights of the sample of army recruits sent to the sergeant-major would not be typical of that of all army recruits if, for example, the recruiting officer knew that the sergeant-major did not like short men and if he disliked the S.M. so much that out of spite he deliberately sent a batch of short men just to annoy him! If no such prejudices entered into the selection of the fifteen – if, for example, they were just fifteen volunteers in the order they presented themselves for enlistment – it is much more reasonable to suppose they would be typical, so far as their heights were concerned, of army recruits in general. It is still, of course, possible that selection in this way might not be typical. Suppose that these fifteen volunteers had all decided to enlist together because they had been made redundant from the local fire brigade; now fire brigades often require certain height restrictions more stringent than those applied by the army in recruiting, so a group of former firemen may not reflect the pattern or distribution of heights among army recruits at large. It would be rather less likely that there would be any selective effect upon heights if the recruits had all been butchers or lawyers. However, there could still be a nagging doubt in these latter cases; are we quite sure that height patterns do not vary between socio-economic groups?

Random Samples

There is only one way of ensuring that we do not take a sample in some way atypical, and that is by selection of a *random sample*. The concept is simple; the practical realization may be extremely difficult. A sample is random if each member of the population has an equal probability of inclusion in the sample. In Chapter 2 (Examples 3 to 8) we considered several cases of drawing numbered tickets from a population of seven tickets; we made the assumption that each had an equal probability of selection, so the sampling was random.

Obtaining a random sample of army recruits is not so easy. We suggested in Chapter 1 that we really wanted to make inferences about a conceptual population of all army recruits past, present and future. At most, at any one time we can only get a sample of recruits currently available or for whom we have existing records of height. A random sample of heights from such records would be as near as we could get to a random sample of heights of all potential recruits.

In practical statistical inference, however, we often have to make inferences from the heights observed for groups such as the 15 recruits sent to the sergeant-major and we must *hope* that they have the characteristics of a random sample. The best we could do in these circumstances is to make such inquiries as we can about any factor likely to make their height distribution atypical (were they all ex-firemen, natives of Aberdeen, or sent to the sergeant-major because they were so short?). If the answer to these and any other questions that may be relevant gives no reason to suspect that they are not *effectively* equivalent to a random sample, it is not unreasonable to proceed to make inferences on the assumption that they are. If, however, there are grounds for suspecting they may be atypical, there must be doubt about the validity of any inferences.

Assuming we are dealing with effectively random samples, what population characteristics might we expect to see reflected in the sample?

Three important aspects of a population are (i) its centre or location, (ii) its spread or dispersion, and (iii) the position regarding symmetry.

In the case of the heights of army recruits, the population is centred near 170 cm., with most young adult males who might volunteer having heights between about 157 and 183 cm. and a fairly high degree of symmetry, as we mentioned on p. 16.

During the first half of 1979 the daily exchange rate between the US$ and £UK averaged about $2·00 (= £1) but fluctuated between about $1·90 and $2·18, showing some slight lack of symmetry.

The number of mistakes a typist makes per thousand words might average about 3, but vary from 0 to 12. The average gives some idea of the location of the 'population' of mistakes. The spread or dispersion from 0 to 12 also indicates a lack of symmetry – she does not (and cannot) get far below the average, but every now and then she has a really bad spell and makes lots of mistakes.

Sample Measures of Location

It is not unreasonable to expect a random sample to give some reflection of the population location, dispersion and symmetry. We shall now discuss some measures of location that might be applied to a sample. Much practical statistical inference – both parametric and non-parametric – is concerned with the use of these to say something about location in the population from which the sample comes.

For samples of measurements there are two commonly used measures of location (sometimes also called measures of centrality); these are the *mean* and *median*; for counts a measure called the *mode* is also used. A lot of rubbish has been written about their relative merits, but which is most useful depends upon the nature of our data and the information we seek from it. We illustrate the concepts by examples.

Example 14

The heights of the 15 recruits sent to a sergeant-major are (in cm.):

163, 171, 174, 177, 176, 181, 173, 176, 168, 172, 175, 169, 174, 179, 168.

What are the mean and median heights of this sample?

The *mean* is perhaps the better known of these concepts; it is also commonly referred to as the average. To get it we add up all the observations and divide by the number we have, 15. A pocket calculator or a few calculations on the back of an envelope gives the total of the above heights as 2,596, so the *mean* height in cm. is

$$\frac{2,596}{15} = 173 \cdot 07.$$

The *median* height of the recruits is obtained by ranking them in order and is the height of the 'middle' recruit; in this case the eighth, there being 7 taller and 7 shorter. Arranging them in order of height we have:

163, 168, 168, 169, 171, 172, 173, 174, 174, 175, 176, 176, 177, 179, 181

whence we see the eighth soldier has a height of 174 cm. This is the sample *median* height. Note that if we had no available record of the heights of individual recruits, we could have obtained the median very easily by taking only one measurement. Our friend the sergeant-major, as we pointed out on p. 15, would soon ask the recruits to line up, tallest on the right and shortest on the left. When this is done, we have only to measure the height of the eighth recruit to obtain the median.

*   *   *

In this example the mean and the median are not very different. Common sense tells us that if the sample reflects accurately the form of the population, this is to be expected; it is a consequence of the symmetry of adult male heights; we expect roughly equal numbers to have heights above and below average in the population and, hopefully, in the sample too; the sample median *by definition* has the property that there are equal numbers above and below it, so the two should not differ greatly.

From the practical viewpoint, such symmetry would be distorted if the army refused to accept male recruits below a certain height and this were sufficient to exclude an appreciable proportion of short people; then the population of army recruits would have slightly different characteristics from those of adult males taken as a whole.

Let us now see when and why a mean and median may differ appreciably.

Example 15

A random sample of the staff of a large organization (including all employees from unskilled workers to top management) has incomes indicated in Table 6 (arranged in ascending order for convenience). Find the sample mean and median salaries.

Table 6   Annual salaries: sample of 25 employees

£4,200	£4,315	£4,420	£4,495	£4,520
£4,580	£4,710	£4,835	£4,950	£5,435
£5,590	£5,800	£6,250	£6,735	£6,940
£7,250	£7,435	£7,680	£7,900	£11,300
£11,800	£11,900	£11,900	£12,100	£58,200

The total of these salaries is £225,240 and dividing this by 25 gives a mean salary of £9,009.60. The median salary is that of the person ranked thirteenth (twelve below and twelve above) in Table 6 and has the value £6,250. Does not the latter seem a better indicator of location or centrality? Nineteen receive lower salaries than the mean and only six receive higher salaries.

*   *   *

If a sample is effectively random, the median is less likely to be influenced by the luck of sampling in a situation like that in Table 6; since there are presumably few senior executives on the pay-roll, there is quite a high likelihood that none may be included in a sample of 25. Suppose the highest salary in the sample had been £16,500 not £58,200, all the others being as in Table 6. The median would be unaltered but the mean would be reduced to £7,341.60.

Lack of symmetry in the salary distribution leads both to the marked difference between mean and median and to the sensitivity of the mean to inclusion or exclusion of one or two high salaries (of which there are relatively few). The mean is more sensitive than the median to outlying values in the 'tail' of a sample or population.

We have defined the sample median as a value such that there are an equal number of observations above and below it. It coincides with a sample value when there is an odd number of observations. If the number is even, it could on this basis fall anywhere between two adjacent sample values. A useful convention is to designate the value midway between the two sample values as the median. Thus the median of the sample values 2, 4, 7, 17, 21, 22, 32, 49 falls midway between 17 and 21, i.e. it is 19.

When our data consist of counts (and also in certain other situations which are of less interest to us in this book) a measure of location called the *mode* is sometimes used. It corresponds to the observation with the highest frequency. Note that the mean and median are also appropriate measures of centrality for counts, and are indeed used more frequently than the mode.

Example 16

The Social Services Department for the town of Big Dollop records the numbers of children born to each of a random sample of 100 couples in the town. These are given in Table 7. What are the mean, median and mode of the number of children per family?

Table 7 Family sizes for 100 couples in Big Dollop

No. of children	0	1	2	3	4	5	6	9
No. of families	23	29	26	9	7	3	2	1

The mean is given by the total number of children divided by the total number of families (100). The total number of children is

$$0 \times 23 + 1 \times 29 + 2 \times 26 + 3 \times 9 + 4 \times 7 + 5 \times 3 + 6 \times 2 + 9 \times 1 = 172.$$

Dividing by 100 gives a mean family size of 1·72. The median family size is such that half the families have that or a smaller number of children and half have that or a greater number of children. Thus we seek for the median a value such that 50 families have that or a smaller number of children. The situation here differs somewhat from our earlier examples as we have large numbers of 'ties'. 23 families have no children. The next smallest observed number of children is 1; this is observed 29 times. Thus, if we arrange our observations in ascending order, we have 23 zeros followed by 29 ones, giving a total of (23 + 29 =) 52 observations. The median falls midway between the 50th and 51st *ordered* observation for a sample of 100. Clearly both these observations are 1, so the median family size is 1.

Since the mode is the family size with highest frequency, this is clearly 1, no other number of children per couple appearing as frequently.

* * *

A practical disadvantage of the mode is that it may not be unique; it could happen that the family sizes zero and two were the most common frequencies; however, where it is unique, it is a useful quick indicator of location.

Despite an obvious skewness in family size the mean has a fair deal of merit as a measure of location in Example 16. The median is trapped as it were in a long string of ties.

In non-parametric methods little use is made of the mode; the median is used more frequently than the mean, although both are used.

Dispersion and Symmetry

In Example 14 there is some clustering of the heights near the mean (or the median, the two differing little in that example); for the income data in Example 15 the clustering is around the median rather than the mean. Also, extremely high incomes are further removed from the median than are extremely low incomes, e.g. the lowest income in Table 6 is £2,050 below the median, the highest income is £51,950 above it. This is an indication of lack of symmetry, usually referred to as *skewness*.

We seek some measures of *dispersion* (i.e. spread) and of symmetry or skewness. In parametric inference a measure of spread called *variance* (or its square root, the *standard deviation*) plays a prominent role. We shall have to say more about it in Chapter 4, but in non-parametric methods we often use another measure of spread called the *interquartile range*. When we have reasonable symmetry the information given by the interquartile range is similar to that given by the standard deviation (although their numerical values are not the same in any particular case). The *quartiles*, which we calculate to obtain this range, also give us information about symmetry or skewness.

The quartiles divide an ordered sample (one in which the observations are arranged in ascending order) in such a way that one quarter of the observations (in a sense about to be described) fall between each pair of quartiles – hence the name. The second quartile corresponds to the median. We have already noted that if there are an even number of observations we conventionally suppose the median to fall midway between two observations; the first and third quartile may also fall between observations. Some convention is needed to give these a unique value. One way of doing this is most easily seen with a diagram like Figure 4, which is drawn for 15 observations. We give each observation a rank, 1 for the lowest, 2 for the second lowest, up to 15 for the highest. The ranks are marked at unit distance apart on the horizontal line in Figure 4.

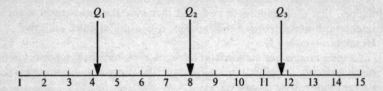

Figure 4 Quartiles for a sample of 15 observations

Now let us associate equal unit intervals with each rank on the scale; that from 0.5 to 1.5 is associated with rank 1, that from 1.5 to 2.5 with rank 2, and so on, with that from 14.5 to 15.5 being associated with rank 15. The total length from 0.5 to 15.5 is 15 units. One quarter of 15 is 3.75. To locate the quartiles we mark points 3.75 units apart starting at 0.5. Thus $0.5 + 3.75 = 4.25$. This gives the position of the first quartile, Q_1. Adding a further 3.75 we get $4.25 + 3.75 = 8.0$, giving the second quartile Q_2 or median. This is the median we got using the 'middle observation' rule. Adding a further 3.75 gives the third quartile at $(8 + 3.75 =) 11.75$. These are marked Q_1, Q_2, Q_3 in Figure 4. Many statistics books are vague about conventions to give unique quartiles and those who do give positive advice often take a different line of argument that leads to not quite identical values; the practical consequences of the differences in definition are slight in all but very small samples. The alternative definition involves the sample cumulative distribution function to be introduced on p. 192.

The interquartile range is defined as $Q_3 - Q_1$. Sometimes one half of this, the *semi-interquartile range*, is used as a measure of spread because its numerical value is usually nearer to that of the standard deviation. If a sample comes from a symmetric population, it can be expected to be reasonably symmetric itself so that Q_1 and Q_3 should be more or less equidistant from, but on opposite sides of, the median, whence $Q_3 - Q_2$ and $Q_2 - Q_1$ should be nearly equal. If these are very different, implying that one of Q_1, Q_3 is further from the median than the other, there is an indication of lack of symmetry.

With large samples – say, 100 or more – it often makes little difference what convention we adopt to get unique quartiles when these fall between observations. Indeed, to get the general picture from a sample of 120, say, it may suffice to take the 30th, 60th and 90th ordered observations as the quartiles rather than values part of the way between these and their neighbours as the various conventions require.

Example 17

Back to the army recruits; what is the interquartile range for the heights in Example 14?

As there are 15 observations we see (Figure 4) that the first quartile occurs one quarter of the way between the fourth (169) and fifth observation (171); i.e. at 'observation' 4·25, whence $Q_1 = 169·5$. Similarly Q_3 lies three quarters of the way between the observations ranked 11 and 12; since these are both 176, that is the value of Q_3 and the interquartile range is $Q_3 - Q_1 = 176 - 169·5 = 6·5$; the semi-interquartile range is $6·5/2 = 3·25$.

*   *   *

In Example 14 we found the median to be $Q_2 = 174$. Thus $Q_2 - Q_1 = 4·5$ and $Q_3 - Q_2 = 2$. This indicates some slight lack of symmetry, but with small numbers of data this is likely to happen even if we are sampling from a symmetric population. The warning here is that any given sample will not mirror all population characteristics exactly. If we took *another* sample of 15, not only would the individual heights be different, but it would indeed be surprising if the mean, median and quartiles were not different. The fact that these characteristics vary from sample to sample is a basic fact of statistical life; an understanding of the pattern of variation is a key notion in statistical inference.

Between them, Q_1, Q_2 and Q_3 provide quite a lot of information about the pattern of variability in a sample, giving information on location, spread and symmetry if examined carefully. Some writers advocate adding to these *summary statistics*, as they are called, the smallest and largest sample value; this provides an informative summary – usually called a *five-number summary* – of the data.

A word though about that expression 'summary statistics'. A statistician refers to any function of the sample values as a 'statistic'; the mean is a statistic; so is the median. The sum of the sample values would be a statistic. In later chapters we shall use the word freely in connection with various functions of the sample values that we use to test hypotheses or to estimate characteristics of the population.

Example 18

Give a five-number summary of the salary data in Example 15 (Table 6).

There are 25 observations, so we rank them 1 to 25; we leave it as an exercise to the reader to show that Q_1, Q_2, Q_3 occur at positions 6·75, 13, 19.25 in the rankings. From Table 6 it is a simple arithmetic exercise to show that $Q_1 = 4,677·5$. This follows because the observations ranked 6 and 7 are respectively 4,580 and 4,710; the difference between them is 130 and three quarters of 130 is 97·5. Adding this to 4,580 gives 4,677·5. We obtained the median $Q_2 = 6,250$ in Example 15; we leave the reader to verify that $Q_3 = 8,750$. Since the minimum and maximum incomes are respectively 4,200 and 58,200, the five-number summary is

$$4,200, 4,677·5, 6,250, 8,750, 58,200.$$

* * *

From the summary we see that the interquartile range $Q_3 = Q_1 = 4,072·5$. Since $Q_2 - Q_1 = 1,472·5$ and $Q_3 - Q_2 = 2,500$, there is a suggestion of a lack of symmetry strongly confirmed by the large distance of the maximum from the median relative to that of the minimum from the median.

Population Characteristics

Having considered some characteristics of samples, we must now say something about the population analogues. We shall deal first with populations of counts and return to one of our earlier examples; the experiment of tossing a fair coin 12 times and noting the number of heads. On p. 51 we gave the following count for a sample of 15:

$$4, 8, 8, 5, 3, 6, 7, 3, 6, 3, 9, 8, 6, 7, 5.$$

We may calculate the mean, median and quartiles for this sample in the usual way. Arranging the number of heads in ascending order we have

$$3, 3, 3, 4, 5, 5, 6, 6, 6, 7, 7, 8, 8, 8, 9.$$

We leave it as an exercise to the reader to check that the sample mean is $88/15 = 5·87$ and the quartiles are $Q_1 = 4·25$, $Q_2 = 6$ and $Q_3 = 7·75$.

We now define analogous quantities for the population. In Table 5 and Figure 3 we have depicted the binomial distribution appropriate to this situation.

Studying Figure 3 we see the obvious symmetry about the central value of 6 heads and the sharply decreasing probability as we move to either extreme. This of course is reflected in our sample by the sample mean being just a little under 6 while the sample median is exactly 6. For a population we define a quantity called the mean (or sometimes the expectation) in rather formidable mathematical terms. For the binomial distribution it always turns out to have the value np. Thus when $n = 12$ and $p = \frac{1}{2}$ the mean is $12 \times \frac{1}{2} = 6$. The median is defined as the smallest value of the random variable (here r, the number of heads) such that the probability of observing that or a smaller number of heads is at least one half. Totting up the probabilities in Table 5, we find that the probability of 6 or fewer heads is

$$\frac{1 + 12 + 66 + 220 + 495 + 792 + 924}{4,096} = \frac{2,510}{4,096}$$

and this gives the median as 6. (Check for yourself that the probability of 5 or less heads is only 1,586/4,096, clearly less than one half.)

Thus, for the binomial distribution, the mean and the median are equal. This is a characteristic of symmetric distributions. Note that the equality is not completely reflected in the sample. In our sample of 15, the sample median exactly equals the population median determined for this distribution; this would not be the case for all samples of 15 generated by coin tossing. Although the sample mean of 5·87 does not quite equal the population mean, it is close to it.

The first quartile for the population is the least number of heads for which there is a probability of at least 1/4 of getting that or a lesser number. In this example it is 5 (since the probability of 5 or less heads is seen by addition to be 1,586/4,096, while that of 4 or less is 794/4,096 which is less than 1/4). By symmetry and a similar and fairly obvious definition the third quartile is at 7 (the probability of 7 or less heads being greater than 3/4 while the probability of 6 or less heads is less than 3/4). Thus the population quartiles are at 5 and 7 while the sample quartiles are at 4·25 and 7·75 using our convention to get a unique value.

The sample mode occurs at 3, 6 and 8, each of these occurring three times; for small samples the mode is not a very worth-while measure. The mode for the population is the value with the highest associated probability, and from Figure 3 we see it is clearly 6.

We see above that there is fair agreement between certain *sample statistics* and the corresponding population characteristics even for this fairly small sample.

Let us now look at a population distribution of counts that is no longer symmetric. Again it is a binomial distribution. We consider a game in which a die is cast and we win a prize only if a 5 or 6 is scored, i.e. 5 or 6 is a 'success'. In 5 plays, what is the distribution of the numbers of successes? Again we have a binomial distribution with $n = 5$ (the number of games) and $p = \frac{1}{3}$ (the probability of success). Using formula (Eq. 12) we get the probabilities in Table 8. Figure 5 is a bar chart like Figure 3 but based on Table 8.

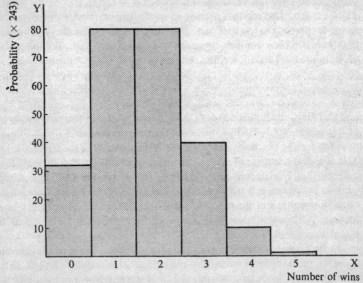

Figure 5 Bar chart for binomial distribution with $p = \frac{1}{3}$, $n = 5$

Table 8   Probabilities of 0 to 5 wins when $p = \frac{1}{2}$

Number of wins	0	1	2	3	4	5
Probability	$\frac{32}{243}$	$\frac{80}{243}$	$\frac{80}{243}$	$\frac{40}{243}$	$\frac{10}{243}$	$\frac{1}{243}$

The most obvious difference between this and the coin-tossing situation is the lack of symmetry. There is a definite element of skewness. The mean $np = 5 \times \frac{1}{3} = 1\cdot67$; the median is 2 since the probability of 1 or less successes $(80 + 32)/243 = 112/243$ is less than one half, whereas the probability of 2 or less successes exceeds one half (it is 192/243). There are two adjacent maximum probabilities corresponding to 2 and 3 successes and these form joint modes. The first and third quartiles (the reader should check) are at 1 and 2 respectively; thus the second quartile (median) and third quartile coincide. The differences $Q_2 - Q_1$ and $Q_3 - Q_2$ are 1 and 0, respectively, reflecting the skewness. The inequality of mean and median is also a reflection of skewness.

What about populations with measurements on interval or ratio scales? We shall try and link the ideas with those we have already developed for counts by first taking measurements on a very crude scale and then refining that scale. This is not unlike what we do in practice. In Example 14, for instance, all the heights of the recruits were recorded in units of one centimetre. To say a person's height is 172 cm. is effectively saying that his true height lies between 171·5 and 172·5 cm. (providing we have not made an error of measurement). This is clearly a useful and sensible practical approximation.

Now consider an even cruder approximation to something we can measure fairly accurately – the lifetime of a machine component. There is a comprehensive mathematical theory on the distribution of lifetimes of these under various circumstances. From this mathematical theory applicable to a *population* of components we can work out the probability of a component failing in various time intervals – these may be quite wide intervals of a year or very narrow intervals of only a few seconds.

Let us consider, without going into the mathematical details, one such model that is quite widely used; for a population having the appropriate distribution, tables freely available give the probabilities, shown in Table 9, of a component failing in specified time intervals after it is put into use. The interval 0–1 means that it fails in less than one year; the interval 1–2 means that it lasts one year but fails at any time between exactly one year and two years after being put into service, and so on; 6+ means that it lasts six or more years.

Table 9   Probabilities of a component failing in given time intervals

Number of years	0–1	1–2	2–3	3–4	4–5	5–6	6+
Probability fails	0·632	0·233	0·085	0·032	0·011	0·005	0·002

Note that the sum of the probabilities in Table 9 is one, as it must be for a set of mutually exclusive and exhaustive outcomes.

We may represent this data on a diagram superficially rather like the bar charts in Figures 3 and 5, but with the difference that the probabilities are no longer associated with integer values as in a count but simply represent the probability of a component failing somewhere in the one year interval between 0 and 1, between 2 and 3, and so on. Such a diagram is called a histogram; if we have unit width for each rectangle on the base line and the height equal to the probability, the area will represent the probability of failure in the given period. A small complication is introduced by the fact that the last entry corresponds to anything over 6 years – it could be 7, 8, 9 or 10 or more years. However, since the associated probability is so small, in practice we may dodge any difficulties because we cannot show anything in this tail with the scale of our diagram. (This sounds like an easy way out, but the real reason we have lumped all lives over 6 years together is precisely because they are so small that we can ignore them for most purposes.)

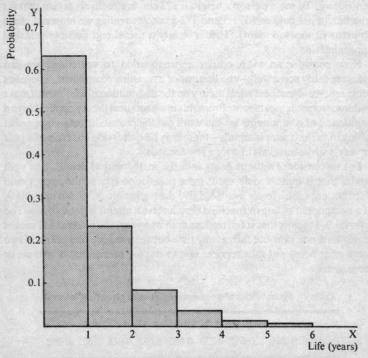

Figure 6 Histogram of life distribution of machine components

Here, as in Figure 5, we do not have symmetry, but there is a definite pattern, the probability of failure being highest in the first year, then rapidly falling off. The division into yearly intervals for the breakdown period is arbitrary. Using the same mathematical model of the lifetime distribution (or time to failure) of the component, we could further break the intervals down into quarters, months, weeks, days, hours or minutes. Had we chosen, say, monthly periods and worked out the probabilities of failure in each month during the first year, their total would still be 0·632, the value for the first year in Table 9, since breakdowns in different months are mutually exclusive events.

In Table 10 we divide the year into quarterly intervals and give the calculated probability of failure in each quarter during the first six years.

Table 10 Probabilities of machine component failures in each quarter

Year		First				Second		
Quarter	1st	2nd	3rd	4th	1st	2nd	3rd	4th
Probability	0·221	0·172	0·135	0·105	0·081	0·064	0·049	0·039
Year		Third				Fourth		
Quarter	1st	2nd	3rd	4th	1st	2nd	3rd	4th
Probability	0·029	0·024	0·018	0·014	0·011	0·009	0·007	0·005
Year		Fifth				Sixth		
Quarter	1st	2nd	3rd	4th	1st	2nd	3rd	4th
Probability	0·0040	0·0032	0·0025	0·0019	0·0014	0·0012	0·0008	0·0007

Check that, apart from round-off, the sum of the probabilities for the four quarters in any year equals the total probability for that year given in Table 9. The information in Table 10 can be put on a histogram. In Figure 6 we adopted the convention that the area of any rectangle indicated the probability associated with the interval on which it was based. Since in that diagram we had unit intervals, the height also equalled the probability. When we now use quarter-unit intervals, to make the area equal to the probability we must make the height of each rectangle four times the probability. In Figure 7 we have adopted this convention and show the rectangles depicting the data in Table 10 by solid lines. The broken lines represent the rectangles for the histogram representation in Figure 6 of the annual data. It is reasonably clear that the total area of the four quarterly rectangles for any year equals that for the annual rectangle with our scale convention (i.e. height = probability and width = 1 unit for annual data; height = 4 × probability and width = ¼ unit for quarterly data. In each case, area = probability associated with the relevant interval).

We repeat the histogram for the quarterly data in Figure 8, but this time we relate it not to the histogram for the annual data but to a smooth curve that passes through the tops of the rectangles and such that the area between the X-axis, the ordinates at the quarterly intervals and this curve is approximately the same as the area of the corresponding rectangle. This

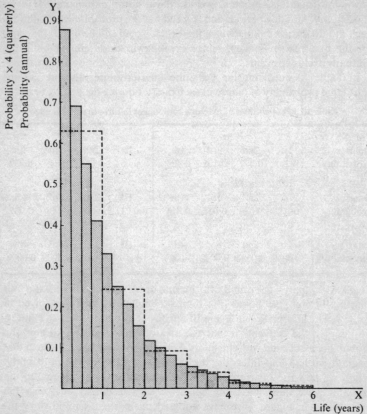

Figure 7 Histogram of life distribution of machine components.
Quarterly basis (annual superimposed)

smooth curve represents a sort of limiting curve we would get if we took shorter and shorter intervals and the rectangles in our histogram got narrower and narrower, so that the steps as we progress from one rectangle to the next become hardly discernible and all we see is a steadily decreasing curve as we move from left to right across the page.

The reader who is familiar with the exponential function in mathematics – usually denoted by the letter e – may recognize the smooth curve as the graph of e^{-x} (but do not worry if you are unfamiliar with this result). Now the area under the curve – by which we mean the area bounded by the curve and the X-axis and the ordinates at any two endpoints – gives the probability of the

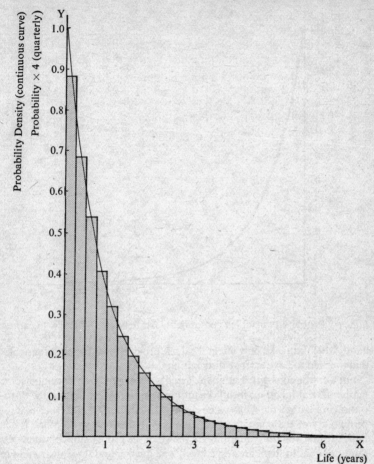

Figure 8 Histogram of life distribution of machine components.
Quarterly basis (smooth curve superimposed)

component having a lifetime in that interval. In Figure 9 the shaded area is
the probability that the component has a life between 3·2 and 4·7 years.

The curve in Figure 9 is an example of what is called the *probability density
function* or *frequency function* for a distribution. Continuous curves are
something we associate with the distribution of random variables that can
be measured on a continuous scale (e.g. those involving interval or ratio
scales). They are said to have *continuous* distributions. Counts, on the other

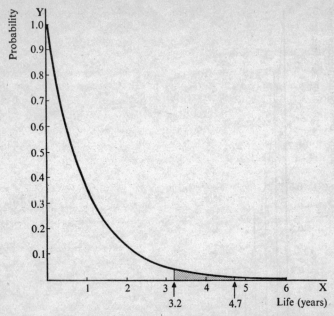

Figure 9 Probability machine component lasts between 3·2 and 4·7 years

hand, which can take only integral values, provide us with random variables that are said to have *discrete* distributions.

For a continuous distribution the mean is defined by a rather cumbersome mathematical function; it suffices for our purpose to say that for the distribution in Figure 9 the mean value is one. The median is a value such that the probability of the continuous variable having that or a lower value is one half; the first and third quartiles are such that the probabilities of values less than or equal to them are respectively one quarter and three quarters. For specific distributions working out the quartiles often means making use of calculus or, sometimes, appropriate tables; for our purposes we need not pursue this further.

For the distribution with probability density function given by the curve in Figure 9, the quartiles can be shown to be $Q_1 = 0·288$, Q_2 (median) = $0·693$, $Q_3 = 1·386$. Have a look at the interquartile range and the differences $Q_3 - Q_2$ and $Q_2 - Q_1$. Does the evidence of skewness reflect itself in these in the way you would expect intuitively from our earlier examples? Note too the difference between the mean and median; just as in discrete distributions, if a continuous distribution is symmetric, the mean and median coincide. We meet a very important example of a continuous distribution in the next chapter.

Applications

The various concepts introduced in this chapter are all relevant to what we shall be doing in Part II; at this stage it is not possible to demonstrate that relevance in a direct way; to do so now would be bringing forward ideas that rightly belong in Part II. Many of the ideas are also relevant in much broader fields of statistical inference, which is always essentially concerned with looking at how well a sample mirrors certain patterns in a population and working from that image back to the population.

Exercises

Working out means, medians and quartiles of samples is largely a matter of practice. A little care and patience is needed. From the point of view of the logic of what one is doing, some thought is required to decide whether the mean or median is more appropriate in any given situation – particularly when there is a lack of symmetry. I will not bore you with too much arithmetic at this stage, but try your hand at the following:

1. On 18 days selected at random from data for several years, the numbers of first-class passengers on a railway sleeper service between two major cities were:

   32 41 73 22 61 80 79 76 78 63 80 19 74 63 78 79 62 79.

Calculate the mean and median of the sample and prepare a five-number summary. Do you think there is evidence to suggest this might be a sample from a non-symmetric (skew) population? Can you suggest any practical reason why a skew distribution might be likely for these data?

2. Table 11 summarizes the number of accidents for each of 88 machine-shop employees in one year. Calculate the mean, median, mode and semi-interquartile range. Comment on the main characteristics of the distribution of accidents.

Table 11   Factory accident data

Number of accidents	0	1	2	3	4	5	6	7
Number of employees	42	18	11	9	3	1	3	1

3. On p. 62 we derived the distribution of a binomial variable with $p = \frac{1}{3}$ and $n = 5$ and associated it with a game of dice in which 5 or 6 was a success, and we counted the number of successes in 5 games. Now take a die and cast it to produce a sample of, say, 20 observations from this distribution. That is, perform the experiment 'casting a die' 5 times and record the number of successes; repeat this 20 times. For your resulting sample of 20, work out the sample mean, median and quartiles and use these to see how well your sample mirrors the characteristics of the population.

4. The Normal Distribution

Scope

We discuss the role of the normal distribution in non-parametric inference. While it has a key role in parametric methods, for us it only plays a supporting one. It provides useful approximations in the case of fairly large samples. We illustrate its use by practical examples and discuss its role as an approximating distribution.

A Paradox

In Chapter 1 we suggested that the heights of army recruits as a 'population' might reasonably be supposed to follow the normal distribution. This distribution has a key role in parametric methods, so it is perhaps ironic that we devote a whole chapter to it in a book on non-parametric methods when one of their prime advantages is that they avoid the often dubious assumption of the parametric approach that the sample comes from a normal population!

However, the distribution has an important subsidiary role in non-parametric inference because it enables us to develop a series of approximate tests that both simplify our arithmetic and save us having to use large and voluminous tables.

We have already alluded to the unfortunate implication of 'abnormality' among other distributions because a particular one is called the 'normal' distribution. The distribution of lives of machine components met with in Chapter 3 (pp. 63–8) has none of the characteristics of the normal distribution, yet it describes, in the everyday meaning of the word, a perfectly 'normal' situation. Although for this reason the alternative name 'Gaussian distribution', a tribute to the eminent mathematician Gauss who discovered it, is to be preferred, the former name is so common that we shall use it in this book.

A Mathematical Idealization

The normal distribution provides a mathematical description of an idealized population with the following important characteristics:

(i) it is so large that for all practical purposes it can be regarded as unlimited in size;

(ii) measurements are on an interval or ratio scale;

(iii) values are symmetrically distributed about the mean;

(iv) values close to the mean occur relatively more frequently than those further away, the frequency falling off according to a certain well-defined pattern.

The mathematical formulation for the idealized population requires a knowledge of only two quantities – the parameters – to describe the distribution. One of these is the mean, a measure of location; the other is a measure of dispersion that we mentioned only in passing in Chapter 3; it is called the standard deviation.

Let us think a little more about the heights of army recruits. Instead of the sample of 15 we talked about in Example 14, suppose we have a very large sample. Typically, although strictly speaking we measure height on a ratio scale, as we have pointed out on p. 63, the height of any individual is only recorded to the nearest centimetre in practice. To say a person's height is 174 cm. effectively means that it lies between 173·5 and 174·5 cm. If the heights of 1,000 recruits are measured and recorded in this way, we can use the data to draw a histogram in much the same way as we did in Figures 7 and 8, except that this time we have observed relative frequencies instead of probabilities. We can then draw a smooth curve to approximate to this histogram, just as we did in Figure 8. This curve is the probability density function or frequency function of the normal distribution appropriate to heights of recruits. A sample of 1,000 heights is given in Table 12 and the histogram and smooth normal probability density function is sketched in Figure 10.

The height of each rectangle in Figure 10 is equal to the proportion or fraction of the 1,000 recruits having the height specified on the base line. For example, the rectangle centred at 168 has a height of 0·054 units since 54 out of 1,000 recruits have this recorded height, i.e. a true height between 167·5 and 168·5 cm. (assuming no measuring or recording errors have been made). In practice there will usually be one or two such errors; it is all too easy to record 167 as 176 with little chance of picking up such an error afterwards; hopefully, mistakes of this sort will affect only a very small number of results.

Table 12   Heights in cm. of 1,000 potential army recruits

Height (cm.)	No. of recruits	Height (cm.)	No. of recruits
158	2	173	82
159	2	174	77
160	5	175	71
161	8	176	66
162	8	177	51
163	10	178	40
164	21	179	35
165	28	180	26
166	34	181	20
167	41	182	12
168	54	183	6
169	66	184	3
170	70	185	4
171	75	186	2
172	80	187	1
		Total	1,000

The smooth curve has the characteristic bell-shaped form widely regarded as the hallmark of normality (although some statisticians query the accuracy of the commonly used description of it as 'bell-shaped'). While it is true that there are other probability density functions that look rather similar in shape but have a different mathematical form, this is a nicety that need not worry us in applications we make.

To draw the smooth curve in Figure 10 accurately we need the values of two parameters that specify the distribution; the mean tells us at what value of the random variable the peak occurs on the probability density curve. With large samples of 500 or more it suffices to take the sample mean as the value of this parameter, for it will be very close to it. It must be realized, however, that if we took another batch of 1,000 recruits and measured their heights, the sample mean would not be exactly identical to that for the set in Table 12, but the difference would almost certainly be very small. For our data we get the sample mean by the method indicated on p. 54. Effectively we total all the heights and divide by the number of observations (here 1,000). From Table 12 we get the sum of all the heights by multiplying each given height by the number of recruits having that height and adding all such products, e.g. since 5 people have a height of 160 they contribute 160 + 160 + 160 + 160 + 160, which is 5 × 160, to the total. The whole operation is easily done with a pocket calculator; there are some short cuts

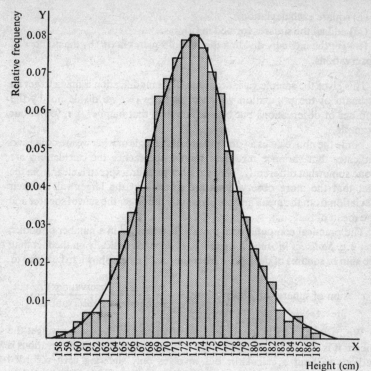

Figure 10 Histogram and normal probability density function for heights

possible if you have not got one, these being described in many elementary statistical texts; see, e.g. Wetherill (1972).

The sample mean turns out to be 172·38. We note in passing that the median is 172 (there being 504 recruits with this or a lesser height but only 424 with a height of 171 or less).

To find the standard deviation, the second parameter needed to specify the normal probability density function relevant to a particular problem, if we have a large sample, we first calculate a quantity which is the square of this and is called the 'variance'. Basically the sample variance is the mean of the squares of the deviations of each observation from the mean. This sounds a bit of a mouthful but we can calculate it step by step as follows:

(i) subtract the mean from each observation to get its deviation from the mean, e.g. for a height of 169 the deviation is $169 - 172·38 = -3·38$ and for a height of 178 the deviation is $178 - 172·38 = 5·62$,

(ii) square each deviation,

(iii) add all the squares formed in (ii),

(iv) get the mean by dividing the sum of squares in (iii) by the number of observations.

This gives the sample variance. One slight modification is made to get an estimate of the population variance; at stage (iv) we divide not by the number of observations but by *one less* than that number, i.e. 999 in our example.

While the above gives a good picture of the logic of what we are doing and indicates that variance measures spread, in practice the calculations are done somewhat differently. That variance measures spread is clear from the fact that the more observations are spread out the larger will be their deviation from the mean and consequently the larger the sum of squares and the mean of that sum.

The practical computational method is described in a number of books; see, e.g. *Statistics in Action*, pp. 77–8. It depends basically on the fact that the sum of squares of deviations from the mean can be shown to be equal to

$$\text{sum of squares all observations} - \frac{(\text{sum of all observations})^2}{\text{the number of observations}}.$$

We have previously found the sum of all observations when we get the mean; it is in fact 172,384. Finding the sum of squares of all observations is tedious without a calculator but involves only squaring each recorded height, multiplying that square by the number of recruits having that height and adding all the resulting products. This gives a value for the sum of squares of 29,740,352, so the sum of squares of deviations from the mean turns out to be

$$29{,}740{,}352 - \frac{(172{,}384)^2}{1{,}000} = 29{,}740{,}352 - 29{,}716{,}243$$

$$= 24{,}109.$$

We estimate the population variance by dividing this by $n - 1 = 999$, giving $24 \cdot 133$. The square root of this is the standard deviation of $4 \cdot 912$.

We emphasize that the method of estimating population mean and standard deviation from a sample will only give very accurate estimates if the sample is large. For small samples we may still make estimates; one of the problems of parametric inference is deciding how good these estimates are.

When we have good values for the mean and standard deviation we may put them in a rather formidable-looking mathematical expression which gives us the values of the probability density function. If we know its value at a number of points, we can plot on a graph the probability density function for the normal distribution which has those *specified* values of mean and standard deviation.

Using the Normal Distribution

Suppose we had been measuring not the heights of army recruits but the weights of frogs in a pond. For adult male frogs it is quite likely that their weights (in grammes, say) would follow a normal distribution. The specific ratio scale (one of weights) and what is being measured are now quite different from that for the heights of recruits. The frogs may turn out to have a mean weight of 52 gm. with standard deviation of 10 gm. If we had weights for a large sample of frogs, we might again get a good fit to our data with a bell-shaped curve; this time it would have a peak at 52 and a spread consistent with a standard deviation of 10.

General values of the parameters mean and standard deviation for a normal distribution are conventionally denoted by two Greek letters:

μ (pronounced *mu*) for the mean and
σ (pronounced *sigma*) for the standard deviation.

We shall use the symbol X to denote a random variable with a normal distribution with mean μ and standard deviation σ. There is a standard result in statistical theory (one we shall assume) that if we subtract μ from every value of X and divide the result by σ, we get a new random variable, which we shall call Z, that still has a normal distribution. It is a rather special normal distribution for which the mean is zero and the standard deviation is one. We call Z a *standard normal variable*. In symbols, if X is a normal variable with mean μ and standard deviation σ, then

$$Z = \frac{X - \mu}{\sigma} \qquad \text{(Eq. 13)}$$

is a standard normal variable.

Technically, if we want to know the probability that a normally distributed random variable X takes a value between any two fixed numbers a and b, we must calculate the area shaded in Figure 11. The argument is similar to that on p. 66.

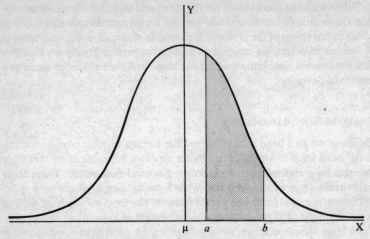

Figure 11 Probability X takes a value between a and b

Readers familiar with calculus will recognize this as a problem of integration, but it is by no means a trivial one and mathematicians have to resort to quite sophisticated numerical methods to get the answer.

Because of the relationship (Eq. 13), we can reduce such problems for any X with known μ and σ to one in the standard normal variable Z. Tables then exist to enable us to solve the problem. The procedure is best illustrated by examples.

Example 19

Suppose the weights of adult male frogs in a certain pond are normally distributed with a mean of 52 gm. and standard deviation of 10 gm. What proportion of the frogs weigh more than 55 gm.?

Using (Eq. 13) with $\mu = 52$, $\sigma = 10$, a value of X greater than 55 clearly implies a value of Z greater than

$$\frac{55 - 52}{10} = 0 \cdot 3.$$

To solve our problem, we therefore need to know the probability that a standard normal variable takes a value greater than 0·3.

Many statistical textbooks and collections of tables give the requisite value. A typical table is Table 24 in *The Penguin Book of Mathematical and Statistical Tables* (1980), which we shall refer to in future simply as the *Penguin Tables*.

What such tables give us directly is the probability that Z is less than 0.3. Figures 12(a) and (b) give the bell-shaped curve for the standard normal distribution with mean at zero. The shaded area in Figure 12(a) is that recorded in the tables opposite $Z = 0.3$; we read this from the tables as 0.6179. The area we want is that shaded in Figure 12(b), which represents the opposite event to that for which the probability is given by shading in Figure 12(a). Thus the associated probability (see p. 29) is $1 - 0.6179 = 0.3821$. Thus, a proportion of 0.3821 or 38.21 per cent of the frogs will exceed 55 gm. weight.

*　　*　　*

Note that the area between the curve and the axis marked Z in Figures 12(a) and (b) is one. Why?

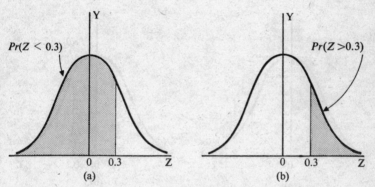

Figure 12 Opposite events and their probabilities for a standard normal variable

Example 20

Given the distribution in Example 19, what is the probability that the weight of a frog differs by less than 3 gm. from the population mean of 52 gm.?

This implies that X lies between 49 and 55 gm. Because of the symmetry of the normal distribution, the probability that X lies between 49 and 52 gm. (below but not more than 3 gm. below the mean) equals the probability that X lies between 52 and 55 gm. (above but not more than 3 gm. above the mean).

The probability that X lies between 52 and 55 is the same as the probability that Z lies between 0 and 0.3, since when $X = 52$, Z is defined by

(Eq. 13) as $(52 - 52)/10 = 0$, and when $X = 55$, we have already seen that $Z = 0.3$. Symbolically we write

$$Pr(0 < Z < 0.3) = Pr(Z < 0.3) - Pr(Z < 0). \qquad \text{(Eq. 14)}$$

Writing the result in this form enables us to read the probabilities direct from the *Penguin Tables*. We already know from Example 19 that $Pr(Z<0.3) = 0.6179$. Clearly, by symmetry (or from the tables, $Pr(Z<0) = 0.5$. Thus the probability that Z lies between 0 and 0.3 is given by (Eq. 14) as $0.6179-0.5 = 0.1179$. We have already seen that this is the probability that X lies between 52 and 55, and this in turn equals the probability that X lies between 49 and 52. Since these are mutually exclusive events, the probability that X lies between 49 and 55 is $2 \times 0.1179 = 0.2358$. Figures 13(a), (b), (c) show the relevant areas on the standard normal probability density diagram.

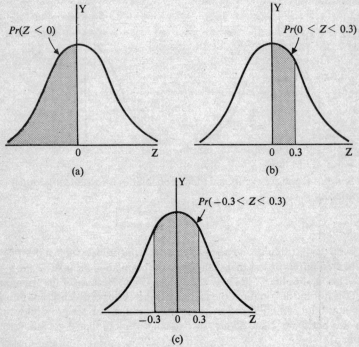

Figure 13 Some probabilities relevant to Example 20

*   *   *

Approximation by a Normal Distribution

The normal distribution is relevant to measurements on a continuous (interval or ratio) scale. We showed in Table 12 and Figure 10 that we got a good approximation even if our data were rounded off (in that case, to the nearest cm.). We can in fact, under certain circumstances, approximate to distributions of counts with a normal distribution. This approximation is particularly relevant to non-parametric methods. In Example 13 (the cream samples), we used the sign test to work out the probabilities of certain unlikely events for a binomial distribution with $p = \frac{1}{2}$; these were the extreme or 'tail' values corresponding to very few or a great many plus signs. Had n been much larger, this would prove rather tedious.

If we represent binomial probabilities by a bar chart as we did for the case $p = \frac{1}{2}$ and $n = 12$ in Figure 10 we see that this has basically the appearance of a histogram. We have reproduced the bar chart in Figure 14 and superimposed on it an appropriate (we shall explain below what we mean by this) normal probability density curve. You see now a reason emerging for our preference for the bar diagram over the simpler representation used in Figure 2.

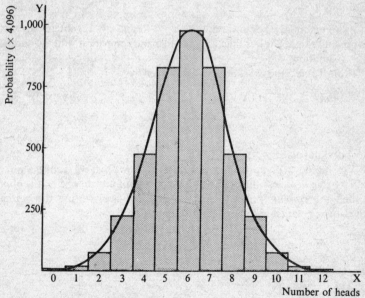

Figure 14 Bar chart for binomial distribution ($p = \frac{1}{2}$, $n = 12$)
and normal probability density curve

The areas to the left of any of the vertical boundaries at 0·5, 1·5, 2·5 composed of the rectangles involved are tolerably well approximated by the areas under the probability density curve to the left of such boundaries. Thus, if we want the probability that X (where X is now the value of the binomial random variable 'number of successes') takes a value of, say, 3 or less, i.e. the probability that $X = 0$ or 1 or 2 or 3, we could approximate it by the area under the smooth curve to the left of 3·5.

What are the values of μ and σ for the normal curve we have fitted? In Chapter 3 we stated the intuitively reasonable result that the mean for a binomially distributed variable is np. This is the value of μ that we take for the normal approximation. In our case, $\mu = np = 12 \times \frac{1}{2} = 6$. We have still to discuss the standard deviation of a binomial variable, but it has in fact the value $\sqrt{(npq)}$, a result we shall assume. When $n = 12$ and $p = \frac{1}{2}$, it follows that $q = 1 - p = \frac{1}{2}$ whence $npq = 12 \times \frac{1}{2} \times \frac{1}{2} = 3$. Thus, $\sqrt{npq} = 1·7321$. This is what we take for σ in the normal approximation.

We now compare the normal approximation with the exact result for $Pr(X \leqq 3)$. The symbol $\leqq$ means *is less than or equal to*.

Example 21

If X is a binomial random variable with $p = \frac{1}{2}$ and $n = 12$, obtain the exact probability that X is less than or equal to 3 and compare it with the normal approximation.

From Table 5 the exact probability is given by

$$Pr(X \leqq 3) = Pr(X = 0) + Pr(X = 1) + Pr(X = 2) + Pr(X = 3)$$

$$= \frac{1 + 12 + 66 + 220}{4,096} = \frac{299}{4,096} = 0·0728$$

to 4 decimal places.

For the normal approximation Figure 14 shows that we want the probability that X is less than 3·5. (The procedure of adding one half is often called the *continuity correction*.) To calculate this, we use the normal distribution with $\mu = 6$ and $\sigma = 1·7321$, according to which

$$Z = \frac{X - 6}{1·7321}$$

is a standard normal variable.

Thus,

$$Pr(X < 3·5) = Pr(Z < \frac{3·5 - 6}{1·7321}) = Pr(Z < \frac{-2·5}{1·7321}) = Pr(Z < -1·443).$$

The *Penguin Tables* (and most others) only give probabilities corresponding to positive values of Z, but Figures 15(a) and (b) show clearly that $Pr(Z < -1.443) = Pr(Z > 1.443)$, and by similar arguments to those used in Example 19, $Pr(Z > 1.443) = 1 - Pr(Z < 1.443)$. From tables we find that $Pr(Z < 1.443) = 0.925$, whence the required probability is $1 - 0.925 = 0.075$. The exact binomial probability was 0.0728, so the normal approximation is correct to 2 decimal places.

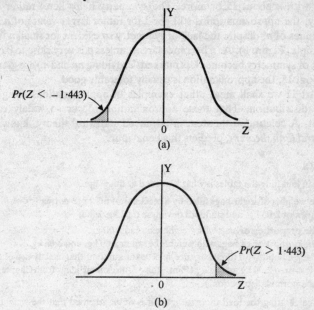

(a)

(b)

Figure 15 Use of symmetry for probabilities corresponding to negative Z

For larger n the approximation is even better.

Example 22

For a binomial distribution with $p = \frac{1}{2}$ and $n = 36$, compare the true probability of $X \leq 13$ with the normal approximation.

By tedious calculation or with appropriate tables if these happen to be available (and they rarely are for such high values of n), the exact probability can be shown to be 0.0662. For the normal approximation, we have a normal distribution with $np = 18$ and $\sqrt{npq} = 3$. Allowing for a continuity correction, we calculate as follows:

$$Pr(X < 13 \cdot 5) = Pr(Z < \frac{13 \cdot 5 - 18}{3}) = Pr(Z < -1 \cdot 5) = Pr(Z > 1 \cdot 5)$$
$$= 1 - 0 \cdot 9332 = 0 \cdot 0668.$$

The results almost agree to 3 decimal places.

* * *

The normal approximation to the binomial distribution is quite good for $p = \frac{1}{2}$ with n about 15 or more. The symmetry helps here; rather surprisingly, the approximation is still good for rather larger values of n and other values of p, despite the lack of symmetry so evident for small n (see, for example, Figure 5). As n becomes larger, unless p is very close to 0 or 1, the lack of symmetry becomes less marked. Providing np and nq are greater than about 15, the approximation is usually tolerably good.

In Part II we shall meet other examples of approximations using the normal distribution. That these approximations occur so widely is no accident. A celebrated theorem in advanced statistical theory, known as the *central limit theorem*, predicts this behaviour.

Exercises

Practice in handling the tables is what is needed at this stage.

1. The weights of sugar bags filled by a mechanical filler are normally distributed with a mean of 2·05 kg. and standard deviation 0·02 kg. Find:

  (i) the proportion of bags with weight less than 2·00 kg.
  (ii) the proportion of bags with weights between 2·00 kg. and 2·08 kg.
  (iii) the probability, if three bags are selected at random, that exactly two of them contain less than 2·00 kg. of sugar? (Hint – this requires some ideas from Chapter 2 as well as the normal distribution.)

2. In calculating the load in an airliner, it is often assumed that the weight of a passenger plus his hand baggage is normally distributed. If this assumption is correct, then it can be assumed that the total weight of 100 passengers and their hand baggage is also normally distributed. If this total has a mean of 8,000 kg. and a standard deviation of 180 kg., find the probability that the total weight of 100 passengers and their hand baggage: (a) exceeds 8,250 kg.; (b) lies between 7,800 and 8,400 kg.; (c) lies within a range of 360 kg. either side of the mean of 8,000 kg.

An airline official correctly declared to me that there was only a probability of 0·01 that the weight of 100 passengers plus their hand baggage would exceed a certain figure. Unfortunately I have forgotten that figure. Use your tables to work it out for me, please.

3. According to what we said above, if we have a binomial distribution with $n = 45$ and $p = 0·9$, the normal approximation may not be very good, since $nq = 4·5$ only. Nevertheless, use it to work out the probability of 43 or more successes. (For comparison, the exact probability of this event is 0·1590.)

Part II

Applied Non-parametric Methods

5. Methods for Single Samples

This is a rather large topic and it is convenient to divide the chapter into two sections – really sub-chapters.

Section A   The Sign Test

Scope

In this section of the chapter we explore the use of the sign test when we are given a single sample of observations. We look at problems that may arise with certain uninformative observations and also consider short cuts that may be introduced with fairly large samples.

We meet for the first time the important concept of a *confidence interval*. The test is extended to inferences about quartiles and a sign test for trend is also described.

More about the Sign Test

The sign test was used in Example 13 with the bacterial counts on cream. We may use it in even simpler situations.

Now we are getting to the core of non-parametric methods, we shall present the techniques largely by way of examples following the pattern indicated on p. 19, although the divisions into 'statistical formulation', 'procedure', etc., will be interpreted fairly broadly to allow free discussion of interesting general points as they arise during the working of an example.

Example 23

The Problem. A professional body conducts a qualifying examination for all who wish to become members; this is a national examination with some

3,000 entrants. In one year the examiners reported that the median mark for all candidates was 54.

Goldbeach College entered 17 candidates and their marks were:

38 29 58 41 82 51 45 39 60 42 36 55 46 61 43 52 64.

The Goldbeach Students Association is not very happy about these marks, considering they indicate a performance below the national average. The College Principal denies this and claims that if we took a random sample of all entrants for the examination we might well get a set of marks like those for his 17 candidates. Can the Principal's claim be substantiated, if the only information we have is the college marks given above and the national median mark of 54?

Statistical Formulation. We are told that the *population* median is 54; the question at issue is whether there is evidence to reject the claim that the above marks are a random sample from such a population. If the sample were a random sample from this population, then there is a probability of one half that any candidate's mark will be less than the median and a probability of one half that it will be greater (ignoring temporarily the possibility that the mark equals the median – a complication we shall deal with on p. 89. We therefore examine the distribution of college marks to determine how many are above and how many are below the hypothetical median of 54; if there are excessive numbers above or below the median, this is evidence against the null hypothesis (p. 41) that the sample comes from a population with median 54; such evidence would imply that Goldbeach students were not a random sample from a population with that median.

We may denote a mark above 54 by a plus and one below by a minus; clearly, under the null hypothesis the probability of each sample mark being a plus is one half; the probability of it being a minus is also one half. The sign test that we introduced in Example 13 is appropriate.

Procedure. The sequence of plus and minus signs for this example, taking the marks in the order given above, is

$$- \ - \ + \ - \ + \ - \ - \ - \ + \ - \ - \ + \ - \ + \ - \ - \ +,$$

a total of 11 minus and 6 plus. Before proceeding further we must decide if a one-tail or a two-tail test (p. 45) is appropriate. While the Goldbeach Students Association have claimed that the results are worse than the national pattern (implying a lower median), this information does not in itself justify a one-tail test; this is just a hunch the Association has; there may be good reason to have anticipated (before the results became known) a better than average performance from Goldbeach students; this may be attributable to higher entrance standards or supposed superiority of teaching. If, on the other hand, it were known that Goldbeach students had only covered half the syllabus and that two lecturers had been sacked for incompetence during the course, these facts might provide grounds for believing that *at best* the Goldbeach students could only reach the national standard and that if they did not, then they certainly would be below it. If we had such evidence we might accept as the only reasonable alternative the hypothesis that the sample came from a population with median less than 54. However, we shall suppose there is no such evidence, so a two-tail test appropriate to the alternative hypothesis that the median of the population from which our sample came is some value other than 54 – it could be above or below – is required.

We could carry out such a test by calculating the probabilities of 6 or less plus signs in 17 observations (which by symmetry is equal to the probability of 11 or more plus signs), using (Eq. 12) for the binomial distribution with $p = \frac{1}{2}$ and $n = 17$. This was the way we did things in Example 13. However the binomial distribution with $p = \frac{1}{2}$ is so commonly used that the results have been tabulated to save us calculating them each time. Table 22 in the *Penguin Tables* is one such table and an abridged version is given in Table A1 in the Appendix to this book. If we enter that table in the row labelled 17 (the value of n) on the left and proceed along that row to the column headed $r = 6$ (the number of plus signs), we find the entry $0 \cdot 166$. This is the probability of getting 6 *or fewer* plus signs when the null hypothesis (implying $p = \frac{1}{2}$) is true. By symmetry the probability of 11 or more plus signs is also $0 \cdot 166$.

Thus the probability of getting our result or one that is less likely, if the null hypothesis is true, is $2 \times 0 \cdot 166 = 0 \cdot 332$, approximately one third.

Conclusion. Since we could expect a result as or more extreme about once in every three samples examined, if the null hypothesis were true, we cannot reasonably reject this hypothesis. Therefore, despite the preponderance of minus signs, we accept that the sample is quite likely one from a population with median 54.

Comments. Remember that continuing to accept the null hypothesis that Goldbeach students are *not atypical* does not prove in an absolute sense that they are typical; it only means that there is insufficient evidence to cast serious doubts upon the null hypothesis. Nevertheless our evidence would support some alternatives even more strongly. One such alternative would be that the data came from a population with median 50; then, applying a sign test, we would have 9 minus and 8 plus signs, about as good a reflection of population characteristics as one could get in a sample of 17. The fact that data may support several different hypotheses will be further considered when we introduce the idea of a confidence interval and confidence limits in Example 25.

*   *   *

Had the logic of the problem in Example 23 indicated a one-tail test, we note that it still would not have given grounds for rejecting the null hypothesis since the probability of 6 or less plus signs was 0·166, well in excess of 0·05, the maximum permissible for significance at the 5 per cent level.

The Influence of Sample Size on Significance

The size of the sample has an influence on our ability to pinpoint departures from hypotheses. Broadly speaking, the greater the number of observations, the more likely we are to detect a departure of a given amount from the null hypothesis, if that departure really exists.

Example 24

The Problem. Suppose that as well as the marks given in Example 23 we had marks for an additional eight Goldbeach students and that these were 29, 43, 81, 52, 53, 42, 49 and 32. Would we still regard it as reasonable to assume the total sample – now $17 + 8 = 25$ – came from a population with median 54?

Statistical Formulation. Similar to Example 23, but we now base our test on 25 candidates.

Procedure. In the first 17 observations we scored 11 minus (below 54) and 6 plus. Corresponding signs for the 8 additional observations are:

$$- - + - - - - -,$$

i.e. 1 plus and 7 minus, making for all 25 observations a total of 7 plus and 18 minus signs with $n = 25$. This is beyond the range of Table A1, so we must resort to more detailed tables. Those in the *Penguin Tables* show us that with $n = 25$ the probability of 7 or fewer plus signs is now 0·022; for a two-tail test we multiply this by 2 to allow for probabilities associated with the symmetric upper tail (18 or more plus signs). The probability of our result or relevant less likely ones is $2 \times 0.022 = 0.044$.

Conclusion. Since 0.044 is less than 0.05, we reject at the nominal 5 per cent significance level the hypothesis that our sample comes from a population with median 54. The evidence points to its coming from a population with a lower median.

Comments. The additional observations have resulted in a dramatic drop (from 0.332 to 0.044) in the probability of a result as or more extreme than that observed even though the proportion of plus signs has only dropped from 6 out of 17 (35·3%) to 7 out of 25 (28%). We shall see in Example 27 that if we quadruple the original sample size from 17 to 68 but keep the proportion of plus signs at the original 35·3 per cent (i.e. 24 plus signs out of 68) we would get a significant result. In the comments on that example we suggest an approximate method of dealing with our sample of 25 that avoids the need for binomial tables.

*   *   *

There is a small logical fallacy in our arguments in Examples 23 and 24 that fortunately has no serious practical consequences. The population median of 54 quoted by the examining authorities *included* the results for the Goldbeach candidates. Strictly, we should have compared Goldbeach candidates with a population of *other* students who could be regarded as typical of the national pattern. Since other students heavily outnumber those from Goldbeach College (total entries being about 3,000), removing the latter from the population would be unlikely to alter substantially the median of 54 used in our calculations and would have little influence on our findings.

The influence of sample size upon our ability to detect significance highlights the fact that *statistical significance* and *practical importance* need not be the same thing. If we have a very large number of observations we can detect very small departures from a null hypothesis, but these may be of little practical importance. This matter is discussed in a more general context in Chapters 2 and 3 of *Statistics in Action*.

Ties

A slight problem would have arisen if one of the Goldbeach students had actually scored a mark of 54; being neither above nor below the population median, we cannot fairly allocate it to either the plus or the minus group. Usually, when performing a sign test, we ignore the observations that are exactly the same as the median specified in the null hypothesis; we reduce the number of observations actually involved in the test by one for each such tie, so that the effective value of n is simply the total number of plus and minus signs.

In Example 57 we face a situation where ties play a more dominant role in a sign test.

Estimating a Median

Suppose we are given a sample and asked to make some sort of informative statement about the median of the population from which it has been obtained. A rather cumbersome way to proceed would be to carry out a large number of hypothesis tests with *assumed* values of the median of the population. If we took a wide range of values, hopefully some of these would be acceptable and others would be rejected. This would give us some idea of a range of acceptable values. Such a procedure would be rather hit-and-miss, not to say time-consuming. However, it does suggest a useful concept, that of defining a range of values that would result in acceptable hypotheses. We might try to do this by using some systematic way of finding the end points of such a range. We may then explore the properties of this range.

We shall consider first a situation where we are given a sample of observations and asked to estimate the median of the population from which the sample is taken. We make no assumption of symmetry and have no other information about the population than that provided by the sample; this is just the situation in which the sign test would be appropriate for hypothesis testing. How to proceed is best illustrated by linking our description to an example.

Example 25

The Problem. A new type of sparking-plug is under test and the manufacturers are interested in the petrol consumption obtainable when it is used in a particular model of car. They carry out tests in accordance with Government-approved procedures for estimating petrol consumption on 12 vehicles of the given model, each fitted with the new type of plug. The petrol consumption figures in miles per gallon are:

42·2 39·7 44·1 43·3 38·7 45·9 51·3 46·8 42·4 44·7 49·3 43·8.

Estimate the median consumption for cars of this model using this type of plug. We shall assume that the 12 cars tested are effectively a random sample from the total output of that model.

Statistical Formulation. We seek a range of potential values of the population median that would be acceptable on the basis of the observed sample and shall endeavour to make some statement of our degree of belief that the true median is among these values. A statement of this sort is necessary because, using the 5 per cent significance level, we shall sometimes reject the null hypothesis when it is true; there is 1 chance in 20 of getting a result in a critical region of size 0·05 (5 per cent) when the null hypothesis is true.

Procedure. Let us first arrange the sample values in ascending order:

38·7 39·7 42·2 42·4 43·3 43·8 44·1 44·7 45·9 46·8 49·3 51·3.

Our definition of sample median (p. 54) tells us that this lies midway between the sixth and seventh ordered observation, i.e. it is $(43·8 + 44·1)/2 = 43·95$. A sign test would certainly accept this as a possible value of the population median, for with this value specified under the null hypothesis our sample would give 6 plus and 6 minus signs. We sometimes refer to this estimate as a *point* estimate of the population median.

Now let us turn our attention to the problem of finding values above and below this that would just be acceptable using a two-tail test with critical region having a size not greater than 0·05. Here Table A1 comes to our aid. We enter it with $n = 12$ and search along that row for an entry which does not exceed *one half* of the size of our critical region, but is as near to this as possible. The relevant entry is 0·019, corresponding to $r = 2$. This tells us that, using a two-tail test, we would reject any hypothesized value of the population median that gave us 2 or less plus signs or, in the symmetrical upper tail, 10 or more plus signs, i.e. the probability of 0, 1, 2, 10, 11 or 12 plus signs is $2 \times 0·019 = 0·038$, and this is the actual size of the nominal 0·05 critical region. For the meanings of actual and nominal in this context see p. 44.

Now, looking at the ordered observations, it is immediately clear that we should have 2 or less plus signs if the hypothesized median exceeded 46·8, and we would have 10 or more plus signs if it were less than 42·2. Values of the hypothetical population median greater than 42·2 but less than 46·8 would all lead to acceptance of the hypothesis; so would the values 42·2 and 46·8 themselves, for we should then have a tie which effectively reduces the sample size by one and increases the probability of 2 or fewer or 10 or more plus signs.

We have thus established a range of acceptable values for the median, i.e. those between 42·2 and 46·8.

However, if we took a further sample of 12 cars, we would get a different set of fuel-consumption figures. They might be (in ascending order for convenience):

37·2 39·1 41·3 42·5 42·8 42·8 43·9 45·4 47·4 47·8 48·0 48·3.

By the arguments used for the original sample, we would accept hypotheses for any population median between 41·3 and 47·8, these being the third largest and third smallest values.

The true population median has some *fixed* but unknown value. Now, if we could repeatedly test the hypothesis that we had a sample from a population that had this median value, in the long run we should reject the null hypothesis in a proportion of 0·038 (i.e. 3·8 per cent) of the tests. This in turn implies that if we take a large number of samples and calculate the range of 'acceptable' values of the population median corresponding to each sample (as we have just been doing), then in 3·8 per cent of the cases the true value would not be included in the range of acceptable values.

Thus if we work out a range for our one sample and make the assertion that the true value lies within this range we shall be correct in our assertion unless we have encountered one of the 3·8 per cent of exceptional cases; there remain $100 - 3·8 = 96·2$ per cent of all cases. This latter percentage represents a *degree of confidence* in the truth of our statement: 'The population median lies in this specified range.' Note that we are not stating that there is an equivalent probability of 0·962 that the true value lies within that range, for the true value is a fixed but unknown constant. The probability refers to the odds of our correctly selecting a range that includes that true value. If we repeated the experiment over and over again, getting a different range each time, the probability refers to the proportion of times we shall be right in asserting: 'This range includes the true value.' It is an expression of our degree of confidence in the statement being true. If we base our interval on a critical region of size α we obtain $100(1 - \alpha)$ per cent confidence intervals. We may speak of actual or nominal intervals. In our case the actual value of α was 0·038, the nominal value 0·05, so our interval is an actual 96·2 per cent confidence interval, as already implied, or a nominal 95 per cent interval. Other nominal levels commonly used are 99 and 99·9 per cent (corresponding to 1 per cent and 0·1 per cent significance levels); the 90 per cent level is also used sometimes. The end points of the interval are usually called the *confidence limits*. The interval is often specified by writing the limits in brackets, e.g. (42·2, 46·8).

Conclusion. For the first sample the point estimate of the population median is 43·95 (the sample median) and nominal 95 per cent (actual level 96·2 per cent) confidence limits are 42·2 and 46·8; in other words, the confidence interval is (42·2, 46·8).

Comments. In this example we have rather mixed the explanation of the logic with the calculation of the answer, but the logic is best explained with the aid of an example.

*   *   *

The choice of conventional nominal levels is a carry-over from parametric methods where the nominal and actual levels usually coincide and where choice of level is often restricted only by availability of appropriate tables.

Generally speaking, the higher the degree of confidence, the wider the interval we get; in other words, by allowing a greater range of acceptable values, we are increasing the chances of our statement: 'This interval contains the population median' being a true statement. Thus from Table A1 when $n = 12$ we see that if we chose a critical region corresponding to 0, 1, 11 or 12 plus signs the size of the critical region would be $2 \times 0·003 = 0·006$. Applying this to the first sample in Example 25, we see that we would accept all hypothetical medians lying between 39·7 and 49·3. Thus a $100(1 - 0·006) = 99·4$ per cent actual (or 99 per cent nominal) confidence interval for the population median would be (39·7, 49·3). Confidence limits and intervals are also discussed in general terms in *Statistics in Action*, pp. 89–93.

Inferences about Quartiles

In Examples 23 and 24 all we knew about the population was that the median value was 54. Suppose the examiners' report had dropped the further pearl of wisdom that 25 per cent of the candidates scored a mark of 47 or less; we would know that the lower quartile for the population was 47. This means that if the Goldbeach College candidates were a random sample from the population, we should expect only about one quarter of them to get a mark below 47.

Example 26

The Problem. Given the Goldbeach College results for 17 candidates in Example 23 (i.e. 38, 29, 58, 41, 82, 51, 45, 39, 60, 42, 36, 55, 46, 61, 43, 52,

64) and the information that the first quartile for the population is 47, is there any evidence that the Goldbeach candidates may not be a sample from the population?

Statistical Formulation. It is convenient to frame the problem as one of testing the null hypothesis that the sample could reasonably be a random sample from a population with a first quartile of 47. Then there is a probability of ¾ that any candidate scores more than 47 and a probability of ¼ that the candidate scores less. If we call a mark above 47 a 'success', then the number of successes will have a binomial distribution with $n = 17$, $p = ¾$ under the null hypothesis. We shall assume a two-tail test is appropriate for the reasons given in Example 23.

Procedure. The marks above 47 are 58, 82, 51, 60, 55, 61, 52, 64 – a total of eight successes. For our significance test we shall require the probabilities of 8 or any lesser number of successes, since any number less than 8 is clearly even stronger evidence against the null hypothesis; in addition there may be very large numbers of successes which have probabilities less than or equal to that for exactly 8 successes; these will also provide evidence against the null hypothesis and should be included in the critical region appropriate to a two-tail test.

With $p = ¾$ we no longer have the symmetry we had for $p = ½$, so we need a different type of table. Table A2 in the Appendix gives the probability of r successes when $p = ¾$ for all n between 10 and 20 inclusive; probabilities are given for each r for which the probability is less than 0·05 and also for the value of r in each tail for which the probability first exceeds 0·05.

We enter Table A2 in the row $n = 17$ and the column $r = 8$ (the number of successes). The entry 0·0093 is the probability of 8 successes. Had the probability exceeded 0·05, we could have terminated the test, concluding immediately that the result was not significant. As it is less than 0·05 we must add the upper and lower tail probabilities for $n = 17$ that are less than or equal to 0·0093. From the table we see that in the lower tail the probabilities of 7, 6 or 5 successes (all mutually exclusive events) are 0·0025, 0·0005 and 0·0001, totalling 0·0031; we may ignore the probabilities of even fewer successes as they are so small as to affect the fourth decimal place at most. In the upper tail the only probability less than 0·0093 is 0·0075 corresponding to 17 successes. Thus the probability of a result as or more extreme than that observed is

$Pr(8 \text{ successes}) + Pr(\text{less than } 8 \text{ successes}) + Pr(17 \text{ successes})$

$= 0 \cdot 0093 + 0 \cdot 0031 + 0 \cdot 0075$

$= 0 \cdot 0199.$

Conclusion. Since the above probability is less than $0 \cdot 05$, we conclude that the result is significant at the 5 per cent level and reject the hypothesis that the sample can reasonably be supposed to come from a population with a first quartile at 47.

Comments. Although we did not reject the hypothesis that the sample came from a population with median equal to that for the national results (Example 23), we now find evidence that there are more candidates in the lower tail than we might expect from information for the results in the country at large; this indicates that the College is probably entering a higher proportion of weak or badly prepared candidates and that there may be some substance in their Students Association's complaints.

* * *

With additional information about the quartile we have reached a conclusion about Goldbeach students we could not have reached with information on the median alone. There is no anomaly here; a sample may indeed come from one of two populations with the same median, but each of these may have a different first quartile.

If we know several features of a population, rather than testing for consistency with each of them in turn, it is sometimes possible and preferable to test for population patterns; this topic is taken up again in Chapter 9, Example 64.

Going beyond the Tables

A characteristic of many parametric tests is that they require little computation if appropriate tables are available. This is true of the sign test. However, we have already seen that if n is greater than 20, we can no longer use Table A1 and have to resort to the *Penguin Tables*; even they can only help us for values of n up to 25. When n is larger than that we can fall back on a useful idea we met in Chapter 4, pp. 79–82. We introduced there the *normal approximation* to the binomial distribution. For the sign test, with $p = \frac{1}{2}$ and a given value of n, the approximation takes the form that z is a standard normal variable where

$$z = \frac{r - \frac{1}{2}n - \frac{1}{2}}{\frac{1}{2}\sqrt{n}}, \qquad \text{(Eq. 15)}$$

r being the greater of (i) the number of plus signs and (ii) the number of minus signs. This is the form of approximation given in Chapter 4 when $p = \frac{1}{2}$ and an appropriate continuity correction is used. A few sketches like Figure 14, looking this time at the top tail, should convince you that we get the correct form for the continuity correction by *subtracting* one half.

Example 27

The Problem. In discussing Examples 23 and 24, we hinted that if we had 68 candidates and got 24 plus signs, i.e. 24 marks above the median, we would get a significant result, although this is only the same proportion of plus signs as we had in Example 23 (6 out of 17). We now show this.

Statistical Formulation. Because $n = 68$ is well beyond the range of our binomial tables we use the normal approximation with (Eq. 15) and use tables of the standard normal variable for our significance test.

Procedure. Here $n = 68$ and since there are 24 plus signs there are $68 - 24 = 44$ minus signs (assuming no candidate scored exactly 54). Using (Eq. 15) with $n = 68$ and $r = 44$ gives

$$z = \frac{44 - 34 - 0 \cdot 5}{0 \cdot 5 \sqrt{68}} = \frac{19}{\sqrt{68}} \approx 2 \cdot 30.$$

For a two-tail test we find that z must exceed $1 \cdot 96$ for significance at the 5 per cent level (since there is a probability of $0 \cdot 025$ that z exceeds $1 \cdot 96$ and a corresponding probability of $0 \cdot 025$ that z is less than $-1 \cdot 96$). For a one-tail test the value required for significance is $1 \cdot 64$.

Conclusion. Since $z = 2 \cdot 30$ exceeds the critical value of $1 \cdot 96$ we reject the null hypothesis that the median is 54.

Comment. The only information we needed to conduct this test was the value of n and r; the individual marks were not needed.

*   *   *

Many practical situations arise where we have to make statistical analyses of such limited information as the number in the sample and the number of plus signs. The original marks of individual candidates may not be available for reasons of confidentiality, or detailed records may not be kept beyond a certain time.

In Chapter 4, p. 82, we indicated that the normal approximation worked reasonably well with $p = \frac{1}{2}$ for values of n in excess of 15 or thereabouts. The reader might like to try using (Eq. 15) for Examples 23 and 24. Using Table 24 in the *Penguin Tables* or other tables of the standard normal variable he should find that for two-tail tests the probabilities he gets with this approximation are respectively 0·332 (in agreement with the exact result) and 0·0456 (compared with an exact result of 0·044 to 3 decimal places).

Similar approximations may be used for tests involving first or third quartiles or indeed for any other value of p, providing n is sufficiently large. In these cases it is useful to think in terms of successes and failures rather than plus and minus signs. If the number of successes exceeds np, denote by r the number of successes; if the number of successes is less than np, denote by r the number of failures (which will then exceed np). Calculate

$$z = \frac{r - np - \frac{1}{2}}{\sqrt{(npq)}} \qquad \text{(Eq. 16)}$$

which is approximately a standard normal variable.

If the only point at issue is that of significance at the 5, 1 or 0·1 per cent levels, to save constant reference to tables of the standard normal variable, it is probably worth remembering the values in Table 13 as the minimum required for significance at these levels.

Table 13 Standard normal variable: minima for significance

Level	5%	1%	0·1%
One-tail test	1·64	2·33	3·09
Two-tail test	1·96	2·58	3·30

A Test for Trend

We often hear assertions such as: 'The number of road accidents is on the increase', 'The winters are getting colder', 'Winters are not as cold as they used to be', 'Examination standards are falling', 'Shoes don't wear as long as they used to'. Given appropriate data, there are several tests to decide whether there is evidence of a recognizable pattern of increase or decrease with time. We shall describe only one of the simplest, which turns out to be in essence a sign test. It was proposed by Cox and Stuart (1955).

Example 28

The Problem. Grandpa Smith alleges that winters are getting colder; his statistically-minded grandson produces figures for the mean January temperature for their part of the world over the previous 20 years. Figures (in degrees C.) in chronological order were:

$$3\cdot2 \quad 3\cdot9 \quad 2\cdot1 \quad 5\cdot7 \quad 2\cdot1 \quad 1\cdot3 \quad -0\cdot2 \quad 1\cdot1 \quad 3\cdot4 \quad 5\cdot2$$
$$3\cdot1 \quad 4\cdot2 \quad 2\cdot1 \quad 1\cdot1 \quad 0\cdot7 \quad 1\cdot1 \quad 0\cdot4 \quad 2\cdot1 \quad 1\cdot1 \quad 1\cdot2$$

Do these data bear out Grandpa's contention?

Statistical Formulation. The grandson sets up the null hypothesis that there is no trend. Despite Grandpa's dogmatic assertion that winters are getting colder, he has been wrong before and they might be getting warmer, so a two-tail test seems appropriate. He selects the Cox and Stuart test which uses the notion that if there is a steady upward trend, values in the second half of the sequence should be consistently above those in the first half, the reverse being true if there is a downward trend. If there is no trend it will be a matter of chance whether those in the second half are above or below those in the first.

Cox and Stuart proposed that in a sequence of 20 (and the idea extends in an obvious way to sequences of any length) we pair up the first and eleventh, second and twelfth, third and thirteenth and so on and record the *signs* of the differences

eleventh – first,
twelfth – second,
thirteenth – third

and so on. If there is no trend, each is equally likely to be positive or negative, so we are back in a situation where the sign test is appropriate. If there is a downward trend, negative signs would predominate; if an upward trend, positive signs.

Procedure. Pairing up the first and eleventh and so on we get a sequence of pairs: $(3\cdot2, 3\cdot1)$, $(3\cdot9, 4\cdot2)$, $(2\cdot1, 2\cdot1)$, $(5\cdot7, 1\cdot1)$, $(2\cdot1, 0\cdot7)$, $(1\cdot3, 1\cdot1)$, $(-0\cdot2, 0\cdot4)$, $(1\cdot1, 2\cdot1)$, $(3\cdot4, 1\cdot1)$, $(5\cdot2, 1\cdot2)$. Mentally subtracting the first from the second in each pair gives a sequence of signs:

$$- \ + \ 0 \ - \ - \ - \ + \ + \ - \ -,$$

a total of 3 plus, 6 minus and one tie.

We have $r = 6$ minus signs when $n = 9$ (reduced from 10 to allow for one tie which is non-informative about any trend). Using Table A1 we see that the probability of our result or one less likely with a two-tail test is $2 \times 0.254 = 0.508$.

Conclusion. There is a better than even chance of getting a result as or more extreme than the one we have observed when the null hypothesis is true, so we certainly have no grounds for rejecting it and Grandpa had best blame old age rather than colder winters for his worsening rheumatics.

Comments. In fairness to Grandpa we must note that mean January temperature is only one aspect of climate. February may really be the month that catches his rheumatics and temperatures for that month may show a trend. Changes in humidity may also be important.

*　　　*　　　*

Fields of Application

Here are some examples of where the sign test could be used:

Insurance The median value of all motor claims paid by a company in 1979 is £280. Early in 1980 a sample of 25 claims include 18 above £280. The sign test can be used to see whether there is convincing evidence of an upward shift in the median.

Medicine The median pulse rate for children of a certain age prior to physical training is known. If pulse rates for a sample are taken after exercise, the sign test is useful in looking for a median shift. Do you think a one- or a two-tail test would be appropriate?

Engineering The median noise level in decibels is known for an aircraft engine of a certain design. The design is modified and comparable noise measurements are made on a sample; if we suspect a median shift, we can use the sign test.

Biology Heartbeat rates of female monkeys in one locality have a known median. Given heartbeat rates for 20 females of the same species from another locality, we might use the sign test for evidence of a shift or to establish confidence limits for the median.

Commerce The median wage of assembly workers in a large plant is known. A sample of wages for workers in another plant enables us to compare median wage levels with a sign test. If the quartiles were known, they too could be compared by a sign test.

Physics Specimens of metal are heated and their hardness is measured at 5° intervals, as temperature increases through a 250° range. The Cox and Stuart test for trend with temperature increase may be useful.

Section B   Tests Based on Randomization

Scope
Very general tests known as *randomization tests* are introduced, but they are shown to have serious practical limitations. A test called the Wilcoxon test is presented as an alternative and its use in hypothesis testing and estimation for medians or means with symmetric populations is discussed. Ties are considered and an approximate test for large samples is given.

Using More of the Data

Two noteworthy points about the sign test are:
   (i) it makes minimal assumptions about the population;
   (ii) it uses very little information from the sample.

In making a hypothesis test, all we assume about the population is that it has a given median; it need not be symmetric and it certainly need not be normal. We discussed the sign test briefly in *Statistics in Action* (pp. 70–75) and then introduced a test called the *t*-test that did a rather better job, *providing* we could assume our sample came from a normal population. The test made use of the numerical values of the observations rather than just the signs of deviations from a given value.

If we can assume that a population is symmetric, then the mean and median coincide and we can make more effective tests for the median (or mean) that take into account not only signs of deviations from the supposed population mean but also their magnitudes. A general test to do this without any assumption of normality has a lot of intuitive appeal, but unfortunately it is not easy to carry out in practice without certain modifications; these were soon discovered by proponents of this approach and have the advantage of simplicity in both calculation and the construction of the necessary tables.

However, the full procedure for general tests – known as 'randomization tests' – illustrates very well some fundamental ideas of non-parametric methods, and I shall demonstrate the process by a simple example. It is important to stress that the test described in Example 29 is in practice usually replaced by the simpler Wilcoxon test to be described later in the chapter.

Example 29

The Problem. To test the effectiveness of an analgesic drug, seven rats are each given an equal dose; after half an hour they are subjected to electric shocks at increasing voltages and a record is made of the minimum voltage that produces a nervous twitch. This varies from rat to rat and the values for the sample are 98, 107, 112, 93, 149, 85 and 122 volts.

It is known that individual rats vary in tolerance to electric currents and experience in a large number of experiments has shown the distribution of tolerances to be symmetric. However, there is a batch to batch variation in the mean. Assuming that the seven rats in this experiment are a random sample from one particular batch, test the hypothesis that the mean for the batch (population) is 95.

Statistical Formulation. Since the population of tolerances is assumed symmetrical, it follows that *not only* have we an equal probability of any observation in our sample being above or below the median (here equal to the mean in view of symmetry), but the probabilities of positive and negative deviations of any given magnitude are equally likely; e.g. we are just as likely to have a sample value between 3 and 4 units *above* the mean as we are to have one between 3 and 4 units *below* the mean. Thus it follows that samples that have a comparable amount of scatter above and below the hypothetical mean support the null hypothesis, whereas samples that have more and larger deviations in one direction than those in the other provide evidence against the null hypothesis. In the 'procedure' section we show how to assess such evidence.

Procedure. If we take as the null hypothesis a population median (or mean) of 95, then for our data the deviations are $98-95 = 3$, $107-95 = 12$, $112 - 95 = 17$, $93 - 95 = -2$ and, continuing in this way, 54, -10 and 27. We may set these out formally as

Negative deviations: 2, 10
Positive deviations: 3, 12, 17, 27, 54.

There are only 2 negative but 5 positive deviations; 4 of the positive deviations are larger in magnitude than either negative deviation. Intuitively, this seems a little unlikely with our assumption of symmetry if the population median really is 95.

We emphasized (p. 17) that it is a characteristic of non-parametric procedures that they are based upon the properties of the sample – in particular, those of the distribution of sample values under the null hypothesis. In this example the relevant question we ask ourselves is: given the *magnitudes* of deviation listed above and considering *all* possible allocations of positive and negative signs attached to them, which allocations fall into a critical region for which we should reject the null hypothesis?

From the remarks made under 'formulation' it is clear that allocations that divide the deviations fairly evenly between positive and negative favour the null hypothesis. The strongest evidence against the null hypothesis and favouring the general alternative that the median does not have the stated value (i.e. that it is either above or below 95) would be all deviations from 95 positive (indicating a median higher than 95) or all deviations negative (indicating a median below 95).

Before we can decide which allocations fall into the appropriate critical region at a specified significance level, we must determine the number of ways we can allocate seven items into two groups, one labelled 'positive' and the other 'negative'. This is a counting problem; to each difference of a given magnitude we may allocate one of two signs. Thus there are two choices of sign for the difference of magnitude 2, two for that of magnitude 3, giving four possible sign combinations, i.e. (2,3), (2,−3), (−2,3) and (−2,−3). Each of these can be combined with 10 or −10 giving $2 \times 2 \times 2 = 2^3 = 8$ different sign allocations to the first three. Continuing in this way we see that there are $2^7 = 128$ different sign allocations for all 7.

Since under the null hypothesis the most likely outcome is a fairly even split between signs, the least likely outcomes are those for which the difference between the sum of the positive deviations and sum of the negative deviations is greatest in magnitude. Let us first consider cases where there are only a few negative deviations; the most extreme case is that when there are none. The sum of the positive deviations, which we shall denote by S_p, is then $S_p = 2 + 3 + 10 + 12 + 17 + 27 + 54 = 125$, while the sum of the negative deviations, S_n, is zero, since there are none. Thus $S_p - S_n = 125$.

If only the deviation of magnitude 2 has a negative sign then $S_n = 2$ and $S_p = 123$, so $S_p - S_n = 121$. It is left as an exercise for the reader to verify that if the negative deviations are 3 only, 2 and 3, 10 only, 2 and 10 or 12 only, the values of $S_p - S_n$ are, respectively, 119, 115, 105, 101 and 101. To calculate these values quickly it is worth noting that we always have $S_p + S_n = 125$, the sum of all the magnitudes, whence

$$S_p - S_n = (125 - S_n) - S_n = 125 - 2S_n \qquad \text{(Eq. 17)}$$

so that to obtain $S_p - S_n$ one need only calculate S_n, double it and subtract from 125. To carry out the test formally, even this is unnecessary, because it follows from (Eq. 17) that as S_n increases, $S_p - S_n$ decreases, so the highest values of the latter correspond to the lowest values of S_n. The combinations giving values of S_n *as low or lower* than that actually observed (negative deviations 2, 10 with $S_n = 12$) are given in Table 14.

Table 14 Samples with $S_n \leqq 12$

Negative deviations	none	(2)	(3)	(2,3)	(10)	(12)	(2,10)
S_n	0	2	3	5	10	12	12

If all the 128 combinations are equally likely the probability associated with each of the 7 mutually exclusive outcomes in Table 14 is 1/128; thus there is a probability of 7/128 of getting a result with the same or lower probability in the 'tail' of the distribution with low S_n. What about the other tail with high S_n? It immediately becomes apparent that if we swop the labels 'positive' and 'negative' on each deviation, we get a set of differences $S_p - S_n$ equal in magnitude but opposite in sign and we can draw up a table similar to Table 14 with positive deviations replacing negative and S_p replacing S_n but the numbers remaining the same. Thus the probability associated with $S_n \leqq 12$ and with $S_p \leqq 12$ is the same, and both equal 7/128; thus the addition rule gives

$$Pr(S_p \leqq 12 \; or \; S_n \leqq 12) = 7/128 + 7/128 = 14/128 \approx 0 \cdot 11.$$

On the other hand the probability that $S_n \leqq 10$ is easily seen from Table 14 to be 5/128 and thus

$$Pr(S_n \leqq 10 \; or \; S_p \leqq 10) = 10/128 \approx 0 \cdot 078.$$

Similarly $Pr(S_n \leqq 3) = 3/128$ whence

$$Pr(S_n \leqq 3 \; or \; S_p \leqq 3) = 6/128 \approx 0 \cdot 047.$$

Thus for a two-tail test at the nominal 5 per cent significance level (actual level 4·7 per cent) we require the lesser of S_n or S_p not to exceed 3. For a one-tail test the appropriate smaller sum S_p or S_n, depending on which side of the null hypothesis the alternative is, may take values not exceeding 10 for nominal 5 per cent significance (actual level 3·9 per cent – make sure you can see why).

Conclusion. Since $S_n = 12$, which exceeds the value required for significance, we cannot reject the null hypothesis that the mean may be 95.

Comments. Obviously, for even a moderate number of observations, it can become quite tedious to list all cases where the allocation of signs could give a higher value to the magnitude of $S_p - S_n$ than that observed. Not only is it tedious but the process can be somewhat liable to error; one has to start from scratch and list the relevant sets for each problem. The full randomization test procedure has considerable intellectual appeal, as it uses all the information in the data, but it is not very practical.

*   *   *

Early workers in this field, notably R.A. Fisher in England and E.J.G. Pitman in Australia, showed that under certain circumstances the results of randomization tests and certain parametric tests were very similar; their findings were published in the 1930s and in the two following decades parametric tests were widely used, often with every justification, but at other times with scant regard paid as to whether assumptions to justify their use really held. In the 1970s there was increasing awareness of the dangers of ignoring assumptions; this has resulted in a new interest in non-parametric methods.

Wilcoxon Signed Rank Test

Wilcoxon (1945) suggested replacing the actual deviations in a case like Example 29 by the rank order of the magnitudes of the deviations. By the magnitude of a deviation we mean its numerical value without regard to sign. Thus both -12 and $+12$ are greater in magnitude than -9 or $+10$, $+5$ is greater in magnitude than -3 and $+7$ and -7 have the same magnitude. We illustrate the method by applying it to the data in Example 29.

Example 30

The Problem. With the same data as in Example 29 (the observations being 85, 93, 98, 107, 112, 122 and 149) we want to test whether it is reasonable to suppose they are a sample from a population symmetrically distributed with median or mean of 95.

Statistical Formulation. We arrange the deviations from 95 in order of magnitude and associate with each rank the *sign* of the corresponding deviation; we then perform a randomization test on these signed ranks.

Procedure. We proceed in a manner similar to Example 29 after arranging the deviations from 95 in order of magnitude and replacing them by their ranks. The 'ordered' differences are -2, 3, -10, 12, 17, 27, 54 and the corresponding ranks with like signs (the *signed ranks*) are $-1, 2, -3, 4, 5, 6,$ 7. There are 128 possible allocations of plus and minus signs to these ranks. As in Example 29, if all or nearly all the ranks are of one sign and any exceptions are of small 'total' magnitude (as indicated by the sum), we have good evidence against the null hypothesis. Also, as in Example 29, it suffices to use the lesser of the sums for positive or negative ranks as the test statistic; we shall here denote these as S_+ (equivalent to S_p in the full test) and S_- (equivalent to S_n).

In this example S_- is $1 + 3 = 4$ and is clearly less than S_+. We get the same or a lower value of S_- if the following sets of ranks are negative: (i) none, (ii) 1 only, (iii) 2 only, (iv) 3 only, (v) 1 and 2 only, (vi) 4 only. Thus our observed case and *six* others, a total of 7, give the same or a lower rank sum for S_-. The probability under the null hypothesis of getting $S_- \leqq 4$ is again 7/128 as in the full randomization test. Also as in that test the probability that $S_+ \leqq 4$ is also 7/128 by symmetry of interchange of plus and minus ranks. Thus we see that for a two-tail test the probability of a result as or more extreme than that observed when the null hypothesis is true is 14/128 – exactly the same as we got for the full randomization test.

Conclusion. Since the probability of S_+ or S_-, whichever is the smaller, not exceeding 4 (the observed value) is 14/128, which is greater than 0·05, we cannot reject the null hypothesis that the median may be 95 at the 5 per cent significance level.

Comments. It is of interest to note that the full randomization test using observed values and the Wilcoxon test using only ranks lead in this case to identical conclusions. This will not invariably be the case, but the practical differences are usually small.

*   *   *

We used a two-tail test in Examples 29 and 30. There may be a situation where a one-tail test would be justified. If, for instance, previous experiments had established that for rats which had not been given the drug the mean of the response distribution to shocks was 95, and that if the drug produced *any* alteration in the mean, it would be to increase it, then a one-tail test would be appropriate. The null hypothesis would be that the mean was 95; the alternative, that the mean exceeded 95; a small sum of negative deviations would favour the alternative. As we saw in Example 30, the probability of S_- taking a value as small or smaller than that observed was $7/128 \approx 0·055$. This narrowly fails to reach formal significance at the 5 per cent level, a fact that should be reported to the experimenter as a 'near miss'.

Tables for the Wilcoxon Test

In practice we do not have to explore fully the smaller values of S_+ and S_- *ab initio*, as we did in Example 30, to establish significance; clearly for *any* sample of size 7 the same rank sums will be critical. Indeed for samples of any fixed size n we can work out a critical value that depends only on n and *not* on the actual numerical values of the observations (apart from slight complications with ties which we discuss on p. 109. This enables us to construct tables of critical values, by which we mean the maximum value of the smaller of S_+ and S_- that permits significance at the relevant level. Table A3 in the Appendix is one that may be used for values of n between 5 and 20. An extended table for values of n up to 30 and with rather more information on actual significance levels is given in the *Penguin Tables* (Table 35).

Table A3 gives exact probabilities associated with one tail that are as near as possible to but do not exceed nominal values $\alpha = 0\cdot05$, $0\cdot025$, $0\cdot01$ and $0\cdot005$; for two-tail tests these probabilities must be doubled. The value recorded as S is the lower of S_+ and S_-. At each probability level for each n we give S and the probability of getting that or a lower value. Thus we have the actual as well as the nominal significance level. For $n = 5, 6, 7$ the lack of an entry means that no test is possible at that level owing to the small sample size.

For $n = 7$ and $\alpha = 0\cdot05$ the table tells us that the probability that the lower of S_+ and S_- is less than or equal to 3 is $0\cdot039$.

The probability that $S \leqq 4$ when $n = 7$ is also recorded in the *Penguin Tables* as about $0\cdot055$ (which equals 7/128) as we established from first principles on p. 105.

A Choice of Tests

Since a sign test may be applied *whether or not* a population has a symmetric distribution, it is still *valid* to carry out a sign test with data such as we had in Examples 29 and 30; but if we did so, we would be ignoring the information that the population is symmetric. The usual result is that we require larger samples to detect a given departure from the null hypothesis.

In Example 23 (the 17 Goldbeach students) the test for a median of 54 fell well short of a significant result when we made no assumption of population symmetry. We now re-examine the problem with this additional assumption.

Example 31

The Problem. Given the marks in Example 23 for 17 Goldbeach College students (38, 29, 58, 41, 82, 51, 45, 39, 60, 42, 36, 55, 46, 61, 43, 52, 64), test the hypothesis that they could be a random sample from a *symmetric* distribution with median 54.

Statistical Formulation. We shall apply the Wilcoxon signed rank test to the deviations from 54 using as the test statistic the smaller of the sums of the positive or negative ranks.

Procedure. The signed deviations from 54 in the order of marks as given are: $-16, -25, 4, -13, 28, -3, -9, -15, 6, -12, -18, 1, -8, 7, -11, -2, 10$. In Table 15 these are rearranged in order of magnitude and the signed ranks are also given.

Table 15   Signed ranks for Goldbeach College marks

Signed difference	1	−2	−3	4	6	7	−8	−9	10
Signed rank	1	−2	−3	4	5	6	−7	−8	9
Signed difference	−11	−12	−13	−15	−16	−18	−25	28	
Signed rank	−10	−11	−12	−13	−14	−15	−16	17	

With the exception of the final entry with rank 17, the positive ranks are small, and it is fairly clear that S_+ is smaller than S_-. $S_+ = 1 + 4 + 5 + 6 + 9 + 17 = 42$. From Table A3 with $n = 17$ we see that for a one-tail test the probability of a sum of 41 or less is $0 \cdot 049$. Table 35 in the *Penguin Tables* shows that $Pr(S \leqq 42) = 0 \cdot 0535$.

Conclusion. If we had external evidence to justify the view that the median could only be *below* 54 we would narrowly fail to establish significance at the nominal 5 per cent level; it is well short of significance if a two-tail test is appropriate.

Comments. In the sign test the one-tail probability of 6 or fewer plus signs was $0 \cdot 166$. The corresponding one-tail probability with the Wilcoxon test is reduced to $0 \cdot 054$. We have in this sense sharpened our result by using a procedure that is justified if the additional assumption of symmetry is reasonable.

*   *   *

The assumption of symmetry could be examined for reasonableness if we knew the mark distribution for all 3,000 candidates. If we knew individual marks for all 3,000 we could test this approximately by drawing a histogram where the heights (or areas) of the rectangles for each class interval were proportional to the number of candidates in that interval. The mark range to specify the width of each class is largely a matter of convenience but would usually be chosen so that some 15–20 classes covered the mark range used.

In Figure 16 we sketch two possible forms for such a histogram. If it looked something like that in Figure 16(a) an assumption of symmetry is reasonable; symmetry could hardly be attributed to the distribution in Figure 16(b).

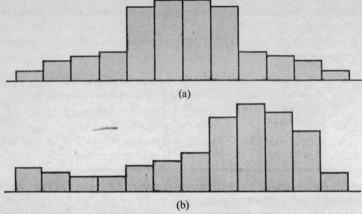

(a)

(b)

Figure 16 Symmetric (a) and non-symmetric (b) distributions

Note that for a skew distribution the mean and the median do not coincide. The sign test is essentially a test for the median; the Wilcoxon test relies essentially upon a median property, but since the mean and median coincide for a symmetric distribution it may be regarded as a test about either.

The Wilcoxon Test for Larger Samples

Although the *Penguin Tables* extend to $n = 30$ and tables for n as high as 50 are given, for example, by Bradley (1968), a normal approximation works quite well for $n > 20$. We shall assume two results that require some knowledge of statistical theory for their derivation; they give the mean and variance of S, where S is the smaller of S_+ and S_-, as $n(n + 1)/4$ and $n(n + 1)(2n + 1)/24$ respectively when the null hypothesis is true. If n is sufficiently large (greater than 20), under the null hypothesis

$$z = \frac{S + \frac{1}{2} - n(n + 1)/4}{\sqrt{\{n(n + 1)(2n + 1)/24\}}} \qquad \text{(Eq. 18)}$$

has approximately a standard normal distribution.

For $n < 30$ if the result is close to the critical value for significance a check in the exact tables is desirable, but if it is well away from the borderline for significance there is little need to worry. The term one half in the numerator of (Eq. 18) is a continuity correction (p. 80).

Example 32

The Problem. Use the normal approximation (Eq. 18) in place of the exact procedure for the data in Example 31.

Statistical Formulation. Calculate S and substitute its value in (Eq. 17) with $n = 17$.

Procedure. As in Example 31 we find $S = 42$. Substitution in (Eq. 17) gives

$$z = \frac{42 \cdot 5 - 17 \times 18/4}{\sqrt{(17 \times 18 \times 35/24)}} = \frac{-34}{21 \cdot 125} = -1 \cdot 609.$$

Since we always take the smaller of S_+ and S_- in (Eq. 18) we find that z is always negative. For a quick check on significance we may still use Table 3, mentally ignoring the minus sign in the calculated value of z. If exact probabilities are required we may use tables for the standard normal variable in the usual way. For example, Table 24 in the *Penguin Tables* shows that the probability of getting a value less than $-1 \cdot 609$, which equals the probability of getting a value greater than $1 \cdot 609$, is $0 \cdot 0538$. A diagram like Figure 15 helps if you have difficulty in seeing how we get this result. The probability of $0 \cdot 0538$ is very close to the exact value of $0 \cdot 0535$ obtained in Example 31.

Conclusion. Essentially the same as we reached in Example 31.

Comments. Although n was less than our recommended value of 20 the approximation worked quite well. Without the continuity correction we would have got a z value of $-1 \cdot 633$ and the probability of getting a value as low or lower than this is (from tables) $0 \cdot 0513$ so the use of the continuity correction increases the accuracy of the approximation. It is, however, less critical in this than in some other applications and many textbooks omit the term '$+ \frac{1}{2}$' in the numerator of (Eq. 18).

Ties

The examples of the Wilcoxon test given so far have avoided one complication that is common with real data. Suppose that our Goldbeach College results had included one candidate with a score of 42 marks and another with 66; their deviations from the supposed median of 54 would be -12 and 12, respectively. This results in 'tied' ranks, one with a positive and one with a negative sign. One way round this difficulty is to replace tied ranks by an average rank with appropriate sign.

Example 33

The Problem. Suppose we have examinations marks for 14 candidates from Goldbeach's rival establishment, Silversands College, and wish to test whether they are consistent with being a random sample from a symmetric population with median 54. For these marks we shall suppose we have worked out the deviations from 54 and (in order of magnitude) they are:

$$3, 5, 7, -8, 8, 9, 15, 15, -15, 17, 19, 21, 21, 24.$$

Statistical Formulation. The Wilcoxon signed rank test is appropriate with due allowance for ties.

Procedure. The deviations of -8, 8 mean a tie for fourth and fifth ranking; give each the mean ranking of 4·5 with appropriate sign. The deviations 15, 15 and -15 tie for seventh, eighth and ninth ranking so give each the mean ranking of 8 with appropriate sign. Proceeding in this way we end up with the 14 deviations ranked as in Table 16.

Table 16   Signed ranks with ties

Signed difference	3	5	7	-8	8	9	15	15	-15	17	19	21	21	24
Signed rank	1	2	3	$-4·5$	4·5	6	8	8	-8	10	11	12·5	12·5	14

In forming the test statistic, here S_-, since this is clearly smaller than S_+, we 'score' a tied rank as in Table 16. Thus $S_- = 4·5 + 8 = 12·5$. From Table A3 with $n = 14$ we see that $S \leqq 12$ implies a probability of 0·0043 in one tail, and this must be doubled for a two-tail test. $S \leqq 15$ implies a probability of 0·008 in a one-tail test.

Conclusion. If a two-tail test is appropriate (and we shall assume there is no outside evidence to indicate otherwise) the result is clearly significant at the nominal 5 per cent level and very close to significance at the nominal 1 per cent level. We reject the hypothesis that the results indicate a symmetric distribution with median at 54. The large number of positive deviations indicates a higher population median.

Comments. The exact test probabilities take no account of the possibility of ties, but in practice, unless these are very common, the tables will give a good approximate indication of significance levels.

*   *   *

The normal approximation may be used with ties, with S calculated as in Example 33.

There is one other complication analogous to the complication of a value corresponding to the median in a sign test. If in Example 33 we had had a candidate who had scored exactly 54, his deviation would have been zero. A zero deviation should not be ranked and the value of n reduced by 1 when using tables like Table A3. The logic in so doing is that the particular observation gives no information about the nature of any alternative hypothesis that might hold.

Estimation of a Population Mean – Symmetric Distribution

We have already discussed (pp. 90–93) the general principles of obtaining an interval estimate for a population median. If we assume symmetry the mean and median coincide. We may therefore regard any confidence limits we form as applicable to either. The estimate for the median in Example 25 did not assume population symmetry; intuitively we feel that if an assumption of symmetry is acceptable, we should do better if we take it into account, as we did in the Wilcoxon test. Our intuition turns out to be correct. Unfortunately the theory of what we do is somewhat beyond the scope of this book and I can only give an intuitive argument to show that what we are doing is reasonable.

Calculation of confidence limits for non-parametric methods sometimes lacks the simplicity of hypothesis testing, but in many cases (the present one being typical) the procedure, once mastered, is no longer or harder than that for the corresponding parametric method and has the advantage that we may be able to avoid the consequences of errors arising from unjustified assumptions of, for example, normality. The consequences of unjustified assumptions in obtaining confidence intervals are even more serious than they are in hypothesis testing.

We shall illustrate the principles by an example that is computationally trivial but demonstrates the essential ideas.

Basically the idea we employ is that of taking every pair of observations in the data and using the mean of each pair as an estimate of the population mean. Since each sample value is equally likely to be above or below the population mean and equally likely to come from either of a pair of intervals symmetrically placed about that mean, these are a sensible sort of estimate. We expect some to be overestimates and some to be underestimates; it is intuitively reasonable to reject some of the smallest and some of the largest. What is not clear to our intuition is just how many we should exclude, and it is the theoretical derivation of this number that is beyond the scope of this book. We shall show in our next example how that number is determined in practice. The theory is described in Lehmann (1975), pp. 182–3.

Example 34

The Problem. Warning devices fitted to aircraft are designed to give a visual and/or audible signal of impending danger when the speed of the aircraft is still some 5 knots above stalling speed. Six of these devices are selected at random from a large production run and tested. The results (in knots above the stalling speed at which the device is triggered off) are as follows:

4·6 5·2 6·0 5·1 5·4 5·8

Past experience has indicated that the population distribution is symmetric. Use the above data to obtain nominal 90 per cent confidence limits for the population median or mean.

Statistical Formulation. We form each 'paired' estimate of the median available from the above sample. By a method described under 'procedure', we use Table A3 to decide how many of these to eliminate; the smallest and largest of those remaining provide confidence limits. The interval between the limits is the required confidence interval. It in fact contains all values that we would accept in a hypothesis test (two-tailed) at, in this case, the rather unorthodox significance level of 10 per cent, since we are seeking a 90 per cent confidence interval. If we require a point estimate of the median, this may be taken as the sample median.

Procedure. It pays to be methodical in setting out the computation, for if we do so, we can shorten the task in a way we explain below in 'comments' on this problem. We first arrange the six observations in ascending order and transcribe them in the first row and column in Table 17. We complete this table by entering the average of first-row and first-column entries at the appropriate row/column intersection. The diagonal entries are the same as the sample values, but they should be looked upon as the *average* of each observation with itself, i.e. the first entry of 4·6 in the body of the table may be looked upon as $(4·6 + 4·6)/2 = 4·6$. The next entry in that row of 4·85 is $(4·6 + 5·1)/2 = 4·85$, etc.

Table 17   Averages used to estimate a median

	4·6	5·1	5·2	5·4	5·8	6·0
4·6	4·6	4·85	4·9	5·0	5·2	5·3
5·1		5·1	5·15	5·25	5·45	5·55
5·2			5·2	5·3	5·5	5·6
5·4				5·4	5·6	5·7
5·8					5·8	5·9
6·0						6·0

Now we enter Table A3 with $n = 6$. From it we note that S (the lesser of S_+ and S_-) must be less than or equal to 2 for significance in a two-tail test at the $2 \times 0.047 = 0.094$ probability level, equivalent to 9·4 per cent. The corresponding confidence level is $100 - 9.4 = 90.6$ per cent. This is the actual level for a nominal 90 per cent level (see p. 92). Now it can be shown that if we delete the two lowest and two highest entries in Table 17 (two entries because $S = 2$), the smallest and largest entries remaining in that table are the 90·6 per cent confidence limits. Clearly the two smallest values are 4·6 and 4·85, so these are deleted. The lower confidence limit is the next lowest value of 4·9. Similarly the upper confidence limit is 5·8, the highest remaining entry in Table 17 after deleting the two highest, 6·0 and 5·9.

Conclusion. Nominal 90 per cent confidence limits are 4·9 and 5·8, so the interval (4·9, 5·8) is the 90 per cent confidence interval.

Comments. The reader may care to verify that if he performs a hypothesis test for a population mean *just* in excess of 4·9 he will find that S_- *exceeds* 2, and with any value slightly less than 4·9 he will find $S_- \leqq 2$. Similar results hold for S_+ on either side of the upper limit of 5·8. When we test hypothetical values of *exactly* 4·9 and 5·8 ties occur. These results are consistent with our observation on p.91 that there is a correspondence between the hypothesis acceptable at 100α per cent significance level and the values in the $100(1-\alpha)$ per cent confidence interval.

The main reason for writing the observations in ascending order in the first row and column of Table 17 was to ensure a concentration of small means in the top left of the table and of large means in the bottom right. Since we need in this example only the three largest and the three smallest means, the remaining 15 need not in practice be calculated at all.

*   *   *

With larger values of n this saving in calculation becomes important. For example, with $n = 17$ (as we had in the Goldbeach College examination marks example), if a nominal 95 per cent confidence interval were required, we require the values of S that have an associated probability less than 0·025 (but as close to that at possible) in each tail. Table A3 tells us that we need $S \leqq 34$ for significance (exact probability 0·0224). Thus, to get the interval we require only the 35 smallest and 35 largest paired estimates (out of a total of 153 such pairs). Thus we need to compute less than half of the possible values.

A Graphical Alternative

Many people prefer a graphical to an arithmetic procedure when either is available. We now describe a graphical method that leads to exactly the same confidence intervals as the arithmetic one used in Example 34.

Example 35

The Problem. Using a graphical method, find a 90 per cent confidence interval for the population median under the same assumptions and with the same data as in Example 34.

Statistical Formulation. Essentially the same as Example 34.

Procedure. We describe the procedure with reference to Figure 17. First we draw (preferably on a sheet of graph paper) a vertical line AB and mark off along it on an appropriate scale points corresponding to each observation. At the point C on this line (midway between the largest and smallest observations of 4·6 and 6·4) draw a horizontal line CD of any convenient length (i.e. a line perpendicular to AB). Join D to the points E and H on AB corresponding to the smallest and largest observation. Through each point corresponding to the remaining four observations we draw lines parallel to HD and ED. At all intersections of these sets of parallel lines (including the original data points) we place a clear dot. If we were to drop lines perpendicular to AB on to AB from each dot (there is no need to do this) we would be able to read off at the points at which they meet AB the 'paired' mean values recorded in Table 17.

To get confidence limits, we look up as before the maximum value of S in Table A3 to indicate significance at the level required for the appropriate confidence interval. In this case $S = 2$, using the same arguments as in Example 34. We now start counting dots *inward* from the top and bottom of the diagram, deleting the two nearest each end as we work down or up the figure. Thus we delete the dots at H and J at the top and at E and F at the bottom. The confidence limits are then given by the vertical scale values corresponding to the next dots in from each end, namely G and K respectively. L is the scale value corresponding to G where GL is drawn perpendicular to AB. On the scale L is at the value 4·9 and clearly K is at 5·8, and these are our limits.

Conclusion. As in Example 34 nominal 90 per cent confidence limits are from 4·9 to 5·8.

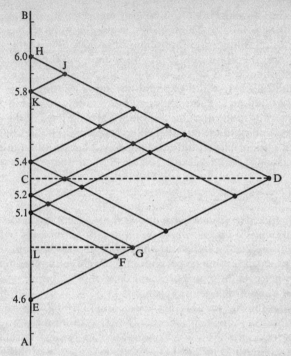

Figure 17 Confidence limits for the mean of a symmetric distribution

Comments. Whether you prefer the arithmetic or the graphical method is clearly a matter of taste – it may well depend on how much you like your pocket calculator!

*　　　*　　　*

Some slight modification to the confidence interval procedures is needed if we have tied ranks arising from two scores being equal. This may result in some inexactness; the main problem arises if we get ties in paired estimates at or near the critical cut-off (or confidence limit) values. For instance, in a table like Table 17, if the four smallest values had been 4·7, 4·8, 4·8 and 4·9, then the two smallest to be deleted would be 4·7 and 4·8, which leaves the 'second' 4·8 as the third smallest. Should this be taken as the lower confidence limit? Here ties again result in some approximation, as the theory is worked out on a 'no tie' basis. It could be argued that since a tie for second and third gives a mean rank of 2·5, we may regard this as being above the cut-off ranking point of 2. This is an intuitive argument rather than one of logical statistical theory, but it is an approximation that is not very misleading in practice. It is reasonable to take 4·8 as the lower confidence limit in these circumstances.

Some modification of the graphical method is also needed when an observation is repeated. Perhaps the best procedure is to draw two parallel lines close together, one fractionally on each side of the point on the vertical scale corresponding to the repeated observation. Two dots should appear where such a pair of lines crosses a single line. An example will be given for a similar situation in the next chapter; Figure 18 shows what is required.

Fields of Application

If we are prepared to assume symmetry, we can use the Wilcoxon test in the relevant examples on p. 99, where we are testing for medians and confidence intervals. Think carefully in which of these examples you might be prepared to add the assumption of symmetry. Would you be prepared to do this, for instance, in the insurance claim example?

Here are three further fields of application:

Psychology Intelligence tests show the median I.Q. for a large number of boys convicted for shoplifting to be 102. The I.Q.s are obtained for a sample of 18 convicted girls. The Wilcoxon test can be used to establish any significant difference in median I.Q.s between the sexes or to obtain confidence limits for the population median I.Q. for convicted girls.

Education A standard test of numerical skills for 12-year-old pupils is widely used throughout a country. The median mark is established as 83. A new method of teaching is introduced in one school and marks for a class of 42 are recorded. The Wilcoxon test can be used to detect median difference associated with the new method. Note here that there may be some doubt about regarding the test group as a random sample of a specific population.

Management Records are used to obtain the median number of days absent from work for all employees in a large factory in a given year. The numbers of days absent for a random sample of 25 employees are noted in the following year. If a symmetric distribution is assumed the Wilcoxon test is appropriate for looking at the possibility of a change in median. If symmetry cannot be assumed the sign test should be used. Do you think symmetry might be a reasonable assumption?

Exercises

1. The weight losses in kilograms for 15 fat ladies who have been on a diet for two months are as follows:

8 12 6 2 4 9 7 0 3 11 6 1 14 5 10.

The firm who sponsor the diet say in their advertisements: 'Lose 10 kg. in two months.' Tackled on what they mean by this, they say it is what a fat lady will lose 'on average'. You are still confused as to what they mean by 'on average', but assuming it is reasonable to regard the 15 observations as effectively a random sample, would it be reasonable to conclude they came from a population with median weight loss 10 kg.? Test this without any assumption of symmetry in the population. What test would be appropriate if you had a further assumption of symmetry? Carry out the latter test.

2. Assuming symmetry, find nominal 95 per cent confidence limits for the population mean, given the observations in Exercise 1 above. Obtain also the confidence limits that would be appropriate if symmetry could not be assumed, and comment on the differences between the results.

3. A pathologist counts the number of diseased plants in random selected areas each 1 yard square in a large wheat field. For 35 such areas the numbers of diseased plants are:

21	17	43	81	32	102	117
42	39	11	67	23	142	7
44	39	82	93	28	145	0
17	77	53	50	60	9	14
40	19	101	104	33	2	22.

Use appropriate non-parametric tests to determine if it is reasonable to suppose the median number of infected plants per square yard for the whole field is 50 (i) without an assumption of symmetry for the population, and (ii) with the assumption of symmetry. Comment on the reasonableness of the latter assumption.

4. A psychologist asserts that the I.Q. of unmarried mothers has a mean of 94. For a random sample of unmarried mothers the I.Q.s are :

93, 107, 88, 122, 89, 113, 102, 93, 95, 123, 102.

Is it reasonable to accept the psychologist's assertion if a symmetric distribution about the mean is assumed? Do you consider an assumption of symmetry is reasonable?

5. Before treatment with a new drug, a number of insomniacs are known to have a median sleeping time of two hours per night. It is known that the effect of the drug, if any, will be to increase sleeping time, but many doctors are doubtful as to whether it will have any effect at all. Is their doubt perhaps justified if the hours sleep per night for the insomniacs after taking the drug are:

3·1, 1·8, 2·7, 2·4, 2·9, 0·2, 3·7, 5·1, 8·3, 2·0, 2·1?

You may *not* assume a symmetrical distribution of sleeping times in the population.

6.   Methods for Paired Samples

Scope

We often have a natural pairing of observations; each person's blood pressure may be recorded before and after administration of a drug; examination marks in French and in Arithmetic may be available for each pupil; we may know weight increases for twin lambs in an experiment where one receives a hormone in its diet and the other does not. In all these situations we are interested in characteristics of the *differences* between paired observations. In this chapter we see how the methods of Chapter 5 may be adapted to this problem, discussing in particular the sign test and the Wilcoxon signed rank test.

Comparison of Pairs

We have already met the basic idea of paired observations in Example 13 where we divided samples of cream into two portions and sent each portion to a different laboratory. In *Statistics in Action*, Chapter 4 is largely devoted to a discussion of the response to a visual stimulus applied either to the right or the left visual field for each of a group of 12 subjects. Educationalists often compare two examining or teaching methods by pairing off students so that each member of a pair is as similar as possible in age, intelligence and previous knowledge of the subject, and then comparing results for each pair. Consistency between examiners can be tested by asking each to mark a series of essays without disclosing the marks they award; the marks for each essay may then be compared to see whether one examiner consistently awards higher marks than the other or whether there appears to be a purely random difference between the marks. In this last example other aspects, such as the relative ordering of candidates by the two examiners, may be of interest, and if this is so, some of the methods for comparing ranks given in Chapter 10 will be relevant.

An agricultural research worker may compare two diets by feeding one to each of two twin lambs and measuring growth over a period, concentrating his attention on growth differences between each twin in a pair. The reason for doing this is obvious; twin lambs on identical diets tend to grow at much the same rate on account of genetic similarity, so any marked differences in growth, when each is fed on a different diet, are likely to be attributable to the effects of diet. Indeed, in all the above examples the aim of pairing was to make conditions as similar as possible within each pair, apart from the factors we were interested in comparing.

It was the sign test we applied to this type of experiment in Example 13. Essentially it was the same sign test that we developed in Chapter 5, but applied not to the original data but to some *one-sample* data derived from it – namely the recorded differences for each sample between the results for the two laboratories. We re-examine this problem in Example 36, being a little more specific about assumptions and making use of Table A1 to avoid the computations we had to make in Example 13.

Example 36

The Problem. Table 18 repeats the data used in Example 13 for 10 cream samples divided into two portions, each analysed by different laboratories. It also gives (for use in a later example) the signed differences for the results which were not considered in Chapter 2. We shall again apply the sign test but consider the implications of what we are doing in the light of Chapter 5.

Table 18 Bacterial counts on cream samples (thousands/ml.)

Sample	A	B	C	D	E	F	G	H	I	J
Lab. *A*	11·7	12·1	13·3	15·1	15·9	15·3	11·9	16·2	15·1	13·6
Lab. *B*	10·9	11·9	13·4	15·4	14·8	14·8	12·3	15·0	14·2	13·1
Lab. *A* – Lab. *B*	0·8	0·2	−0·1	−0·3	1·1	0·5	−0·4	1·2	0·9	0·5
Sign	+	+	−	−	+	+	−	+	+	+

Statistical Formulation. The only assumption needed to justify using the sign test is that, if there is no systematic difference between the laboratories, we are prepared to accept that we are equally likely to get a higher reading from either laboratory. In that case the sign of the difference is equally likely to be positive or negative. As we shall see when we discuss tests that take into account the actual magnitude of the signed differences, there are several different patterns of distribution possible that will make positive or negative differences equally likely, but which is operating need not concern us here. If positive or negative differences are equally likely, we are really testing whether the differences have median zero, so the signs of the differences observed are equivalent to the signs of the deviations from the hypothetical population median which is now zero.

Procedure. We may now use Table A1 with $n = 10$ and note immediately that the probability of three or fewer minus signs is $0 \cdot 172$ (the same result as we got in Example 13).

Conclusion. We again conclude, precisely as in Example 13, that there is no evidence to reject the null hypothesis.

Comments. The sign test makes no use of the actual differences. We shall see in Example 37 that we may use these fruitfully.

*   *   *

The sign test is particularly useful when we cannot score observations on an ordinal or more sophisticated scale but can only classify the difference in some form such as *better or worse*, *higher or lower*, etc. For example, people may be asked to try two headache remedies on the next two occasions on which they had headaches. To avoid any bias, they should be told in which order to use the remedies, labelled A and B without further means of identification (the decision on order being determined by using a randomization method such as tossing a coin). Each subject then reports which he considers to be the better headache cure and we may get a series of *plus* and *minus* scores for individuals where a plus sign indicates a preference for remedy A and a minus sign a preference for remedy B. Use of the sign test is then virtually the only way to analyse the results.

When one has actual difference scores such as the Lab. A – Lab. B readings in Table 18, it seems logical to try and make use of these data as a *single sample* derived from our paired observations. We recall that the single-sample Wilcoxon signed rank test is essentially one for tests about the median or mean of a population assumed to be symmetric. Now if we consider the bacterial tests in Examples 13 and 36 and wish to test the null hypothesis that for each sample the two laboratories produce results that are identically distributed (i.e. that any differences observed are attributable to random sampling from the *same* distribution), we can see that if the hypothesis is true the differences will be symmetrically distributed about zero. On the other hand, if the two populations have different medians (e.g.

if one laboratory in the bacterial count example consistently tends to overestimate), the differences will not be symmetrically distributed about zero. There are, however, circumstances where the two laboratories may produce results that are not identically distributed, yet the differences are still symmetric; this would be the case if the distributions for the two laboratories were *different* symmetric distributions but each had the same mean. It is well to be aware of such subtleties, but by far the most common use of the Wilcoxon test on differences is to decide between the null hypothesis of identical distributions (for each laboratory in our example) and the alternative of a shift in location, as indicated by a difference betweeen the medians.

Example 37

The Problem. As for Example 36, but now we test the assumption that the results for Lab. *A* and Lab. *B* for each cream specimen are identically distributed, so the null hypothesis is that the differences Lab. *A* – Lab. *B* represent a sample from a symmetric population with median (or mean) zero.

Statistical Formulation. The alternative to the null hypothesis is that the median is not zero; this alternative would hold if the two laboratories had different population medians; it might also hold if the distribution of results for the two laboratories were *not* symmetric and differed from one another *in some respect* even if they had identical medians. The most likely practical alternative is the former, i.e. that the results for one laboratory show a shift in location (a change in median) relative to the other.

Procedure. The differences in Table 18 must be ranked in order of magnitude since these represent deviations from the assumed population mean of zero. These and the corresponding signed ranks are given in Table 19, ties being dealt with in the manner described on p. 109.

Table 19   Ranked differences for bacterial counts

Differences	−0·1	0·2	−0·3	−0·4	0·5	0·5	0·8	0·9	1·1	1·2
Ranks	−1	2	−3	−4	5·5	5·5	7	8	9	10

The test statistic is $S- = 1 + 3 + 4 = 8$. We now enter Table A3 with $n = 10$ and we see that for a one-tail test the probability that $S \leqq 8$ is 0·024. The corresponding two-tail probability is $2 \times 0·024 = 0·048$.

Conclusion. Since the probability of getting either S_+ or S_- as small or smaller than that observed is less than 0·05 we reject the hypothesis of zero mean (or median) difference at the 5 per cent significance level.

Comments. The Wilcoxon test here shows itself to be sharper than the sign test; this is because we are using the additional information provided by the magnitudes of the differences. From Table 19 we see that those with negative signs are generally smaller than those with positive signs, as well as being fewer in number.

*   *   *

Generally, when there are ordinal scores, tests for shift of the median, *if this is believed to be the only distinguishing feature between the populations*, should be carried out using signed ranks. It is better not to use the sign test except when we have only *preferences* between two members of a pair.

We may wish to test for hypothetical differences between medians other than zero or to obtain confidence limits for such differences. For paired samples these are special applications of the methods introduced in Chapter 5 and we illustrate them in Examples 38 and 39.

Example 38

The Problem. Twelve children are given an arithmetic test; after three weeks' special tuition they are given a further test of equal difficulty (something we say more about in the 'comments' below). Their marks in each test and the individual differences are given in Table 20. Do these indicate that the average improvement due to extra tuition is 10 marks (more about this in the comments, too)?

Table 20   Marks in an arithmetic test

Pupil	A	B	C	D	E	F	G	H	I	J	K	L
First test	45	61	33	29	21	47	53	32	37	25	42	81
Second test	53	67	47	34	31	49	62	51	48	29	48	86
Second – first	8	6	14	5	10	2	9	19	11	4	6	5

Statistical Formulation. We may take the question to ask essentially whether, if these children can be regarded as a random sample from some hypothetical population (perhaps children of the same age trained in the same educational system), it is reasonable to suppose the median difference between before and after is 10.

Procedure. We apply Wilcoxon's signed rank test to the population of differences in the last line of Table 20, now considering whether these are consistent with a population median difference of 10. In the order given in the table, the deviations from 10 are $-2, -4, 4, -5, 0, -8, -1, 9, 1, -6, -4$ and -5. We omit the zero difference (see p. 111) and arrange the others in order and assign ranks as in Table 21. The sum of the positive ranks is clearly the smaller and $S_+ = 1\cdot5 + 5 + 11 = 17\cdot5$.

Table 21 Ranked deviations from 10 of test score differences

Signed deviation	1	−1	−2	4	−4	−4	−5	−5	−6	−8	9
Signed rank	1·5	−1·5	−3	5	−5	−5	−7·5	−7·5	−9	−10	11

From Table A3 we see that with $n = 11$ (not 12, since we had one zero deviation) there is no question of significance even with a one-tail test for any value of S exceeding 13.

Conclusion. We do not reject the hypothesis that the median difference could be 10.

Comments. A conscientious statistician (as all good statisticians should be) may have two worries about this problem as posed. First, how does one determine whether two tests are of equal difficulty? Might not the improved marks in the second really reflect the fact that in some sense the second test was the easier? The most the statistician can do here is to seek assurances from the educationalists conducting the tests that reasonable precautions had been taken to ensure equal difficulty. Sometimes in situations like this, standard tests are used that have been tried on large groups of students with results that have shown pretty convincingly that they are of equal difficulty.

The second worry may be whether there is really much purpose in testing whether there has simply been a shift in medians between the two tests. One may doubt the realism of this; sometimes pupils who are good to start with will benefit little from extra tuition; very bad pupils may likewise show little benefit from extra tuition. It may only be those in the middle of the ability range that show appreciable benefit. This is something the statistician may find evidence for when he looks at the data; he may spot that candidates with very high or very low marks change less than those with a moderate mark. In such circumstances he would be wise to discuss with the experimenter just what is being tested. For the data used in this example there seems to be no such evidence; nevertheless, deciding the appropriate test to make is often a matter for fruitful discussion between the statistician and experimenter.

*   *   *

Example 39

The Problem. Using the data in Example 38, obtain nominal 95 per cent confidence limits for the median improvement in score, using both an arithmetic and a graphical method.

Statistical Formulation. On the basis of the recorded differences in Table 20 we form the sequence of all possible paired means using either the arithmetic or graphical methods described in Chapter 5. We then use Table A3 to determine the limits.

Procedure. We consider first the arithmetic method, limiting the calculations to essential values only. To decide how many we need calculate, we first consult Table A3. For 95 per cent confidence limits we require a value of S with a one-tail associated probability for that or a lower value not exceeding 0.025. We see that this implies $S = 13$ with an associated probability of 0.021 ($S = 14$ would in fact give a probability of 0.026). We must, however, compute the 14 lowest and the 14 highest pairs, as we reject 13 at each end and require the 14th to give us the actual limit.

We set out the relevant calculations in Table 22, using a similar pattern to Table 17. The entries for the first row and column are the differences in Table 20 rearranged in ascending order.

A study of Table 22 soon indicates that all remaining potential entries are irrelevant. Arranged in order the 14 smallest paired means are 2, 3, 3·5, 3·5, 4, 4, 4, 4·5, 4·5, 5, 5, 5, 5, 5 and the largest 14 in descending order are 19, 16·5, 15, 14·5, 14, 14, 13·5, 12·5, 12·5, 12·5, 12, 12, 12, 11·5. Excluding the top and bottom 13 leaves the confidence limits of 5 and 11·5.

The graphical method is similar to that used in constructing Figure 17, the only complication being the tied observations at 5 and 6 where we need *double* lines as intimated on p.116. We represent these as a pair of lines slightly separated. The method is illustrated in Figure 18 and the reader is recommended to construct the figure himself on the general pattern described in Example 35, remembering to put 2 dots at an intersection of double and single lines, 4 dots at the intersection of a pair of double lines, etc.

Table 22   Paired means of arithmetic test score differences

	2	4	5	5	6	6	8	9	10	11	14	19
2	2	3	3·5	3·5	4	4	5					
4		4	4·5	4·5	5	5						11·5
5			5	5								12
5				5								12
6												12·5
6												12·5
8												13·5
9											11·5	14
10											12	14·5
11											12·5	15
14											14	16·5
19												19

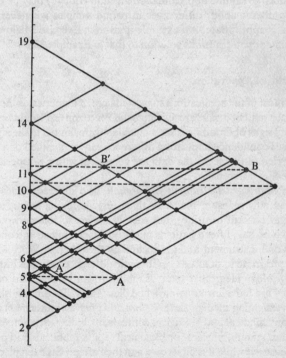

Figure 18 Graphical procedure for obtaining confidence limits (with ties)

Again, to get the limits, we count in 14 dots from top and bottom and read off on the vertical scale the value corresponding to the fourteenth dot. The limits are determined from the dots marked A and B in Figure 18. Note that these choices are not unique; we could equally well have chosen A' and B' and got the same limits. Again, as in the arithmetic method, the limits are 5 and 11·5.

Conclusion. Using either the arithmetic or graphical methods the nominal 95 per cent (actual 95·8 per cent) confidence limits are 5 and 11·5.

* * *

Large Sample Approximation

The large sample approximation given in (Eq. 18) may be used for testing hypotheses about differences in paired samples whenever the Wilcoxon test is appropriate. An example is given in Exercise 3 below and it follows a similar pattern for its solution to that in Example 32.

Fields of Application

In most of the applications suggested here, if numerical values of differences in the matched pairs are available the Wilcoxon test would be appropriate; if only signs of differences are available we are limited to the sign test. In most cases confidence limits for a difference can be obtained or a hypothesis test carried out to see if the data are consistent with a prespecified population median difference.

Laboratory Instrument Calibration Two different kinds of instrument reputedly measure the same thing (e.g. hormone levels, blood pressure, sugar content of urine), but each is subject to some error. Samples from each of, say, fifteen patients might be divided in two and one part analysed by one instrument and the second by the other. A Wilcoxon procedure is appropriate to detect any systematic difference between instruments.

Biology Heartbeat rates of rabbits might be observed before and after they are fed a hormone-enriched diet. The Wilcoxon test is appropriate for investigating median shift. *Before* and *after* measurements are common in many medical and biological contexts, including experiments on drugs and other stimuli, physical or biological (e.g. a rabbit's blood pressure may be measured while it is on its own and then after it has been placed in a cage for half an hour with one of the opposite sex).

Medicine An instrument called a Vitalograph is used to measure lung capacity. Readings may be taken on a sample of workers at the beginning and end of a work shift to study the effect of fumes inhaled in some industrial process.

Agriculture In a pest control experiment each of 10 plots may contain 40 lettuce plants. Each plot is divided into 2 halves; one half chosen at random is sprayed with one insecticide, the other half with another. Differences in numbers of uninfested plants can be used in a Wilcoxon test to detect differences in effect of the insecticides.

Trade Two different check-out systems are being compared in a supermarket. At randomly selected half-hour periods during a week the numbers passing through each system are recorded to provide data for a Wilcoxon test.

Psychology For sets of identical twins where it is known which was the first-born, times taken to carry out a manual task are compared to see if there is any indication that the first-born is in general quicker; Wilcoxon is again appropriate for testing.

Road safety Drivers' reaction times in dangerous situations may be compared before and after each has consumed a specific amount of alcohol.

Space Research Potential astronauts might have the enzyme content of their saliva determined before and after they have been subjected to a zero gravitational field in a simulator. Such biochemical evidence is important in determining physiological reactions to space travel.

Exercises

1. Blood pressures of 11 patients are measured before and after administration of a drug that is known not to raise blood pressure but might have the effect of lowering it. The differences for each patient in systolic blood pressure (recorded as pressure before minus pressure after) are:

$$7 \ 5 \ 12 \ -3 \ -5 \ 2 \ 14 \ 18 \ 19 \ 21 \ -1.$$

Perform an appropriate non-parametric test to see if the sample (assumed effectively random) contradicts the null hypothesis of no systematic change in blood pressure.

2. Obtain nominal 95 per cent confidence limits for the median difference in bacterial cream counts between Laboratory A and Laboratory B using the signed differences given in Table 18. We suggest you try both the arithmetic and graphical methods.

3. A hormone is added to one of the otherwise identical diets given to each of 40 pairs of twin lambs. Growth difference over a three-week period is recorded for

each pair. Signed ranks were allocated for the 40 differences. The lower rank sum of 242 was that for the negative differences. If it is not known *a priori* whether any effect the hormone might have would be to increase or to decrease the growth rate, investigate the acceptability of the hypothesis that the hormone has no effect on growth rate.

4. A psychologist interviews both the father and mother of each of 17 unrelated but mentally handicapped children asking each one individually a series of questions aimed at determining how well they understand the problems their child is likely to face in adult life. He records for each family whether it is the husband (H) or the wife (W) who shows the better appreciation of these potential problems for their handicapped offspring. For the 17 families his findings are:

H W W H H H W H H H H H H H W H H.

Is the evidence sufficiently strong to conclude that by and large husbands have a better understanding of the situation?

7. Methods for Two Independent Samples

Scope

We often wish to decide whether two independent samples can reasonably be supposed to come from the same population or from populations that differ only with respect to the median (or its equivalent, the mean, if they are symmetric). The methods of Chapter 6 are no longer appropriate as we cannot reduce this to a single-sample problem. After describing one very simple test, we devote most of the chapter to two more widely used procedures.

These are essentially two versions of the same test, but there is confusion over nomenclature; the test is sometimes called the Wilcoxon *rank sum* test ('rank sum' to distinguish it from 'signed ranks' met in Chapters 5 and 6) and sometimes the Mann–Whitney test. Their inventors developed the same basic idea with rather different detail in the late 1940s. While one formulation illustrates the theory more clearly, many people find the other easier to use.

A Simple Test

Let us look first at a simple test devised in 1959 by a very inventive American statistician, John Tukey.

Example 40

The Problem. Hotpot Stoves have a standard method of insulating the ovens in the stoves they make. To test its effectiveness they take random samples from the production line and heat the ovens to 400°C., noting the time it takes them to cool to 360°C., when the power is switched off. For a random sample of 8 ovens the times in minutes are:

$$15 \cdot 7 \quad 14 \cdot 8 \quad 14 \cdot 2 \quad 16 \cdot 1 \quad 15 \cdot 3 \quad 13 \cdot 9 \quad 17 \cdot 2 \quad 14 \cdot 9.$$

They decide to explore the use of a cheaper form of insulation and use this on a further random sample of 9 ovens and note the times taken for the same temperature drop to be:

$$13 \cdot 7 \quad 14 \cdot 1 \quad 14 \cdot 7 \quad 15 \cdot 4 \quad 15 \cdot 6 \quad 14 \cdot 4 \quad 12 \cdot 9 \quad 15 \cdot 1 \quad 14 \cdot 0.$$

The firm want to know whether they have reasonable grounds for considering that the cheaper insulation performs as well, in the sense that the population median times for given heat loss may reasonably be assumed to be the same.

Statistical Formulation. The null hypothesis is that the samples come from the same population and the alternative is that the second sample (with the cheaper insulation) represents a population with lower median, there being ample grounds based on physical properties of the substances used, etc., for rejecting any hypothesis that the cheaper product could possibly be more efficient. Thus we shall be interested in a one-tail test. We shall base this on the degree of overlap of the two samples. Clearly, if the two sets of sample measurements did not greatly overlap one another this would be fairly convincing evidence of different medians.

Procedure. If our alternative hypothesis were true it would be supported by values in the first sample being generally higher (the heat being retained longer) than in the second. Tukey's proposal bears this in mind. We proceed as follows. We first determine whether *any* value in the second sample is lower than *every* value in the first sample. If not, stop the test and automatically accept the null hypothesis of equal medians. In our case, however, the value of $12 \cdot 9$ in the second sample is less than $13 \cdot 9$, the smallest value in the first sample. We next look at the top end and see if the largest value in the first sample is larger than every value in the second; we find it is, $17 \cdot 2$ being greater than any value in the second sample. Had there not been such a value, we should again stop the test and accept the null hypothesis.

The situation is depicted in Figure 19 where the samples are represented by dots on parallel lines with identical scales. There is a range of overlapping values, but if the test is to continue sample 1 must have its top tail extending to the right of this range as in Figure 19, and sample 2 must have its lower tail extending to the left of this range.

If the test is not yet terminated, we count the total number of observations in sample 2 that are less than *all* those in sample 1; there are two, $12 \cdot 9$ and $13 \cdot 7$. We also count the number of observations in the first sample that are larger than *all* those in the second; there are three, $15 \cdot 7$, $16 \cdot 1$ and $17 \cdot 2$. Thus there are five observations in the non-overlapping part of the sample

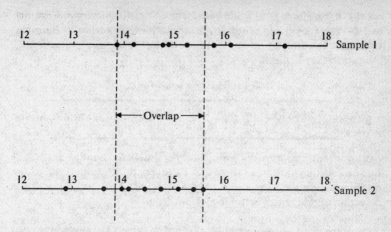

Figure 19 Diagrammatic representation of oven insulation data

range. This total, usually denoted by T, is our test statistic. The theory of *Tukey's Quick Test*, as it is usually called, is complicated but gives the remarkable result that, providing the size of each sample is not more than about 20 and the sample sizes are not very different, for a one-tailed test we have significance at the 2·5 per cent level if $T = 7$ or more, at the 0·5 per cent level if $T = 10$ or more and at the 0·05 per cent level if $T = 13$ or more.

Conclusion. In our case with $T = 5$ we do not have significance at any of the above levels.

Comments. Although a one-tail test was appropriate in our problem, for a two-tail test under the same conditions the values $T = 7$, 10, 13 are the minima for significance at the 5, 1 and 0·1 per cent levels (double the levels for the one-tail test).

*   *   *

Ties may occur between the largest member of one sample and a member of the other or the smallest in one sample and a member of the other. In such cases a tied observation is given a count of one half in evaluating T.

Example 41

The Problem. A hardness testing machine measures in arbitrary units the hardness of samples of a certain zinc and aluminium alloy. Random samples are taken from large production batches made by two different processes, A and B. Table 23 gives the results (arranged for convenience in ascending order) for the samples tested. Is there evidence to support a difference in the population medians?

Table 23 Hardness tests on an alloy

Process A	4·7	5·3	9·8	13·4	15·1	16·7	17·2	17·4	17·7	19·2
Process B	2·9	3·7	4·2	5·9	11·2	13·3	14·4	14·6	15·1	

Statistical Formulation. We form Tukey's T statistic counting any ties as one half if they occur at the end of the overlap. A two-tail test will be appropriate in the absence of any prior evidence on limitation of the direction of differences between medians.

Procedure. From the ordered observations in Table 23 it is easy to see that process B has three values 2·9, 3·7 and 4·2 *below* any for process A and that process A has 5 values 16·7, 17·2, 17·4, 17·7 and 19·2 *above* any for process B. There is also one tie at this top end at 15·1 which scores one half. Thus $T = 3 + 5 + 0·5 = 8·5$.

Conclusion. Since T lies between 7 and 10 and the sample sizes are not very different, we reject the hypothesis that the medians are equal at the 5 per cent but not at the 1 per cent level.

*   *   *

If the numbers in the two samples are very different, tables are required to get the T values needed for significance. Conover (1971), Table 21, p. 408, is suitable.

Tukey's test is quick to use, and in many cases one only has to remember the magic numbers 7, 10, 13 as T values for significance. However, the theory of the test is more complicated than that for some non-parametric tests, and it clearly uses only a small amount of the available information.

We now consider a more widely used test where it is also easier to outline the theory.

The Wilcoxon Rank Sum Test

The general philosophy of this test has something in common with the Wilcoxon signed rank test used in Chapters 5 and 6. Suppose we are given data like those in Example 40 and rank the observations for the two samples *jointly* in order of magnitude from smallest to largest. If both samples were from the same population it would be a matter of chance which sample produced the smallest observation, the next smallest and so on; indeed we would expect a pretty fair mix of low-, medium- and high-ranking observations in each sample. If a great many of the low-ranking and few of the high-ranking observations occur in one sample, this is evidence that the samples may come from different populations. Let us illustrate the situation in a very simple case. Suppose we have 9 observations altogether; we may think of their ranks from 1 to 9 as labels attached to tickets; suppose we want a random sample of 4 of these, the remaining 5 to be regarded as a second sample. Mechanically we could generate such samples by drawing 4 tickets from the hat for the first-sample ranks; those left in the hat would form the second sample.

Drawing samples like (1, 5, 6, 8), (1, 3, 6, 7) or (2, 5, 8, 9) would not surprise us at all. We would be a little surprised if our sample turned out to be (1, 2, 3, 4) or (6, 7, 8, 9). Why should we be surprised? If we are selecting at random, *any* sample of four has an equal probability of selection. Our surprise really stems from the fact that these last samples contain *all* the low and *all* the high ranks, respectively, whereas the others contain a good mix of ranks. This is reflected in the sums of the ranks. A moment's reflection will show that there are many more samples with a rank sum of, say, 17, than there are samples with rank sum 10 or rank sum 30. Indeed (1, 2, 3, 4) is the *only* sample with rank sum 10 and (6, 7, 8, 9) is the only sample with rank sum 30. However (1, 3, 6, 7) or (2, 4, 5, 6) or (1, 2, 5, 9) or (1, 2, 6, 8) or (2, 3, 5, 7) do not exhaust all those which add up to 17. Can you find at least one other? This property of the sums simply reflects the fact that samples with a good mixture of ranks are more common than those with extreme ranks only. The extreme samples are therefore those that provide evidence *against* the null hypothesis; they are more likely to result from different populations.

To associate probabilities with the various sample sums we need first to know how many different samples of four we can get from nine. This is a simple combinations problem: in how many ways can we select 4 items from 9 (without regard to order)? It is

$$^9C_4 = \frac{9 \times 8 \times 7 \times 6}{1 \times 2 \times 3 \times 4} = 126.$$

Since all 126 selections are equally likely, each has a probability of 1/126. Since (1, 2, 3, 4) is the only sample with sum 10, the probability of this sample sum is 1/126. A sum of 11 only arises with the sample (1, 2, 3, 5), so it also has a probability of 1/126. A sum of 12 may be got from (1, 2, 3, 6) or

(1, 2, 4, 5), so the probability of a sample rank sum of 12 is 2/126. Since the events 'sum is 10', 'sum is 11' and 'sum is 12' are mutually exclusive, the probability of a sum less than or equal to 12 is the sum of these three probabilitites, i.e.

$$\frac{1}{126} + \frac{1}{126} + \frac{2}{126} = \frac{4}{126}.$$

Clearly, if we are testing the hypothesis that the samples of 4 and 5 are from the same population against the general alternative that the populations differ in location (i.e. in their median in any case and in their median or mean if we assume they are symmetric), then a two-tail test is appropriate. In Example 42 we develop such a test for a numerical example from first principles. Example 43 is an example of a practical application making use of tables.

Example 42

The Problem. A pharmaceutical firm market a product that they claim will reduce the absorption of alcohol into the blood stream. To test the claim, nine volunteers are each asked to drink three pints of beer; four of the nine selected at random are given the product to take. After 30 minutes a blood sample is taken from each of the nine and the blood alcohol content in mg./100 ml. for each is given in Table 24. Is there sufficient evidence to conclude that the preparation influences the alcohol level in the blood stream?

Table 24   Blood alcohol content after 3 pints beer (mg./100 ml.)

Given product	79	85	105	93	
Not given product	99	102	107	117	108

Statistical Formulation. We seek the rank sum associated with the sample of four given the product. If there is no prior indication that the only effect of the drug could be to reduce alcohol intake into the blood, a two-sided test would be appropriate and a *low* or a *high* rank sum would be evidence against the null hypothesis of no difference. If there were prior evidence (say from the biochemical angle) that, if the drug had any effect, it would necessarily reduce uptake, then a one-tail test would be appropriate with a low sum of ranks indicating significance.

Procedure. First, we jointly rank all observations. This is done in Table 25 where we print in italic observations and ranks for those given the product. A useful dodge when working with pencil and paper is to underline them.

Table 25   Blood alcohol content ranked for two samples

Observation	79	85	93	99	102	*105*	107	108	117
Rank	1	2	3	4	5	6	7	8	9

The sum of the ranks for those given the product is $1 + 2 + 3 + 6 = 12$ and we have already seen in the discussion before this example that the probability of a sum of 12 or less in this situation is 4/126. Thus, if a one-tail test is appropriate, the probability of a result as or more extreme than we have observed is $4/126 \approx 0.032$. If, however, a two-tail test were appropriate, we would find that the probabilities associated with a sum of 30, 29 and 28 are also, respectively, 1/126, 1/126 and 2/126 – all as or less likely than a sum of 12. In fact, there is a *symmetrical* upper tail; we leave it as an exercise to verify this by writing down the samples that give sums of 30, 29 and 28. Thus for a two-tail test the probability of a result as or less likely than that observed is $4/128 + 4/128 = 8/128 \approx 0.063$.

Conclusion. If a one-tail test is appropriate the relevant tail probability is less than 0·05, so we reject the hypothesis of no difference at the nominal 5 per cent level. If we cannot justify a one-tail test on *a priori* grounds we have insufficient evidence to reject the hypothesis at the nominal 5 per cent level, but it is worth drawing attention to the fact that the result falls not far above the critical level needed for significance.

Comments. Some unease may arise because the ranks associated with the larger sample who do not take the product are ignored. However, once we know the sum of ranks for one sample, that for the other is automatically determined. The total of all ranks from 1 to 9 is 45; thus if the sum of the ranks for the first sample is 12, that for the second must be $45 - 12 = 33$. This is easily verified from Table 25.

*   *   *

In general the sum of the ranks of n items (i.e. the sum of the numbers 1, 2, 3, . . . , n) turns out to be $n(n + 1)/2$. This is easily checked in simple cases and for $n = 9$ we find it is $9 \times 10/2 = 45$. Thus in general if Q denotes the sum of ranks for all n units in the two samples and S_1 and S_2 the sums of the ranks for samples 1 and 2, respectively, we have $Q = S_1 + S_2 = n(n + 1)/2$ and $S_2 = n(n + 1)/2 - S_1$.

Example 43

The Problem. Apply the Wilcoxon rank sum test to the problem considered in Example 40 on oven insulation.

Statistical Formulation. We assume as in Example 40 that there are *a priori* grounds for performing a one-tail test. We must now rank the data and find the value of an appropriate statistic based on rank sums to make the necessary test.

Procedure. In Table 26 we give the ordered cooling times for the data in Example 40, the eight values in italic corresponding to the standard method of insulation. Ranks are also given.

Table 26   Oven cooling times ordered and ranked

Time	12·9	13·7	*13·9*	14·0	14·1	*14·2*	14·4	14·7	*14·8*
Rank	1	2	*3*	4	5	*6*	7	8	*9*

Time	*14·9*	15·1	*15·3*	15·4	15·6	*15·7*	*16·1*	17·2
Rank	*10*	11	*12*	13	14	*15*	*16*	17

Working out the probabilitites associated with all possible rank sums for a total of 8 out of 17 would be very tedious; fortunately, tables come to our aid. An abridged table is given in Table A4 in the Appendix, and more extensive tables are given by Lehmann (1975) as Table B, p. 410, and by Daniel (1978) as his Table A8, p. 408.

To use such tables we first calculate S_1 or S_2. It does not matter which, but generally speaking it is easier to calculate either a sum for the sample that tends to involve the smaller ranks or else for the sample with the smaller number of observations.

The sum S_1 (the sample using the standard insulation) is:

$$3 + 6 + 9 + 10 + 12 + 15 + 16 + 17 = 88.$$

Now the tables do not involve S_1 or S_2 directly but related statistics T_1 or T_2. If m_1, m_2 are, respectively, the number of observations in the first and second sample then

$$T_1 = S_1 - m_1(m_1 + 1)/2 \qquad \text{(Eq. 19)}$$

and

$$T_2 = S_2 - m_2(m_2 + 1)/2 \qquad \text{(Eq. 20)}$$

The reader who enjoys algebraic manipulations might like to deduce from (Eq. 19) and (Eq. 20) that

$$T_2 = m_1 m_2 - T_1 \qquad \text{(Eq. 21)}$$

but if you do not like algebra we suggest you take this last and useful result on trust. We shall check the result numerically for our example. We have $S_1 = 88$, $m_1 = 8$, $m_2 = 9$ whence by (Eq. 19)

$$T_1 = 88 - (8 \times 9)/2 = 88 - 36 = 52.$$

Thus, (Eq. 21) gives

$$T_2 = (8 \times 9) - 52 = 72 - 52 = 20.$$

This is the way to get T_2 in practice, but as verification of (Eq. 21) we may calculate T_2 as follows:

$$S_2 = 1 + 2 + 4 + 5 + 7 + 8 + 11 + 13 + 14 = 65,$$

whence by (Eq. 20)

$$T_2 = 65 - (9 \times 10)/2 = 65 - 45 = 20.$$

Table A4 gives the maximum value of the lesser of T_1 and T_2 indicating significance in a one- or two-tail test as appropriate. Entering Table A4 with $m_1 = 8$ and $m_2 = 9$ we find that in a one-tail test 18 is the maximum value indicating significance. Our T_2 value of 20 therefore provides no reason to reject the null hypothesis in a one-tail test at the 5 per cent level. The more extensive tables given by Lehmann indicate that the probability (one-tail) of a T_2 value less than or equal to 20 is in fact 0·0694, so the result is not far short of significance.

Conclusion. There is insufficient evidence to reject the hypothesis that the second material has the same median time for the given heat loss as the first, but there is probably a sufficient element of doubt to justify a larger experiment before the manufacturer changed to the new material if he considered any difference likely to be of importance.

Comments. At this stage the manufacturer may well feel it useful to have confidence limits for the likely difference in median times. We show how these are calculated in Example 47 and Exercise 3 at the end of the chapter is devoted to calculating these for the data used in this example.

*   *   *

The use of T_1 and T_2 rather than S_1 and S_2 as a test statistic may seem somewhat artificial; however, it has advantages for tabulation, since the minimum of S_1 differs for each sample size, but the minimum of T_1 (and T_2) is always zero. Can you see why? (Hint – what is the sum of the numbers 1, 2, 3, . . . m_1? See p. 135.

On p. 129 we mentioned the equivalence of the two tests known as the 'Wilcoxon rank sum test', which we have just described, and the 'Mann–Whitney test'. It is the procedure for obtaining T_1 and T_2, usually associated with the name 'Mann–Whitney', that is different. We describe it by reworking the previous example; T_1 and T_2 are now obtained directly, another reason for their use in tables.

Example 44

The Problem. The same as in Example 43, but solution to proceed by the Mann–Whitney method.

Statistical Formulation. Again we order the sample, but instead of determining a sum of ranks we look at the number of observations in one sample exceeding (i.e. ranked higher than) each member of the other sample. The total obtained will be either T_1 or T_2. For our one-tail test, if the alternative hypothesis that the second material is inferior is correct, we expect relatively few values in the second sample to exceed those of the first. Determining the number of cases in which this occurs leads directly to T_2.

Procedure. Table 27 illustrates the method. In the first column we set out all first-sample values in the order given on p. 129 (there is is no need to order them). We then count the number of values in the second sample exceeding each of these. These have been listed in Table 27, but in practice there is no need to do so; only the total numbers recorded in the final column are needed.

Table 27 Calculations for the Mann-Whitney statistic

First Sample	Higher values in second sample	Number of higher values
15·7	—	0
14·8	15·4 15·6 15·1	3
14·2	14·7 15·4 15·6 14·4 15·1	5
16·1	—	0
15·3	15·4 15·6	2
13·9	14·1 14·7 15·4 15·6 14·4 15·1 14·0	7
17·2	—	0
14·9	15·4 15·6 15·1	3
	Total	20

The total 20 in the last column of Table 27 is the value of T_2.

Conclusion. For this example we have established the same value for the test statistic as in Example 43.

Comments. This equivalence is general, although we shall not prove it.

*   *   *

Many people feel that the Mann–Whitney procedure is easier to use in practice to calculate T_1 or T_2; once one is obtained, the other may be worked out from (Eq. 21). The choice of method for obtaining the statistic T_1 or T_2 is clearly a matter of personal preference. However, the Wilcoxon procedure has two merits: its family resemblance to the Wilcoxon signed rank test and its simplicity, which means that the rationale of the procedure is easy to follow.

Ties

Ties are dealt with in a manner reminiscent of the Wilcoxon signed rank test. We assign to tied ranks their mean if we use the Wilcoxon rank sum approach. If we use the Mann–Whitney approach we count one half for each tied value in different samples. The critical value of the test statistic T_1 or T_2 is then only approximate, but unless ties are very common, the result should not be seriously misleading. We illustrate the method by an example.

Example 45

The Problem. The parts per million of an impurity in a metal refined by a certain process are recorded for 7 specimens (sample A). Similar readings are obtained for 5 specimens refined by a new process (sample B). The values are given in Table 28. Test the hypothesis that there is no difference between the sample medians.

Table 28   Parts per million of an impurity in a metal

Sample A	12	15	17	15	11	13	16
Sample B	12	15	13	14	10		

Statistical Formulation. The appropriate test is the Wilcoxon/Mann–Whitney test with $m_1 = 7$, $m_2 = 5$ and ties being present. Since there is no *a priori* reason for a one-sided alternative a two-tail test is appropriate.

Procedure. We shall calculate T_1, T_2 by both the Wilcoxon and Mann–Whitney methods. The appropriate ranks for the combined samples are given in Table 29 where italic indicates sample *A* values.

Table 29   Ranks for metal impurity data

Sample values	10	*11*	*12*	12	*13*	13	14	*15*	15	15	*16*	17
Ranks	1	2	3·5	3·5	5·5	5·5	7	9	9	9	*11*	*12*

Make sure you are clear about the method of allocating ranks to ties; if not, turn to p. 109 for details.

For the smaller sample $S_2 = 1 + 3·5 + 5·5 + 7 + 9 = 26$; since $m_2 = 5$, (Eq. 20) gives $T_2 = 26 - (5 \times 6)/2 = 11$ and (Eq. 21) gives $T_1 = (5 \times 7) - 11 = 35 - 11 = 24$. Thus T_2 is the appropriate test statistic.

While we do not have to rank the data for the Mann–Whitney count, we may as well take advantage of having done so and use the last line of Table 29 to get T_2 by counting the number of times each sample *A* ranking (in italic) is exceeded by a sample *B* ranking, counting one half in the case of a tie. Proceeding from the smallest to largest sample *A* value, we see 2 is exceeded by 3·5, 5·5, 7 and 9 so scores 4; 3·5 is equalled by 3·5 and exceeded by 5·5, 7 and 9 so scores 3·5; 5·5 is equalled by 5·5 and exceeded by 7 and 9 so scores 2·5; each 9 in sample *A* is equalled by the 9 in sample *B* rankings so each scores 0·5. Clearly 11 and 12 score zero. Adding these scores

$$T_2 = 4 + 3·5 + 2·5 + 0·5 + 0·5 = 11$$

as before. From Table A4 with sample sizes 5, 7 we see that the lower of T_1, T_2 must not exceed 5 for significance at a nominal 5 per cent level in a two-tail test.

Conclusion. We have insufficient evidence to reject the null hypothesis that there is no difference between the population medians.

Large Sample Approximation

Table A4 only extends to m_1, $m_2 = 15$ although other tables such as those in Daniel (1978) cover values from 16 to 20 in addition. Note that Daniel's tables effectively give values of $T' = T + 1$ where T is the lesser of T_1 and T_2.

When m_1, m_2 exceed 15, a normal approximation may be used. With the usual continuity correction it can be shown that, under the null hypothesis, if T is the smaller of T_1 and T_2, then

$$z = \frac{T + \frac{1}{2} - \frac{1}{2}m_1 m_2}{\sqrt{\{m_1 m_2 (m_1 + m_2 + 1)/12\}}} \qquad \text{(Eq. 22)}$$

has approximately a standard normal distribution. For significance at the 5 per cent level we require $z < -1\cdot64$ in a one-tail test and $z < -1\cdot96$ in a two-tail test.

Example 46

The Problem. A mathematics examination is given to 20 boys and 18 girls in the same class. On the assumption that the class can be regarded as an effectively random sample of children in the country, the teacher wishes to test the hypothesis that the median scores for boys and girls are the same (i.e. that the sample of scores for boys comes from the same population as the sample of scores for girls). He calculates T_1 for boys and T_2 for girls, finding T_2 is lower than T_1 and that $T_2 = 113$. Carry out the appropriate test.

Statistical Formulation. Since m_1, m_2 both exceed 15 we may use the approximation (Eq. 22). A two-sided test will be appropriate since there is no *a priori* reason for expecting one sex or the other to be better, despite the old wives' tales about girls not being so good at mathematics.

Procedure. With $m_1 = 20, m_2 = 18$ and $T = 113$, (Eq. 22) gives

$$z = \frac{113\cdot5 - (20 \times 18)/2}{\sqrt{(20 \times 18 \times 39/12)}} = \frac{113\cdot5 - 180}{1\sqrt{1170}}$$

$$= \frac{-66\cdot5}{34\cdot21} = -1\cdot94$$

This falls just short of the critical value of $-1\cdot96$ required for significance at the 5 per cent level.

Conclusion. There is not quite sufficient evidence to formally reject the hypothesis of no difference between boys and girls, but the result only narrowly fails to reach significance.

Comments. Tables such as those given by Daniel show that the approximation is not bad; had the value of T_2 been 112 (only one lower), significance would have been attained at the 5 per cent level. The reader may care to verify that with this lower value of T in (Eq. 22) we would get $z = -1\cdot97$, so significance would just be reached with the approximation also.

*   *   *

142 QUICK STATISTICS

Confidence Limits for the Difference Between Two Medians

As in the case of the single-sample situation, the interval estimation problem of determining confidence limits and intervals requires for a rigorous presentation theory that is beyond the scope of this book. Again, however, the method has many similarities to the one-sample process. An arithmetic or a graphical method both lead to the same results. If we check back and do a hypothesis test of a type to be described in Example 50, we find the limits are just on the boundaries of acceptability.

The confidence intervals we require are those for the *difference* between the two population medians. We base them on the idea that each difference between sample values gives an estimate of the difference between medians. Again it is the more extreme differences that we reject as unlikely. The theory which we are not presenting here tells us the number of extreme cases to reject; it turns out that if we want, for example, nominal 95 per cent confidence limits we look up the value of T (the smaller of T_1, T_2) that would *just* be significant at the 2·5% level in a one-tail test and exclude that number from each tail. There is a striking similarity here to what we did in the one-sample or paired-sample case.

Example 47

The Problem. In order to compare two different keyboard layouts for a pocket calculator they are designing, a company divide 21 volunteers into a group of 10 and a group of 11, allocating individuals randomly to the groups. (Why is this a wise thing to do?) Each group is asked to carry out the same standard series of calculations, group A using the first type of keyboard and group B the second. The total times (in minutes) for each individual to carry out the complete sequence of computations are recorded in Table 30. Use an arithmetic method based on the Wilcoxon rank sum procedure to obtain nominal 95 per cent confidence limits for the differences in median times between the two layouts.

Table 30   Times (minutes) to complete calculations

| Group A | 23 | 18 | 17 | 25 | 22 | 19 | 31 | 24 | 28 | 32 | |
| Group B | 24 | 28 | 32 | 28 | 41 | 27 | 35 | 34 | 27 | 35 | 33 |

Statistical Formulation. We require all possible differences between group A and group B observations. We reject the T smallest and T largest of these differences where T is the value of T_1 or T_2 that would just indicate significance at the 2·5 per cent level in a two-tail test. From Table A4 we find

$T = 26$. The largest and smallest differences not to be rejected give the required limits; the interval between these limits is the nominal 95 per cent confidence interval.

Procedure. In Table 31 we tabulate all the 110 differences although, as we shall see in our 'comments', it is in practice not necessary to calculate them all if we are systematic. The group *B* times are written in ascending order in the first row of Table 31 and the group *A* times in ascending order in the first column. In the body of the table any entry is the result of subtracting the group *A* entry in its row from the group *B* entry at the top of its column. Thus the diagonal entries are $24 - 17 = 7, 27 - 18 = 9$, etc.

Table 31   Differences between Group A and Group B times

	Group B										
	24	27	27	28	28	32	33	34	35	35	41
17	7	10	10	11	11	15	16	17	18	18	24
18	6	9	9	10	10	14	15	16	17	17	23
19	5	8	8	9	9	13	14	15	16	16	22
22	2	5	5	6	6	10	11	12	13	13	19
23	1	4	4	5	5	9	10	11	12	12	18
24	0	3	3	4	4	8	9	10	11	11	17
25	−1	2	2	3	3	7	8	9	10	10	16
28	−4	−1	−1	0	0	4	5	6	7	7	13
31	−7	−4	−4	−3	−3	1	2	3	4	4	10
32	−8	−5	−5	−4	−4	0	1	2	3	3	9

(rows labelled under "Group A")

We note that the 26 smallest values of the differences occur in the bottom left of the table and the 26 largest in the top right. The 26 smallest are −8, −7, −5, −5, −4, −4, −4, −4, −4, −3, −3, −1, −1, −1, 0, 0, 0, 0, 1, 1, 1, 2, 2, 2, 2, 2. The next smallest difference is 3; this is the lower confidence limit. Similarly, the 26 highest differences include values from 24 down to 12, but, after eliminating 26 entries, we still have some differences of 12 left, so 12 is the upper limit. The reader should check the calculation of this upper limit.

Conclusion. The nominal 95 per cent confidence limits for the median difference are 3 and 12; that is, we have 95 per cent confidence in the truth of the statement that the median time for the layout used by group *A* is between 3 and 12 minutes quicker than that for the layout used by group *B*.

Comments. If we wanted a point estimate for the difference an obvious one to take would be the difference between the medians for groups *A* and *B*.

We leave it as an exercise to show that the median time for group A is 23·5 minutes and for group B is 32 minutes, giving a difference of 8·5 minutes.

Since zero is not in the confidence interval, we would reject the hypothesis that the medians were the same.

We have noted that in Table 31 all the high values occur in the top right of the table and all the low values in the bottom left. After a little practice it is unnecessary to calculate all differences; all that is needed is to write down sufficient values in the appropriate corners to obtain the limits.

*   *   *

We now consider a graphical method of solving this problem.

Example 48

The Problem. The same as in Example 47 but a graphical method is to be used.

Statistical Formulation. We construct a graph by the method given under 'procedure' and use this to obtain confidence limits identical with those in the previous example.

Procedure. It is almost essential to use graph paper if the procedure is to be carried out quickly and accurately. We described the method by reference to Figure 20 where OX and OY are horizontal and vertical axes with origin at O. The same scales must be used on each axis and are so chosen that all values in group A (i.e. from 17 to 32) can be represented on the X-axis (horizontal) and all values in group B (i.e. from 24 to 41) can be represented on the Y-axis (vertical). Through each point on the X-axis corresponding to an observed value we draw a line parallel to the Y-axis. AB in Figure 20 is such a line through the observation 19. Also through each observation point on the Y-axis we draw a line parallel to the X-axis. CD is such a line corresponding to the observation 34. When an observed value occurs twice, as do 27, 28 and 35 in group B, it is best to draw two parallel lines close together, one slightly displaced to each side of the value, mentally noting that ideally they should merge with each other.

The lines PQ and RS are equally inclined to the axial directions (i.e. they make an angle of 45 degrees with each axis). They are so drawn that in the bottom right of the graph there are at least 27 intersections of lines of the type AB, CD *on or below PQ*, where intersections with 'double' lines (circled in the diagram) correspond to repeated observations and count as two. Similarly RS is placed so that there are at least 27 observations on or above it at the top left.

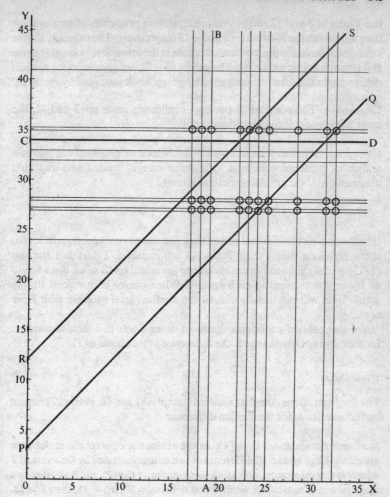

Figure 20 Graphical method for obtaining a confidence interval

The reason we choose the number 27 is that it is one greater than the critical value of $T = 26$ obtained from Table A4. In the previous example we deleted the 26 smallest and the 26 largest pairs.

In our example there are 26 intersections *below PQ* and 33 *on or below* it; there are 25 intersections *above RS* and 28 *on or above*. *PQ* and *RS* cut the Y-axis at 3 and 12 respectively. Elementary properties of graphs show they would cut the X-axis at -3 and -12 respectively. The values 3, 12 give confidence limits for the median difference in the form: 'layout used by group B – layout used by group A'. The values of -12, -3 give limits for median difference in the form: 'layout used by group A – layout used by group B.'

Conclusion. The nominal 95 per cent confidence limits are 3 and 12, the same as those determined arithmetically.

Comments. Whether one adopts the arithmetic or graphical method is a matter of personal choice; a little more care is needed with repeated observations if the graphical method is used.

* * *

If one wants to know actual rather than just the nominal confidence levels, more elaborate tables than Table A4 are required. Tables in Lehmann (1975) already referred to enable one to get actual levels when there are 10 or fewer observations in each sample. When one or both exceed 10, the actual level will not usually exceed the nominal level by more than 1 per cent.

We may obtain confidence limits at other levels in a similar manner. Essentially the only change is the difference in the choice of T.

Example 49

The Problem. Given the data used in Examples 47 and 48, obtain 99 per cent confidence limits for the median difference.

Statistical Formulation. Using either the arithmetic or graphical method we eliminate large and small differences to an extent indicated by the value of T which is the maximum indicating significance at the 0·5 per cent level in a one-tail test. From tables we find that with $m_1 = 10$, $m_2 = 11$, then $T = 18$. (N.B. Table A4 does not give the requisite values; tables such as those given by Daniel (1978), p. 410, may be used.)

Procedure. If we use the arithmetic procedure, Table 31 is relevant. We exclude the 18 smallest and 18 largest differences. The 18 smallest are -8, $-7, -5, -5, -4, -4, -4, -4, -4, -3, -3, -1, -1, -1, 0, 0, 0, 0$. The next smallest entry, 1, is the lower confidence limit. The 18 largest differences are 24, 23, 22, 19, 18, 18, 18, 17, 17, 17, 17, 16, 16, 16, 16, 16, 15, 15. Since there still remains a difference of 15, this is the upper limit.

If we use the graphical procedure we must shift PQ, RS in Figure 20 outward until there are at least $18 + 1 = 19$ points on or outside each line. It is left as an exercise to the reader to show that these new lines cut the Y-axis at the above limits.

Conclusion. A 99 per cent confidence interval for the median difference is from 1 to 15.

*   *   *

Hypothesis Tests for Non-zero Differences

Sometimes one wishes to test the hypothesis that the median difference between two populations has a certain specified value. If this hypothesis is true, then if we increase all values of the population with the lower median by this specified value, we shall have populations with the same median. Thus, given a sample of values from each, if we add the specified difference to each of the sample values from the population with the lower median, we should have samples from populations with equal medians and the test can proceed as in Examples 43 to 46.

Example 50

The Problem. Given the data in Table 30, test the hypothesis that the median of the population from which the group A sample is taken is 3 units less than that for the group B sample.

Statistical Formulation. We add the supposed difference of 3 to each sample value in group A. We now test the hypothesis that these *revised* values are a sample from the same population as the group B sample, using the Wilcoxon rank sum test.

Procedure. Table 32 gives the combined ordering and ranks for the observations in Table 30 after 3 has been added to *each* group A observation. Ties are dealt with in the usual manner. The modified group A values are printed in italic. From Table 32 we get

$$S_1 = 1 + 2 + 3 + 5 + 6 + 8 + 11 + 13 + 16{\cdot}5 + 19 = 84{\cdot}5.$$

Since $m_1 = 10$ and $m_2 = 11$ we get from (Eq. 19) and (Eq. 21)

$$T_1 = 84{\cdot}5 - (10 \times 11)/2 = 84{\cdot}5 - 55 = 29{\cdot}5$$

and

$$T_2 = 110 - 29{\cdot}5 = 90{\cdot}5.$$

Table 32   Rankings for testing a median difference

Ordered data	20	21	22	24	25	26	27	27	27	28
Ranks	1	2	3	4	5	6	8	8	8	11

Ordered data	28	28	31	32	33	34	34	35	35	35	41
Ranks	11	11	13	14	15	16·5	16·5	19	19	19	21

From Table A4 we see that the maximum value of T indicating significance at the 5 per cent level in a two-tail test is 26.

Conclusion. We do not reject the hypothesis that the population median difference may be 3.

Comments. In Example 48 we established that the lower 95 per cent confidence limit was 3 and the upper 95 per cent limit was 12. We have remarked earlier (p. 91) that all hypothetical values in a confidence interval should lead to acceptable values of the appropriate related null hypothesis. Since 3 is a value within our confidence interval (even if only just), it is therefore not surprising that it is acceptable with a 5 per cent significance level test. We should expect any value less than 3 to be unacceptable in such a test. The reader may care to verify, by applying the procedure of this test for a supposed difference of, say, 2·9, that T_1 is thereby reduced to 26 so that the difference is just significant.

* * *

While the approach demonstrated in the above example may sometimes be useful in practice, the reader should be gaining some appreciation of the greater value of the confidence interval approach in that it gives us in one operation a complete range of acceptable hypotheses. More importantly perhaps, it gives some indication of how precisely our observations reflect the relevant population characteristic. In Example 47 we established with 'reasonable certainty' that the median difference lay between 3 and 12. If the manufacturer of the calculators only wanted firm evidence that there was a difference in median times, this information might suffice. If he wanted to know whether the median time difference was at least ten seconds we could not assure him firmly that this were so. We might suggest he try a larger experiment with more people. As we remarked on p. 88, a larger experiment may detect differences that are missed by a small experiment. In the context of confidence intervals, generally speaking a larger experiment will yield shorter confidence intervals than a small experiment; in technical jargon we refer to this as an increase in *precision*.

Three or More Samples

It would clearly be desirable to extend the comparison methods of this chapter to three or more independent samples. The stove manufacturer may wish to compare several types of insulation; the manufacturer of calculating machines may wish to compare four keyboard layouts.

The reader familiar with the parametric branch of statistics using normal distribution theory will recognize this as analogous with the extension of methods based on Student's 't' to analysis of variance. See, e.g. Chapters 4 and 5 of *Statistics in Action*.

There are similar extensions in the non-parametric field which essentially follow the Wilcoxon idea of comparing ranks. The best-known procedures in this area are associated with the names of Kruskal and Wallis and are described by Daniel (1978), to whom the interested reader is referred.

While non-parametric methods have a role to play in 'several-sample' problems, they lack the flexibility for dealing with a variety of alternative hypotheses that is a valuable feature of the analysis of variance; however, tests based on this parametric method require for their validity reasonable conformity with assumptions that are sometimes clearly violated. This is a major reason for the increasing interest during the last decade in non-parametric and other robust methods.

Fields of Application

It does not take a very vivid imagination to think up realistic situations where one might wish to compare the medians or means of two populations on the basis of independent samples. Then the Wilcoxon rank sum test or the corresponding Mann–Whitney approach is an appropriate non-parametric attack. Here are three relevant situations:

Medicine If we wish to compare the value of two drugs for reducing blood pressure, independent samples may be almost essential; because of 'interaction' or 'hangover', it might be quite inappropriate to give both drugs to any one person, even after a quite considerable time-lapse.

Sociology To explore the possibility that town and country children may attain different levels of physical fitness, samples of each might be scored in a fitness test and results compared non-parametrically.

Mineral exploration A mining company has options to develop two sites but only wishes to develop one. Sample test borings are taken on each and the percentage of the metal of interest contained in each boring is determined; this information can be used to test for population differences in mean or median levels of the metal; clearly, if there is evidence of one site being the richer, the company will want to develop it (assuming development costs and other factors are about the same for either site).

We leave it as an exercise for the reader to think up typical situations involving two independent samples in fields such as manufacturing, commerce, accountancy, agriculture, biology, physics, psychology and engineering.

Exercises

1. Apply Tukey's quick test to the calculator data given in Table 30.

2. This exercise demonstrates the use of the Wilcoxon rank sum test where we have only ordering and no actual measurements. Suppose an alloy is composed of zinc, copper and tin in certain proportions. It may be made at one of two different temperatures and we wish to know if one temperature produces, on the whole, a harder alloy than the other. We make 7 batches at the lower temperature and 9 at the higher. We arrange them in order of hardness, using the test described on p.13 (i.e. scraping each specimen against every other specimen to see which produces the deeper scratch). The final rankings in order of hardness are given in Table 33, where H stands for high- and L for low-temperature production. Rank 1 is the softest and rank 16 the hardest specimen. Test the hypothesis of equal hardness against the alternative that one temperature produces an alloy of greater median hardness than the other.

Table 33   Ranking of an alloy by hardness

Production temperature	H	L	H	H	H	L	H	L	L	H	H	L	L	L	L	L
Rank	1	2	3	4	5	6	7	8	9	10	11	12	13	14	15	16

3. Using the data in Table 26 on oven cooling times, obtain nominal 95 per cent confidence limits for the difference in median cooling times for the two types of insulation. Try both the arithmetic and graphical method and see which you prefer.

4. In Example 50 we showed that for the data in Table 30 the hypothesis of a median difference of 3 (exactly equal to the lower 95 per cent confidence limit) would not be rejected using a hypothesis test with the 5 per cent significance level, whereas we would reject a hypothesis of a difference less than 3. Verify that an analogous situation holds for the upper confidence limit of 12.

5. A psychologist is interested to know whether men or women are more upset by delays in being admitted to hospital for routine surgery. He devises an anxiety index to measure the degree of anxiety shown by patients one week before their scheduled admission. He has an index measurement for 17 men and 23 women. He ranks these 1 to 40 on a scale of increasing anxiety. If the sum of the ranks S_1 for the 17 men is 428, is there evidence against the null hypothesis that anxiety is independent of sex? If there is, which sex appears to show the greater anxiety?

8. Categories and Counts

Scope

Many observations take the form of counts; in particular, items or individuals may be classified according to whether or not they possess certain characteristics. We often look for associations between such characteristics. For example, if we have counts of numbers of smokers and non-smokers in a sample who do and do not contract lung cancer, we may ask if these give strong evidence of a link between smoking and lung cancer.

We shall find that very often the tabular forms in which data are presented may look similar but that the questions that can be asked and answered are rather different.

A test known as the *chi-squared test* often provides a good approximation to more exact non-parametric tests.

Counts versus Measurements

There are many situations where we count numbers of responses rather than measure a specific magnitude or level of response. In Table 24 we gave actual measurements of blood alcohol content; instead we might have asked volunteers to undergo a breathalyser test and simply recorded *positive* or *negative* responses according to whether or not the crystals changed colour.

Example 51

The Problem. From a group of 21 volunteers 11 are selected at random and given a drug that is claimed to inhibit alcohol absorption into the system; the remaining 10 are given no such drug. Each subject then drinks three double gins and one hour later is given a breathalyser test where a colour change indicates a likely excess of alcohol in the bloodstream. The results are given in Table 34. Do these indicate that in the population from which the volunteers are taken we should reject the null hypothesis that the proportion in the population showing a positive response is not influenced by the drug? We shall assume a two-tail test is appropriate, there being no prior evidence that the drug could only have a depressing effect on intake.

Table 34   Results of breathalyser test

	Positive Result	Negative Result	Row total
Given drug	2	9	11
Not given drug	7	3	10
Column total	9	12	21

Statistical Formulation. We consider this in very general terms. The appropriate null hypothesis is that the proportion giving a positive response in the population would be unaltered by administration of the drug. To devise a non-parametric test we now ask ourselves: *if the null hypothesis is true* and we take samples of 10 and 11 (corresponding to those not given and given the drug, respectively), are we likely to get only 2 positive responses from 11 in one of these samples and 7 from 10 in the other? One's intuitive reaction is that this is rather unlikely. Statistically, what we now ask is this: suppose our 21 people in the two samples are going to produce 9 positive and 12 negative responses (the totals observed in Table 34), what is the probability, if we split the 21 randomly into two groups of 10 and 11, that 7 of the positives will fall into the group of 10 and only 2 into the group of 11? We shall also want to know the probabilities of any less likely divisions of positives between the two groups.

We could simulate this sampling situation by supposing we had 21 tickets in a hat, 9 labelled P for positive and 12 labelled N for negative. The allocation of a sample of 11 is achieved by random selection. Those remaining in the hat represent the second sample of 10. on p. 154 we shall show how to work out the probability of each outcome of such a procedure. This method has been used to obtain the probability of each possible outcome illustrated in Table 35. Once we have these probabilities we add the probabilities associated with our observed outcome and any equally or less likely outcomes; we regard our result as significant if the total associated probabilities are sufficiently low.

Procedure. We show all possible outcomes together with the associated probabilites (calculated as described on p. 154) in Table 35, where a tableau of the form

$$\begin{matrix} 1 & 10 \\ 8 & 2 \end{matrix}$$

(Eq. 23)

has the format of Table 34, i.e. there is 1 P and 10 Ns in our sample of 11 and 8 Ps and 2 Ns in our sample of 10. All tableaux have the row and column totals shown in Table 34. Note that in forming each tableau, this condition on the totals implies that once we write down the number of Ps in the top line all other entries are *automatically* determined to give the correct row and column totals. This idea of the minimum amount of information needed to complete each tableau is associated with the concept of *degrees of freedom* we shall be introducing on p. 155.

Since the outcomes listed in Table 34 are mutually exclusive and exhaustive, the sum of the associated probabilities should be unity. The reader should check that this is so, apart from a small allowance needed for rounding off. In practice only the probabilities of the few tableaux as or less likely than that observed need be calculated.

Table 35   Permissible samples of 10, 11 from 21

(a)	(b)	(c)	(d)	(e)
0 11	1 10	2 9	3 8	4 7
9 1	8 2	7 3	6 4	5 5
$p = 0.000034$	$p = 0.001684$	$p = 0.022454$	$p = 0.117885$	$p = 0.282924$

(f)	(g)	(h)	(i)	(j)
5 6	6 5	7 4	8 3	9 2
4 6	3 7	2 8	1 9	0 10
$p = 0.330078$	$p = 0.188616$	$p = 0.050522$	$p = 0.005613$	$p = 0.000187$

We observed tableau (c); those less likely are (a), (b), (i) and (j) and all are appropriate in a two-tail test. The total associated probability is:

$$0.000034 + 0.001684 + 0.022454 + 0.005613 + 0.000187 = 0.02997.$$

Conclusion. Since the result lies in a critical region of actual size 0.02997, which is less than 0.05, the result is significant at a nominal 5 per cent level, so we reject the hypothesis that the drug has no effect and conclude it does alter the alcohol level.

Comments. Had we enough prior chemical and biological evidence to know that the drug, if it did anything, could only *reduce* intake, a one-tail test would be appropriate, associated tail probabilities being provided by tableaux (a), (b) and (c) and totalling:

$$0.000034 + 0.001684 + 0.022454 = 0.024172,$$

again giving significance at the nominal 5 per cent level although the actual level of significance is of course slightly higher (remember that the lower the tail probability, the higher the significance).

* * *

Calculating the Probabilities

We now look at the calculations for those probabilities in Table 35. First, what is the number of distinct samples of 11 tickets from 21 if we ignore order but regard each ticket as distinguishable (perhaps by a number)? This is a simple combinations problem – the answer if $^{21}C_{11}$. Suppose now we want the probability that a sample of 11 contains exactly 4 Ps; this implies it also contains 7 Ns. This corresponds to the configuration (e) in Table 35. Since we select 4 from 9 Ps this can be done in $^9C_4$ ways; similarly there are $^{12}C_7$ ways of selecting 7 from 12 Ns. Since we may combine any selection of 4 Ps with any selection of 7 Ns there are $^9C_4 \times {}^{12}C_7$ samples with the desired property and all are equally likely. There are $^{21}C_{11}$ equally likely possible samples. Thus by the basic probability definition, p. 26, the probability of configuration (e) in Table 35 is

$$\frac{^9C_4 \times {}^{12}C_7}{^{21}C_{11}}$$

By writing the combinations out in factorial form the reader may like to verify that the probability may be written

$$\frac{9! \times 12! \times 11! \times 10!}{21! \times 4! \times 5! \times 7! \times 5!} \qquad \text{(Eq. 24)}$$

There is still quite a bit of arithmetic needed to evaluate this and a pocket calculator helps. Tables of logarithms of factorials are also included in some statistical tables. The value may be shown to be $0 \cdot 282924$.

The result (Eq. 24) may be generalized to any tableau of the form (Eq. 23).

We write such a tableau

$$\begin{matrix} a & b \\ c & d \end{matrix} \qquad \text{(Eq. 25)}$$

where we regard the row totals $a + b$, $c + d$ and the column totals $a + c$, $b + d$ as fixed (often referred to collectively as the *marginal* totals). A generalization of the argument used for the particular case leads to an expression for the probability of the configuration in (Eq. 25) which reduces to an analogue of (Eq. 24)

$$\frac{(a+b)!\,(c+d)!\,(a+c)!\,(b+d)!}{n!\,a!\,b!\,c!\,d!} \qquad \text{(Eq. 26)}$$

where $n = a + b + c + d$.

The calculation of these probabilities for all possible tableaux would be tedious if we had to start from scratch each time; however, once the probability has been calculated for one tableau in a table like Table 35, that of its neighbour may be obtained by a few simple multiplications and divisions. This is quite easy for the mathematically inclined, providing that a little care is taken to avoid round-off errors, but we do not give details as we shall seldom need to carry out the exact test used in Example 51.

Before we develop a simple alternative, we return to the point made on p. 153 that with fixed marginal totals we need to know only one entry in a tableau like (Eq. 23) to complete the tableau for that particular random selection. In other words, we associate *one degree of freedom* with the tableau. The concept of degrees of freedom in this and other situations is discussed in Chapters 3, 4 and 5 of *Statistics in Action*.

The test applied in Example 51 is known as *Fisher's exact test*. In many circumstances it is well approximated by a test described in Chapter 3 of *Statistics in Action* known as the chi-squared test ('chi' is pronounced 'ki' and refers to the Greek letter written $\varkappa$). For those not familiar with the test, it is described here. We extend its scope somewhat beyond that given in *Statistics in Action*.

The Chi-squared Test

Given the marginal totals in a case like that in Table 34, it is easy to work out the expected numbers in each position in the table. These positions are often referred to as *cells*. The expected numbers are based on the null hypothesis; since there are 21 observations with 9 positives (P), then in a sample of 11 the expected number of Ps is the proportion in 21, i.e. 9/21 multiplied by the sample size 11, i.e.

$$\frac{9}{21} \times 11 = \frac{99}{21} \approx 4\cdot71.$$

A rule of thumb (based on the above reasoning) for obtaining the expected number in any cell involves the row and column total associated with that cell as well as the grand total (n) and is

$$\frac{(\text{row total}) \times (\text{column total})}{\text{grand total}} \qquad \text{(Eq. 27)}$$

Since Table 34 has two rows and two columns, it is often called a 2 × 2 (pronounced 2 by 2) table. The expected number of Ps among those taking the drug, i.e. the expected number for the first cell of the table, has been worked out above as 4·71. Applying (Eq. 27) to the cell corresponding to a negative response among those not given the drug (the cell in the second row and second column) the expected number is $12 \times 10/21 \approx 5·71$. The reader should calculate the expected numbers for the two remaining cells in a like manner. They are given in Table 36 where it will be noted that the row and column totals for the *expected* numbers equal those for the *observations* in Table 34.

Table 36   Expected numbers under null hypothesis

	Positive result	Negative result	Row total
Given drug	4·71	6·29	11
Not given drug	4·29	5·71	10
Column total	9	12	21

Thus if we have worked out one expected number, say 4·71, we may get the others by a series of subtractions from the known marginal totals, e.g. $11 - 4·71 = 6·29$ and $9 - 4·71 = 4·29$; the final value of 5·71 is obtained either as $12 - 6·29$ or $10 - 4·29$.

As a matter of good statistical practice, to check for arithmetical slips it is sensible to calculate two of the expected values, say those in the first row, using (Eq. 27), check that they add to the row total and then get the remaining two by subtraction.

If the null hypothesis is true the observed and expected numbers will not differ greatly. Large discrepancies between observed and expected numbers indicate departures from the null hypothesis. It would seem intuitively reasonable to base a test on the *magnitudes* of the differences between observed and expected numbers in each cell. However, we should also take into account the size of the numbers involved; if we expect 84 and we observe 87 the discrepancy is 3; if we expect 4 and observe 1 the discrepancy is also 3. Yet in the latter case we rightly feel the discrepancy justifies more doubt about the hypothesis on which we have based our expected numbers. Think of this in terms of coin-tossing if you like. Toss a coin 8 times and the expected number of heads is 4; it is a little surprising if we only get 1 head. Toss a coin 168 times and the expected number of heads is 84; we are not very surprised if we actually observe 87.

To overcome this problem we try and relate the magnitude of the discrepancy to the expected number; what we do is to express the square of the magnitude as a fraction of the expected number and calculate for each cell

$$\frac{(\text{observed number} - \text{expected number})^2}{\text{expected number}}.$$

We add the results for all cells to form a statistic called the chi-squared statistic and denoted by the symbol x^2.

Example 52

The Problem. For the results given in Example 51, use the x^2 statistic to test the null hypothesis that the drug does not influence the proportion responding positively to the breathalyser test.

Statistical Formulation. We calculate the x^2 statistic and then use tables in the manner described under 'procedure' to decide upon significance.

Procedure. Taking the observed and expected numbers from Table 34 and 36, respectively, we get:

$$\begin{aligned}
x^2 &= \frac{(2-4\cdot71)^2}{4\cdot71} + \frac{(9-6\cdot29)^2}{6\cdot29} + \frac{(7-4\cdot29)^2}{4\cdot29} + \frac{(3-5\cdot71)^2}{5\cdot71} \\
&= \frac{(2\cdot71)^2}{4\cdot71} + \frac{(2\cdot71)^2}{6\cdot29} + \frac{(2\cdot71)^2}{4\cdot29} + \frac{(2\cdot71)^2}{5\cdot71} \\
&= (2\cdot71)^2 \left(\frac{1}{4\cdot71} + \frac{1}{6\cdot29} + \frac{1}{4\cdot29} + \frac{1}{5\cdot71} \right) \\
&= 7\cdot3441 \, (0\cdot2123 + 0\cdot1509 + 0\cdot2331 + 0\cdot1751) \\
&= 7\cdot3441 \times 0\cdot7795 \\
&\approx 5\cdot72,
\end{aligned} \qquad \text{(Eq. 28)}$$

all of which can be done in one step on many pocket calculators. We have written the steps in full to show the general method of calculation. There is a short cut formula for the 2×2 table, but since it does not generalize we shall ignore it.

The x^2 statistic will clearly be larger the greater the discrepancies between observed and expected numbers, so we shall look to large numbers for significance. Tables like Table 32 in the *Penguin Tables* tell us how large, but Table A5 in the Appendix is an abridged table that suffices for our purposes.

The value that indicates significance at a given level depends upon the 'degrees of freedom', seen in our problem to be *one*. The first column in Table A5 gives the degrees of freedom. The remaining columns give the minimum chi-squared value for significance at the 5, 1 and 0·1 per cent level in a two-tail test. For significance at the 5 per cent level we see that x^2 must exceed 3·84, while for significance at the 1 per cent level it must exceed 6·64.

Conclusion. There is evidence that the proportion of positive responses differs between those who do and do not take the drug; the difference is significant at the 5 but not at the 1 per cent level.

Comments. The significance levels given in Table A5 are both actual and nominal. The chi-squared distribution on which Table A5 is based is related to the normal distribution mathematically and its use as an approximation in this example can only be justified as a *large-sample* approximation. We use it in much the same spirit as we use the normal approximation to the sign test or to the Wilcoxon tests.

*   *   *

We need some guidelines about how large a sample is sufficient to justify the approximation. In our example it seems to have worked reasonably well: the exact probability given by Fisher's test was 0·03, whereas more extensive tables of chi-squared show that the probability of getting a value in excess of 5·72 is approximately 0·02. The difference is due to our sample being a little small, and this brings us back to the need for guidelines. The following rule of thumb is commonly given: avoid chi-squared if the expected number in any cell is less than 5. This is, perhaps, overcautious but is normally used, since it is very difficult to find any other satisfactory general rule.

With the normal approximations in earlier chapters a continuity correction was introduced. With x^2 statistics in general there are strong technical arguments against continuity corrections – indeed, they generally make little difference. However, in the case of 2×2 tables a continuity correction may be used, but as it tends to underestimate significance, it acts conservatively. The appropriate correction is to subtract one half from the *magnitude* of the difference between observed and expected numbers in each cell before squaring. It will be noted in (Eq. 28) that for each cell the magnitude of this difference was 2·71; subtracting one half from this gives a magnitude of 2·21. Replacing 2·71 by 2·21 in the numerators of (Eq. 28) reduces the value of the x^2 statistics from 5·72 to 3·81, a value that *just* fails to reach significance at the 5 per cent level. This conservative tendency of the correction prevents us making false claims of significance. For rather larger samples, with all or most of the expected numbers about 10 or more, the approximation to the exact test using the continuity correction is generally very good.

If the result of a chi-squared test is close to significance, it is appropriate, where the numbers are small and a *precise* measure of significance is required, to perform Fisher's exact test.

The 2×2 table – sometimes referred to as a *contingency* table – is a cross-classification of responses by two attributes. In Example 51 the responses were classified by *nature* (positive or negative) and *applied condition or treatment* (drug or no drug). The aim of testing the null hypothesis is to see whether the proportions when we classify by one of the attributes are independent of the other, or whether there is an association between attributes. In Example 51 we framed this by asking: 'Are the proportions of positive and negative responses observed indicative of a real difference in the population between those taking and those not taking the drug, or could they be attributed to sampling variation?' Our conclusion in this case was that there is some association between taking the drug and response, i.e. taking the drug influences response.

Extension to More Than Two Categories

In many experiments there will be more than two categories for either or both attributes. Example 53 typifies such a situation.

Example 53

The Problem. A manufacturer of washing machines issues instruction leaflets for their use in English for the UK and US markets, in French for the French market, German for the German market and Spanish for the Spanish and Argentinian market. He conducts a survey of randomly selected customers in each country and asks them to classify the instructions (in the language appropriate to their country) as *excellent*, *reasonable* or *poor*. The responses are set out in Table 37. I have done a bit of cheating with the results to make the arithmetic easy for illustrative purposes.

Does the survey indicate that the leaflet is more acceptable in some countries than in others?

Note that although the same instruction leaflet (the English-language version) is issued in both the U K and the U S, it is worth testing adequacy in the two markets separately, since what is clear to somebody in the UK may not be so clear in the US, owing to differences in idiom. For example, in the UK cars have *boots* and in the US, *trunks*; English cars run on *petrol;* American, on *gas*. For similar reasons, separate samples were taken in Spain and Argentina, although both speak basically the same language.

Table 37   Responses to washing machine instructions

	Excellent	Reasonable	Poor	National totals
UK	42	30	28	100
US	20	41	19	80
France	17	31	12	60
Germany	25	24	11	60
Spain	21	30	19	70
Argentina	25	44	11	80
Grade totals	150	200	100	450

Statistical Formulation. Our null hypothesis is that the appropriate language instructions are equally acceptable (or unacceptable) in all countries and that any differences in proportions may reasonably be attributed to the vagaries of sampling. We shall test this using a chi-squared test.

Procedure. We must first work out the expected numbers in each cell under the null hypothesis. Thus, for the UK, since the overall proportion finding the instructions excellent are 150 out of 450, or one third, the expected number in the UK is one third of the UK respondents, i.e. one third of 100 or 33·33. Indeed for any country and any grading the expected number may be calculated by (Eq. 27) as in the 2 × 2 table. Table 38 gives the expected numbers in each cell. The reader should check that each row or column total for expected numbers equals that for the observed numbers given in Table 37 (apart from minor discrepancies due to rounding off).

Table 38   Expected numbers in each cell

	Excellent	Reasonable	Poor
UK	33·33	44·44	22·22
US	26·67	35·56	17·78
France	20·00	26·67	13·33
Germany	20·00	26·67	13·33
Spain	23·33	31·11	15·56
Argentina	26·67	35·56	17·78

What are the degrees of freedom for our test? We argue along similar lines to those for the 2×2 table, i.e. given the fixed marginal totals, what is the minimum number of entries we must have in the cells before we can complete the table? Clearly, if we have the first two entries in each of the first five rows, we can complete all those rows. Also, with this information we can proceed to complete the sixth and final row to give the correct totals. A moment's reflection will show that with fixed marginal totals this is the least information necessary to complete the table. In other words, we must have at least 2 entries in each of 5 columns to complete the table – 10 entries in all. We associate 10 degrees of freedom with our test. Further reflection shows that if we have r rows and c columns, given all row and column totals, the minimum number of cell values we must have to complete the table is $(r - 1) \times (c - 1)$. In this example $r = 6$, $c = 3$. We now calculate x^2 using Tables 37 and 38. No continuity correction is used when r and c exceed 2, so for each cell we just calculate

$$\frac{(\text{observed number} - \text{expected number})^2}{\text{expected number}}$$

and add the results. Thus, for the second column and third row ('France'/ 'reasonable') we get:

$$\frac{(31 - 26 \cdot 67)^2}{26 \cdot 67} = \frac{(4 \cdot 33)^2}{26 \cdot 67} = 0 \cdot 703$$

All the terms contributing to x^2 are given in (Eq. 29) below, which uses the differences between observed and expected numbers in each cell. The terms are arranged in order, working across each row of the tables in turn:

$$x^2 = \frac{(8 \cdot 67)^2}{33 \cdot 33} + \frac{(14 \cdot 44)^2}{44 \cdot 44} + \frac{(5 \cdot 78)^2}{22 \cdot 22} + \frac{(6 \cdot 67)^2}{26 \cdot 67} + \frac{(5 \cdot 44)^2}{35 \cdot 56} + \frac{(1 \cdot 22)^2}{17 \cdot 78}$$

$$+ \frac{(3 \cdot 00)^2}{20 \cdot 00} + \frac{(4 \cdot 33)^2}{26 \cdot 67} + \frac{(1 \cdot 33)^2}{13 \cdot 33} + \frac{(5 \cdot 00)^2}{20 \cdot 00} + \frac{(2 \cdot 67)^2}{26 \cdot 67} + \frac{(2 \cdot 33)^2}{13 \cdot 33}$$

$$+ \frac{(2 \cdot 33)^2}{23 \cdot 33} + \frac{(1 \cdot 11)^2}{31 \cdot 11} + \frac{(3 \cdot 44)^2}{15 \cdot 56} + \frac{(1 \cdot 67)^2}{26 \cdot 67} + \frac{(8 \cdot 44)^2}{35 \cdot 56} + \frac{(6 \cdot 78)^2}{17 \cdot 78}$$

$$= 19 \cdot 97. \tag{Eq. 29}$$

This is a tedious calculation without a pocket calculator with a memory store or a facility for chain operations involving multiplications, divisions and additions.

Table A5 is now entered with 10 degrees of freedom. We see that x^2 must exceed 18·31 for significance at the 5 per cent level and 23·21 for significance at the 1 per cent level.

Conclusion. We reject the hypothesis of no association between language and acceptability grade at the 5 per cent significance level.

Comments. The manufacturer may well want to know in which countries the instructions are found less satisfactory. Some idea of this may be gained by finding which cells make the major contribution to x^2. Let us make a purely arbitrary rule, which, however, seems intuitively reasonable, and consider only those cells that contribute more than one unit to x^2. In such cells, if the observed number exceeds the expected number we call it a *plus*; if the observed number is less we call it a *minus*. An inspection of (Eq. 29) tells us which cells contribute more than one to x^2; then examination of Tables 37 and 38 tells us whether we label each contribution *plus* or *minus*. The results of this inspection are given in Table 39. No entry indicates that the corresponding cell contributes less than one to x^2.

From Table 39 we see that in the UK a higher proportion than average thought the instructions very good or very poor rather than just reasonable. In the US a smaller proportion found them excellent. This finding reinforces our comment that although the official languages in the two countries are the same, differences in idiom (and perhaps differences in the educational systems) may result in different reactions to the instructions.

Table 39   Main differences from expectation in Example 53

	+ *observation exceeds expectation*		
	− *observation less than expectation*		
	Excellent	*Reasonable*	*Poor*
UK	+	−	+
US	−		
France			
Germany	+		
Spain			
Argentina		+	−

A larger proportion than average found the German instructions excellent; perhaps the person who wrote them did a better job than his colleagues (or perhaps German housewives are more easily pleased). It would seem that in Argentina the Spanish instructions were regarded as reasonable relatively more frequently than in Spain itself.

*   *   *

The company may well want to take a closer look at some aspects of the results. For instance, if we take the English version alone, is there strong evidence that it is better geared to the UK market than it is to the US market?

An obvious approach to this would be a test of association applied to the data for just these two countries, i.e. the data in the first two rows of Table 37.

Example 54

The Problem. In Table 40 we give the data from Table 37 for the UK and US only, together with certain expected numbers obtained in a way described under 'procedure'. Is there evidence that the proportions responding in the various grades differ significantly between the countries?

Table 40   Responses to English-language instructions

	Excellent	Reasonable	Poor	National totals
UK	42(34·44)	30(39·44)	28(26·11)	100
US	20(27·56)	41(31·56)	19(20·89)	80
Grade totals	62	71	47	180

Statistical Formulation. The null hypothesis is that the proportions in the population gradings for both countries are the same. A two-tailed test using x^2 is appropriate.

Procedure. The expected numbers given in brackets after each observed number in Table 40 are based on the marginal totals in *that* table; the totals in Table 37 are no longer relevant as they are based on additional data that does not interest us here. Using these expected numbers we get:

$$x^2 = \frac{(7·56)^2}{34·44} + \frac{(9·44)^2}{39·44} + \frac{(1·89)^2}{26·11} + \frac{(7·56)^2}{27·56} + \frac{(9·44)^2}{31·56} + \frac{(1·89)^2}{20·89}$$

$$= 9·12.$$

How many degrees of freedom? If you do not agree the answer is 2, go back and check the argument for determining these on p. 161. Entering Table A5 in the row for two degrees of freedom we find that x^2 must exceed 5·99 for significance at the 5 per cent level and 9·21 for significance at the 1 per cent level.

Conclusions. The results almost reach significance at the 1 per cent level. Inspection of Table 40 shows that the main difference is that the proportion of UK purchasers finding the instructions excellent is higher; the proportions finding them poor do not differ markedly.

Comments. Many people find conclusions of this type easier to grasp if we express the results in tables of proportions or percentages. Expressions as proportions or percentages are reasonably easy to interpret if they are based on large samples, but care is needed in considering percentages when numbers are small. Two out of five is 40 per cent, but three out of five is 60 per cent. If two drugs are each tried on five patients and one drug cures three of them but the other only two, the percentage cures are respectively 60 and 40. The difference looks impressive as a percentage, but if there is only a fifty-fifty chance of cure with each drug, it is a matter of equal chance whether 2 or 3 out of 5 will be cured. Our only possible cure proportions in a sample of five are 0, 20, 40, 60, 80 or 100 per cent.

For the rather larger numbers in Table 40 it is reasonable to compare percentages. As we have a sample of 100 from the UK, the data are equivalent to percentages. To get the US percentages we multiply the number in each grade by 100 and divide by 80 (the total size of the US sample). The percentages are given in Table 41.

Table 41   Percentage responses to English language instructions

	Excellent	Reasonable	Poor
UK	42	30	28
US	25	51·25	23·75

While Table 41 is fine for visual comparisons between the proportions, note that the x^2 test is done on – and is only valid for – the actual numbers. It is not valid if performed on tables of percentages.

*   *   *

Have you any qualms about doing tests on complete sets of data like Table

37 and then separate tests on selected parts, ignoring the rest? If not, you should have. We must emphasize that hypotheses to be tested should be selected *before* data is obtained. By testing all and then selected parts of the data, inconsistencies may arise, as a simple example shows.

Example 55

The Problem. Just before an England v. Scotland football match 80 Englishmen, 75 Scotsmen and 45 Welshmen selected at random from those on their way to the stadium are asked who they think will win the game. Their answers are set out in Table 42, the numbers in brackets being the expected numbers calculated in the usual way from marginal totals.

Table 42   Likely winners of a football international

	English	Scots	Welsh	Total
England	55 (48)	40 (45)	25 (27)	120
Scotland	25 (32)	35 (30)	20 (18)	80
Total	80	75	45	200

Is there evidence that the proportions expecting each side to win are influenced by nationality? Different proportions might reflect hopeful biases on the parts of Englishmen and Scots, the Welsh perhaps taking a more neutral viewpoint. We have assumed for the sake of simplicity that each interviewee has been asked to plump for the winner, no draws being allowed.

Statistical Formulation. The null hypothesis is that the proportions in the population are the same for all three nationalities. The x^2 test is appropriate.

Procedure. Calculating the x^2 statistic in the usual way (left as an exercise), we find it has the value 4·38. With 2 degrees of freedom Table A5 shows that we need a value of at least 5·99 for significance at the 5 per cent level.

Conclusion. We do not reject the null hypothesis.

Comments. Suppose somebody looks at the figures and says that, despite the lack of significance, the departures from the expected numbers look more marked for the Scots and English than for the Welsh, and that since the Welsh are presumably neutral in their allegiance, we should concentrate on English and Scottish views. We then have the problem in Example 56.

*   *   *

Example 56

The Problem. We extract the data for English and Scottish fans from Table 42. Is there now evidence that the proportions expecting an English win differ between nationalities?

Statistical Formulation. We now have a 2×2 table and perform a x^2 test on it.

Procedure. Table 43 gives the relevant observed and expected numbers based on the marginal totals in that table.

Table 43   Football forecasts by Englishmen and Scotsmen

	Englishmen	Scotsmen	Total
England	55 (49·03)	40 (45·97)	95
Scotland	25 (30·97)	35 (29·03)	60
Total	80	75	155

We leave it as an exercise to show that $x^2 = 3.88$.

Conclusion. With 1 degree of freedom this just reaches significance at the 0·05 level.

Comments. We have two conflicting results; for all three nationalities we have insufficient evidence to say the proportions differ, yet for a selected two we conclude they do. It is not the statistics that have gone wrong; it is a consequence of testing hypotheses suggested by the data. We have selected a part of the data because it *looks* as though it might be different. A safe rule to use is to avoid such tests when the data as a whole show no significance. If the data as a whole show significance, then do *separate* tests on sub-portions of the data only if they have been nominated on *a priori* grounds as worthy of attention. This we assumed to be the situation with the instruction leaflet data in Examples 53 and 54.

There is perhaps one crumb of comfort – had we used a continuity correction in this example, the x^2 value would have fallen below that required for significance!

*   *   *

The whole area is one of considerable complexity. There is a subtle distinction between doing separate tests on parts of the data (what we did in Examples 54 and 56) and using information from the whole data to test hypotheses about parts of it; this is something that is often done in more complex problems than any we meet in this book; one parametric situation where it is common is in problems tackled by the analysis of variance. A discussion of relevant techniques is beyond the scope of this book.

To give a very extreme illustration of how one might prove anything just by looking at part of the data, let us take a coin-tossing experiment. We can show by similar arguments to those used in Example 13, p. 38, that if we toss a coin 6 times and get 6 heads or 6 tails, this is sufficient evidence to reject the hypothesis that the coin is true. In practice, if we toss a coin a few thousand times we are *almost certain* to get a run of at least six heads or at least six tails at some stage. If we ignore all other observations and say that these are the only six that interest us, we conclude the coin is not true. Since the probability of getting such a sequence in several thousand tosses is very close to *one* we are testing not at a 5 per cent level but at something perilously close to a 100 per cent level! A far-fetched example perhaps, but people who analyse bits of data testing only those things that look interesting – particularly small portions of data from large experiments – are going down a dangerous and slippery statistical path.

Fields of Application

Tests of association, such as the tests just described, are appropriate in many disciplines. Here are 5 situations where we might test for association with a x^2 test (or perhaps Fisher's exact test if numbers were small):

Rail transport A railway may be worried whether its image is better with second-class passengers than with first-class ones. It may ask samples of each to grade the service as 'excellent', 'good', 'fair' or 'poor', setting up a 4×2 table of responses.

Television viewing A government TV service competes with a commercial service. We ask samples of men and women which service they prefer, expressing the results in a 2×2 table, differences in preference ratings between the sexes being of interest.

Similar examples to the two above occur in many market research projects.

Medicine A doctor compares two treatments for curing drug addiction. With each he classifies withdrawal symptoms for each patient as 'severe', 'moderate' or 'slight'. He examines the 2×3 table for evidence of association between treatments and severity of withdrawal symptoms.

Sociology A social worker may be interested in whether blonde or brunette teenage girls who frequent public houses are more likely to drink spirits; a 2 × 2 table with the categories 'spirits'/'non-spirits' and 'blonde'/'brunette' is appropriate.

Public health After a contaminated food episode on a Jumbo jet where some passengers showed mild cholera symptoms, the airline authorities are anxious to know if those previously vaccinated showed a higher degree of immunity. They conduct an enquiry to ascertain which passengers had and had not been vaccinated and their records tell them which in each category showed symptoms, so they can test for association.

Rain making In low-rainfall areas experiments are carried out in which rain-bearing clouds are 'seeded' to induce precipitation. Randomly selected cloud formations are either seeded or not seeded and it is observed whether or not local rainfall follows.

A Deceptive Similarity

The appropriate statistical test always depends on the logic of the situation and not on the manner in which a particular batch of data is set out. Thus the x^2 test applied to a 2 × 2 table as in Examples 52 or 56 is appropriate because we are testing equality of proportions or lack of association; it is not a consequence of the data being presented in a 2 × 2 table. The data in Table 44 have a very similar format to those in Table 34, but the appropriate method of analysis is different.

Example 57

The Problem. Political parties are very keen to know whether their party political broadcasts influence voters. To get some ideas about this, suppose the Labour party asked a group of 300 randomly selected voters how they intended to vote *before* such a broadcast; they then arranged to obtain the voting intentions of the *same* 300 after the broadcast. This could be done by giving each a reply-paid postcard to fill in and return after the broadcast, asking if they had changed their intentions. There would in practice be a problem of non-response in such a survey – a difficult problem for which some allowance can be made in practice, but how to do so is a matter of sampling theory, not of non-parametric methods, and is beyond the scope of this book.

Clearly, if the broadcast has been effective the Labour party would hope that more voters will have swung from Conservative to Labour than in the opposite direction. To obtain any meaningful test we have to assume that the broadcast is the only feature likely to have influenced voters between the two surveys. Perhaps this is a rash assumption in a political context, but in applications of the test to fields such as psychology and medicine (see below) it is often reasonable to ascribe systematic changes to one factor. Table 44 summarizes the result of the survey.

Table 44 Effect of a political broadcast on electors

		Pre-broadcast voting intention	
		Labour	Conservative
Post-broadcast	Labour	140	15
voting intention	Conservative	4	141

The question of interest to the Labour party is – do these results give evidence that the broadcast really encouraged a swing to Labour?

Statistical Formulation. While the structure of Table 44 looks not unlike that of Table 43, we no longer base the split on independent samples; rather it is based on two questionings of the same sample. The situation reminds us of the paired-sample situation. We take an observation (assessment of voting intention) on each of 300 subjects; we submit each subject to a treatment (listening to a party political broadcast) and we assess his response to that treatment (has political allegiance changed and, if so, in which direction?).

Our *null hypothesis* would be that the broadcast is neutral in its effect; in the population it is equally likely to swing people either for or against the Labour party or else leave them unchanged in their views. What is really interesting is the number of label changes. The situation has analogies with others in which we have used the sign test. We may associate a *positive* sign with a switch Conservative to Labour, a *minus* sign with a switch Labour to Conservative and all remaining cases can be regarded as *ties*. Our null hypothesis can be framed in a slightly different equivalent form; that a shift in allegiance, if it occurs, is equally likely to be in either direction. Since there is some evidence that party political broadcasts can lose as well as gain support for the party sponsoring them a two-tailed test seems appropriate.

Procedure. We note that the number of plus switches – Conservative to Labour – in Table 44 is 15; the number of minus switches is 4; there are $140 + 141 = 281$ ties. Under the null hypothesis we have a binomial distribution with $p = 1/2$ and $n = 19$. From Table A1 we find the probability of 4 or fewer minus signs is 0.01; doubling this for a two-tail test we get a probability of 0.02.

Conclusion. Since this probability is less than 0·05, we have reasonable grounds for rejecting the hypothesis of 'no effect' at the 5 per cent level and we may conclude there is evidence that the broadcast has benefited the Labour party (assuming no other factors are responsible for the swing).

Comments. We have demonstrated the solution in terms of the sign test. In this type of example it is often called *McNemar's test.* It may seem both surprising and wasteful that our test is based on the behaviour of only 19 units in a sample of 300. The remaining 281 observations are not wasted, however, as they make up 'bulk' for our sample. Even the most optimistic party manager would only expect a small proportion of the electorate to be influenced sufficiently by one party broadcast to change party allegiance; a five per cent gain might be considered very satisfactory. Thus, to measure change affecting only a small proportion of the sample units, a large sample is required. Had we taken only a sample of 50 electors, we might have had 4 changes in one direction and 1 in the other; this would be insufficient to reach a conclusion of significance – think of the analogy of tossing a coin 5 times and observing 1 head and 4 tails; this would give no significant indication of bias.

*   *   *

The above example over-simplifies politics by ignoring minor parties. We could have allowed for them by using the classifications 'Labour' and 'non-Labour'.

The Binomial, Normal and Chi-squared Distributions

On p. 79 we showed we could approximate binomial variable probabilities by those for the standard normal distribution. Although the numbers in Example 57 are rather small for a normal approximation it works quite well with a continuity correction. Without such a correction we would use the approximation

$$z = \frac{r - np}{\sqrt{(npq)}}$$

with $n = 19, p = q = \frac{1}{2}$. With $r = 15$ (plus signs) we find

$$z = \frac{15 - (19 \times \frac{1}{2})}{\sqrt{(19 \times \frac{1}{2} \times \frac{1}{2})}}$$

$$= 2\cdot524.$$

The reader may care to check that with the usual continuity correction (think carefully whether we add or subtract the correction – remember we are interested in the probability of 15 or more *plus* signs) z will reduce to 2·295.

From Table 24 in the *Penguin Tables* or other tables of the standard normal variable we find that in a *two-tail test* the probability that z exceeds 2·524 in magnitude is 0·0116 and the probability that it exceeds 2·295 in magnitude is 0·0211; thus with the continuity correction we have good agreement with the exact binomial probability calculated in Example 57.

It is sometimes recommended that McNemar's test be conducted as a chi-squared type test using the relevant cells in Table 44 or a similar table in a way we now illustrate.

Example 58

The Problem. We seek a chi-squared approximation to the solution of the problem in Example 57.

Statistical Formulation. The relevant cells in Table 44 are those representing changes in voting allegiance with entries 4 and 15. The appropriate chi-squared statistic is based on the deviation of these from their expected values under the null hypothesis with $n = 19$ and $p = 1/2$, implying an expected value $np = 9·5$. The nature of the x^2 statistic will become apparent when we form it.

Procedure. For each of the two cells we form the contribution to x^2 in the manner of earlier examples, i.e.

$$x^2 = \frac{(15 - 9·5)^2}{9·5} + \frac{(4 - 9·5)^2}{9·5}$$

$$= \frac{(5·5)^2}{9·5} + \frac{(5·5)^2}{9·5}$$

$$= 6·3684.$$

Once we know n and the number of plus signs we automatically know the number of minus signs, so it seems reasonable to suppose x^2 has one degree of freedom. The value required for significance with 1 degree of freedom at the 1 per cent level is found from Table A5 to be 6·64, so our value just fails to reach significance at that level. This looks consistent with the normal approximation without continuity correction.

Let us now take the square root of the x^2 value 6·3684. It is 2·524, exactly the value we got using the normal approximation (p. 170).

Now let us try x^2 with a continuity correction – subtracting one half from the *magnitude* of each deviation prior to squaring. We then get

$$x^2 = \frac{(5)^2}{9\cdot5} + \frac{(5)^2}{9\cdot5} = 5\cdot2632.$$

The square root of this is 2·294 and (apart from round-off) this is the value given by the normal approximation with continuity correction on p. 171.

Conclusion. The chi-squared approximation to McNemar's test is exactly equivalent to the normal approximation to the binomial.

Comments. This link between the standard normal distribution and chi-squared with *one degree of freedom* is quite general; indeed chi-squared is the square of a standard normal variable in the one degree of freedom case. There is also a relationship of a somewhat more complicated nature between normal variables and chi-squared with 2 or more degrees of freedom. We shall not pursue this here. The relationship is reflected in the tables; in a two-tail test with a standard normal distribution, z must exceed 1·96 in magnitude for significance at the 5 per cent level; the corresponding x^2 value with 1 degree of freedom is 3·84 and $(1\cdot96)^2 = 3\cdot84$.

*   *   *

The normal distribution plays an important role in linking together ideas that at first sight may not be obviously related.

Fields of Application

McNemar's test has perhaps been most widely used in psychology and education; there are also applications in medicine. We give 2 examples:

Educational research If children are to be exposed to an ordeal which some may fear but which holds no terrors for others, it is sometimes argued that some explanation of the nature of the ordeal should be given before it is actually faced. This, of course, may reduce fear in some who are initially frightened but implant fear in others who were originally fearless. If numbers who are influenced by an explanation prior to the ordeal can be obtained, McNemar's test gives some indication of whether the explanation does more harm than good.

Medicine In comparing two drugs, one of which is definitely a placebo and the other a drug that might or might not affect a cure, sufferers might be given the drugs in random order and asked to note which, if either, is effective. Some will claim both are, some neither and some one but not the other. McNemar's test can be used to test whether the results for different responses favour the placebo, the drug under test, or neither.

Exercises

1. In a psychological test for pilot applicants in the Utopian Air Force, applicants are classified as 'introvert' or 'extrovert' and are subjected to a test for pilot aptitude which they may pass or fail. The results for 120 applicants break down as in Table 45. Is there evidence of an association between pilot aptitude and personality type?

Table 45   Personality and pilot aptitude

	Introvert	Extrovert
Pass	14	34
Fail	31	41

2. Palpiteria is a country where everybody who goes to the doctor has to pay a bill. A political party produces the information in Table 46 to support their claim that the poorer people are inhibited from seeking medical aid by the cost. The figures may be taken to represent a random sample from the wage-earners of Palpiteria. The incomes are given in Palpiliras (P), the country's unit of currency. Do the figures really support the claim that the poor make proportionally less use of the medical services?

Table 46   Visits of wage-earners to doctors

Time since last visit to doctor	Income		
	Over 10,000 P.	5–10,000 P.	Under 5,000 P.
Under 6 months	17	24	42
6–12 months	15	32	45
Over 12 months	27	142	271
Never been	1	12	127

3. Would your conclusions in Exercise 2 have been any different if the data were in only two income groupings: (i) under 5,000 P. and (ii) over 5,000 P., i.e. if columns 1 and 2 had been lumped together in Table 46?

4. One hundred salesmen are asked whether or not they think it is in the interests of public safety to prohibit people from drinking any alcohol less than 3 hours before

driving a car. They are then given a lecture on the causes of car accidents and shown a film on the relevance of alcohol in some serious accidents. They are again asked their opinions on the desirability of bringing in the above ban. Do the results given in Table 47 indicate a significant change in attitudes has been induced by the film and lecture?

Table 47   Changed attitudes towards alcohol and driving

| | | Before lecture and film | |
		In favour	Against
After lecture	In favour	31	16
and film	Against	8	45

5. Finally, one for the more energetic. Here is an example where the numbers are too small for a chi-squared test. Would you like to try your hand at Fisher's exact test for this one?

Six boys and six girls are each subjected to the same endurance test. If they manage to endure their suffering for 30 hours without falling asleep, they pass; otherwise, they fail. Do the data in Table 48 provide firm evidence of a different endurance capacity for the two sexes?

Table 48   Endurance test for the sexes

	Pass	Fail
Boys	1	5
Girls	4	2

9. Testing for Fit

Scope

In Chapters 5, 6 and 7 we were concerned largely with hypothesis testing and estimation concerning *location* of populations. We dealt mainly with medians or means. In this chapter we consider more general questions of the type: is this sample consistent with its having come from a population with a specified distribution? Is it reasonable to assume that these two samples come from the same distribution?

We shall find two broad classes of test are relevant; one class invokes the χ^2 statistic, the other involves statistics generally referred to by the name Kolmogorov–Smirnov.

Fit to a Discrete Distribution

If we consider families of, say, five children, the number of boys will be 0, 1, 2, 3, 4 or 5. Given sample data we may often use a chi-squared test for certain hypotheses about the general form of the population. Example 59 provides an illustration.

Example 59

The Problem. Table 49 gives the numbers of families, each of 5 children, with a specified number of boys from a total sample of 200 families. Are these data consistent with the hypothesis that the number of boys has a binomial distribution with $p = 1/2$? Biologically this hypothesis implies that the sex of each child is independent of that of any other child in the family and that each is equally likely to be a boy or a girl.

Table 49   Numbers of boys in each of 200 families of 5

Number of boys	0	1	2	3	4	5
Number of families	6	36	58	66	25	9

Statistical Formulation. The null hypothesis is that the sample is one of 200 from a binomial distribution with $n = 5$ and $p = 1/2$. We can work out the probability of each number of boys between 0 and 5 using (Eq. 12), whence Pr (no boys) $= 1/32$, Pr (one boy) $= 5/32$, Pr (2 boys) $= 10/32$, Pr (3 boys) $= 10/32$, Pr (4 boys) $= 5/32$, Pr (5 boys) $= 1/32$. From these we can work out the expected numbers in 200 families and under certain conditions, which we discuss in the 'comments' section, we may use a chi-squared test to see if it is reasonable to assume our sample was generated by the binomial 'mechanism' described above.

Procedure. First we must calculate the expected number of families of each size assuming the null hypothesis holds. Since the probability of any one family having no boys is 1/32, in 200 families the expected number is $200 \times (1/32) = 6 \cdot 25$; similarly for one boy the expected number is $200 \times (5/32) = 31 \cdot 25$; for two boys it is $200 \times (10/32) = 62 \cdot 5$. Because of the symmetry of the binomial distribution with $p = 1/2$, for 3, 4 and 5 boys the expected numbers are respectively $62 \cdot 5$, $31 \cdot 25$ and $6 \cdot 25$. Table 50 shows both observed and expected numbers.

Table 50   Observed and expected numbers of boys

Number of boys	0	1	2	3	4	5
Number of families:						
Observed	6	36	58	66	25	9
Expected	6·25	31·25	62·5	62·5	31·25	6·25

For each number of boys we calculate

$$\frac{(\text{observed no. of families} - \text{expected no. of families})^2}{\text{expected no. of families}}$$

and add the results to get the x^2 statistic. Thus

$$x^2 = \frac{(6 - 6 \cdot 25)^2}{6 \cdot 25} + \frac{(36 - 31 \cdot 25)^2}{31 \cdot 25} + \frac{(58 - 62 \cdot 5)^2}{62 \cdot 5}$$

$$+ \frac{(66 - 62 \cdot 5)^2}{62 \cdot 5} + \frac{(25 - 31 \cdot 25)^2}{31 \cdot 25} + \frac{(9 - 6 \cdot 25)^2}{6 \cdot 25}$$

$$= 0 \cdot 010 + 0 \cdot 722 + 0 \cdot 324 + 0 \cdot 196 + 1 \cdot 25 + 1 \cdot 21$$

$$= 3 \cdot 712.$$

How many degrees of freedom do we associate with x^2? The only fixed total we have is the number of families, 200. Only if we know the number of families with, say, 0, 1, 2, 3 and 4 children can we complete the table of observed or expected numbers by subtraction from the total. We could not complete Table 49, for instance, with less information. The degrees of freedom are therefore 5, since, given the sample size, we need 5 of the 6 observations to complete the table, or, in other words, once we know 5 of them we automatically know the sixth. With 5 degrees of freedom we find from Table A5 that x^2 must exceed 11·07 for significance at the 5 per cent level.

Conclusion. There is no reason to reject the null hypothesis.

Comments. In essence the x^2 test is only reasonable when the sample size is sufficiently large to validate it as an approximation to some exact test; although it is difficult to give hard and fast rules, in practice the test works fairly well as a test of *goodness of fit* when the expected numbers are all round about 5 or more.

*   *   *

The next example illustrates a useful device when a few of the expected numbers fall below five.

Example 60

The Problem. A machine part is regarded as satisfactory if it operates for 90 days without failure. If it fails in less than 90 days it is unsatisfactory as this results in a rather costly stoppage of the machine. A supplier of the part claims that the probability of a satisfactory life for each part he supplies is 0·95. Each machine requires four of these parts all of which must be functional for its successful operation. To test the manufacturer's claim, 100 machines are each fitted with 4 new parts at the start of a 90-day period and the numbers surviving 90 days in each machine are recorded in Table 51. Do these results support the supplier's claim?

Table 51   Number of parts lasting 90 days in each machine

Number surviving	0	1	2	3	4
Number of machines	2	2	3	24	69

Statistical Formulation. The null hypothesis is that we are sampling from a binomial distribution with $n = 4$ and $p = 0.95$.

Procedure. Using (Eq. 12) under the null hypothesis we have for each machine

$$Pr\text{(none survive)} = {}^4C_0(0\cdot95)^0(0\cdot05)^4 = 0\cdot00000625$$
$$Pr\text{(one survives)} = {}^4C_1(0\cdot95)^1(0\cdot05)^3 = 0\cdot000475$$
$$Pr\text{(two survive)} = {}^4C_2(0\cdot95)^2(0\cdot05)^2 = 0\cdot0135375$$
$$Pr\text{(three survive)} = {}^4C_3(0\cdot95)^3(0\cdot05)^1 = 0\cdot171475$$
$$Pr\text{(four survive)} = {}^4C_4(0\cdot95)^4(0\cdot05)^0 = 0\cdot81450625$$

(Check that these probabilities sum to unity – why should they?)

We multiply each probability by 100 to get the expected numbers of machines with the various numbers of parts surviving 90 days. Table 52 gives observed numbers as in Table 51 and expected numbers rounded to 2 decimal places.

Table 52   Machine parts – observed and expected numbers

Number of parts surviving		0	1	2	3	4
Number of machines:	observed	2	2	3	24	69
	expected	0·00	0·05	1·35	17·15	81·45

Here the expected numbers corresponding to 0, 1 or 2 parts surviving are all less than 5 – their sum is only 1·40. Only by pooling these with the case of three survivors can we get an expectation greater than five; thus the expectation of *three or fewer* survivors is $0\cdot00 + 0\cdot05 + 1\cdot35 + 17\cdot15 = 18\cdot55$. We now carry out our test on the 'pooled' data in Table 53.

Table 53   Pooled data for machine parts

Number surviving		3 or less	4
Number of machines:	observed	31	69
	expected	18·55	81·45

We calculate

$$x^2 = \frac{(31 - 18\cdot55)^2}{18\cdot55} + \frac{(69 - 81\cdot45)^2}{81\cdot45}$$
$$= 8\cdot36 + 1\cdot90 = 10\cdot26.$$

In Table 53 we have in effect evaluated expected numbers for only two frequency classes. With a fixed total, once we know the observed or expected numbers for one we automatically know those for the other, so there is one degree of freedom. From Table A5 we see that x^2 is clearly significant at the 5 per cent level and also at the 1 per cent level, just failing to reach significance at the 0·1 per cent level.

Conclusion. We reject fairly decisively the manufacturer's claim. The number of cases in which all four parts survive 90 days is well below expectation, suggesting either that p is not so high as the manufacturer claims or that the assumption of a binomial distribution is unjustified.

*   *   *

Distributions Other Than the Binomial

The binomial distribution has associated with it rather stringent conditions of independence and only two possible outcomes. The chi-squared test is non-parametric in the sense that we may use it for tests of compatibility with a wide range of distributions involving quite different and unrelated parameters. In this section we consider its use with two other distributions commonly associated with counts – the *uniform distribution* and the *Poisson distribution* – and demonstrate how x^2 may indicate whether a sample can reasonably be accepted as one from a population having these distributions.

A discrete random variable is said to have a uniform distribution if there is an equal probability of it taking each of a number of permitted values. If it may take any of n values, then the probability of its taking each is $1/n$.

Example 61

The Problem. It is well known that for most telephone exchanges the first digits of subscribers' numbers are by no means random. Sometimes all the numbers begin with one or two digits – perhaps 5 or 6. However, it is widely believed that the final digits of subscribers' numbers on a reasonably large exchange are random; that is, they are equally likely to be any of the digits 0, 1, 2, 3, 4, 5, 6, 7, 8 or 9. To test this, the Tayside directory covering part of Eastern Scotland was opened at p. 32 and the last digit noted for subscribers on the page whose exchange was Dundee. The number of times each digit occurred in the final position for the 153 Dundee subscribers listed on that page is given in Table 54. Are these consistent with the hypothesis that each digit is equally likely?

Table 54   Final digits in a sample of Dundee telephone numbers

Digit	0	1	2	3	4	5	6	7	8	9
Times observed	18	18	18	11	11	15	21	14	18	9

Statistical Formulation. Our null hypothesis is that any of the ten digits are equally likely; thus, the probability associated with any digit is 1/10, so the expected number of times each would occur in a sample of 153 is 15·3.

Procedure. To work out x^2 we subtract 15·3 from each observed number of occurrences, square the results, divide each by 15·3 and add. Thus

$$x^2 = \frac{(2\cdot7)^2 + (2\cdot7)^2 + (2\cdot7)^2 + (4\cdot3)^2 + (4\cdot3)^2 + (0\cdot3)^2 + (5\cdot7)^2 + (1\cdot3)^2 + (2\cdot7)^2 + (6\cdot3)^2}{15\cdot3}$$

$$= \frac{140\cdot1}{15\cdot3} = 9\cdot16.$$

Similar arguments to those used in the examples on the binomial distribution indicate that we have 9 degrees of freedom (one less than the number of digits). For significance at the 5 per cent level Table A5 indicates that we require a minimum value of 16·92.

Conclusion. There is insufficient evidence to reject the hypothesis that the digits are random.

Comments. We must bear in mind that failure to reject a hypothesis does not prove it is correct. There is at least one sound practical reason why final digits may not be completely random. Subscribers with multiple exchange lines often only have the first of these listed; very often this ends in a 1 or 2, e.g. a firm might have the numbers 48211 to 48216 inclusive, but only the first would be listed.

*   *   *

A population will have a Poisson distribution if events occur independently of one another in time subject to certain criteria that give rise to a *Poisson process*, a concept discussed in *Statistics in Action*, pp. 155–6. For example, a typist may make on average three mistakes in every thousand words. If these mistakes occur in a purely random fashion and we count the number of mistakes in each thousand words she types, we may occasionally find no mistakes, more often one, two, three or four mistakes and, rather less frequently, five, six, seven, eight or more mistakes.

If mistakes occur in a random fashion at a constant average rate (e.g. there is not a tendency for mistakes to be more common late in the day or after the typist has had a telephone call from her boyfriend), there is a formula that gives us the probability of each number of mistakes per thousand words. If the average rate of occurrence of the phenomenon we are interested in (here mistakes per thousand words) is λ (Greek, pronounced *lambda*) then the probability of observing r of the events per unit (in our case per thousand words) is

$$Pr(r \text{ events}) = \frac{e^{-\lambda}\lambda^r}{r!} \qquad \text{(Eq. 30)}$$

where e is a number called the *exponential*. It is a bit like that famous number π, the ratio of the circumference to the diameter of a circle, in that we can express it to any number of decimal places. Correct to 3 decimal places $e = 2 \cdot 718$ and this is the value we shall use in calculations. We previously met e in Chapter 3, p. 66.

We may be interested in various aspects of a typist's error-making potential. We may want to test somebody's claim that her *average* error rate is actually 3 per 1,000 words; alternatively, we may wish to test whether her mistakes really occur in an independent fashion; once she has made two or three mistakes does she get rattled and tend to make mistakes more frequently? Or, alternatively, does she try and improve her concentration and as a result make fewer mistakes for the next few pages? Again, she may be erratic, and although mistakes may be independent of each other, the rate at which she makes them may change due to factors such as increasing tiredness or the differing complexity of the work she is typing.

In Example 62 we test the hypothesis that errors occur randomly at a specified rate of 3 per thousand words. In Example 63 we consider the more general test of whether data accord with a Poisson process, λ not being specified in advance.

Example 62

The Problem. It is claimed a typist makes random errors at an average rate of 3 per thousand words typed, giving rise to a Poisson process. A random sample of 100 sets of 1,000 words from all her output is examined and the number of mistakes counted in each set. Table 55 summarizes the results; are they consistent with the above assertion?

Table 55   Errors per thousand words typed

Number of errors	0	1	2	3	4	5	6	7
Number of samples	6	11	16	18	12	14	12	11

Statistical Formulation. The null hypothesis is that the sample of 100 comes from a Poisson distribution with $\lambda = 3$. The expected number of times each error occurs will then be proportional to the probabilities calculated by (Eq. 30). These are tedious to evaluate without a pocket calculator although there is no difficulty in principle and once the probability of r errors is obtained that for $r + 1$ is given by multiplying the result for r by $\lambda/(r + 1)$.

Direct calculation of the probability of two errors gives

$$Pr(2 \text{ errors}) = \frac{(2 \cdot 718)^{-3} \times 3^2}{2!}$$

$$= \frac{3^2}{(2 \cdot 718)^3 \times 2} = \frac{9}{20 \cdot 0793 \times 2}$$

$$= 0 \cdot 2241.$$

Tables giving values of e^{-x} for various values of x are available as an aid to calculation. See, e.g., Table 14 in the *Penguin Tables*.

Since the probability of 2 errors is $0 \cdot 2241$, the expected number of times two errors will occur in a sample of 100 is $22 \cdot 41$. We may easily calculate the probabilities of any number of mistakes between 0 and 6 and for that matter of 7, 8 or 9 mistakes or even more. However, the greatest number observed in Table 55 is 7; since, theoretically, the typist could make more errors, it seems appropriate to pool all expectations of 7 or more errors. Since the different numbers of mistakes are mutually exclusive we have

$$Pr(7 \text{ or more errors}) = 1 - Pr(6 \text{ or less errors}) \qquad \text{(Eq. 31)}$$

$$= 1 - \text{sum of the probabilities of } 0, 1, 2, 3, 4, 5 \text{ or } 6 \text{ errors.}$$

Procedure. The relevant probabilities and expected numbers in the sample (obtained by multiplying each probability by the sample size 100) are given in Table 56. The probability of 7 or more errors is calculated using (Eq. 31) once the other probabilities have been evaluated.

Table 56 Probabilities and expected numbers, $\lambda = 3$

Number of errors	0	1	2	3	4	5	6	7 or more
Probability	0·0498	0·1494	0·2241	0·2241	0·1681	0·1008	0·0504	0·0333
Expected numbers	4·98	14·94	22·41	22·41	16·81	10·08	5·04	3·33

To calculate x^2 we compare observed and expected numbers in each of the eight 'cells' in Tables 55 and 56. We note, however, that the expected numbers for no errors and for 7 or more are both below 5. That for no errors is only just below, so we accept it for the x^2 calculation, but we pool *7 or more* with *exactly 6*, giving an expected value $5 \cdot 04 + 3 \cdot 33 = 8 \cdot 37$. Then

$$x^2 = \frac{(6 - 4 \cdot 98)^2}{4 \cdot 98} + \frac{(11 - 14 \cdot 94)^2}{14 \cdot 94} + \frac{(16 - 22 \cdot 41)^2}{22 \cdot 41} + \frac{(18 - 22 \cdot 41)^2}{22 \cdot 41}$$

$$+ \frac{(12 - 16 \cdot 81)^2}{16 \cdot 81} + \frac{(14 - 10 \cdot 08)^2}{10 \cdot 08} + \frac{(23 - 8 \cdot 37)^2}{8 \cdot 37}$$

$$= 32 \cdot 42.$$

The number of observations involved in calculating x^2 is reduced to 7 as the result of pooling, leaving 6 degrees of freedom for x^2. Table A5 shows that with 6 degrees of freedom x^2 need only exceed 22·46 for significance at the 0·1 per cent level.

Conclusion. The result is very highly significant. We reject at the 0·1 per cent level the hypothesis that the errors have a Poisson distribution with $\lambda = 3$.

Comments. Having rejected the hypothesis, what sort of alternatives should we consider? One possibility is that λ does not equal 3. The mistakes may still occur independently at random, but perhaps at a higher rate since the really big discrepancy between observations and expectations is that the typist makes 6 or more mistakes much more often than we would expect if $\lambda = 3$. An intuitively reasonable thing would be to try and *estimate* λ from the sample. An obvious estimate would be the average number of mistakes per thousand words noted in our sample of 100. We may then make a further x^2 test to see if we have consistency with a Poisson distribution with this new value of λ.

*   *   *

Example 63

The Problem. Given the data in Example 62, but making no assumption about the value of λ, test the hypothesis that the data are consistent with a Poisson distribution.

Statistical Formulation. We first estimate λ as the mean number of mistakes per thousand words in the samples. We then perform a x^2 test of goodness of fit; we discuss the appropriate degrees of freedom under 'procedure'.

Procedure. We use the data in Table 55 to estimate λ. Since we observe 1 mistake in 11 samples, 2 in 16 samples and so on, the total number of mistakes is obtained by multiplying 1 by 11, 2 by 16 and so on and adding the results. Thus, the average number of errors per thousand words in the sample is

$$\frac{(0 \times 6) + (1 \times 11) + (2 \times 16) + (3 \times 18) + (4 \times 12) + (5 \times 14) + (6 \times 12) + (7 \times 11)}{100} = 3 \cdot 64$$

Calculation of the expected numbers with this value of λ requires evaluation of $e^{-3 \cdot 64}$. Table 14 of the *Penguin Tables* gives the value of this as 0·0263. Substituting this value in (Eq. 30) gives

$$Pr(r \text{ errors}) = \frac{0.0263 \times (3.64)^r}{r!}$$

Table 57 Probabilities and expected numbers, $\lambda = 3.64$

Number of errors	0	1	2	3	4	5	6	7 or more
Probability	0.0263	0.0957	0.1742	0.2114	0.1924	0.1400	0.0850	0.0750
Expected numbers	2.63	9.57	17.42	21.14	19.24	14.00	8.50	7.50

In Table 57 the expected number with no errors is below 5, so we combine this cell with that for 1 error, getting the observed number for 0 or 1 error as $6 + 11 = 17$ and the expected number as $2.63 + 9.57 = 12.20$. Table 58 shows the observed and expected numbers relevant for the calculation of x^2.

Table 58 Observed and expected numbers of errors, $\lambda = 3.64$

Number of errors	0 or 1	2	3	4	5	6	7 or more
Observed	17	16	18	12	14	12	11
Expected	12.20	17.42	21.14	19.24	14.00	8.50	7.50

This gives a x^2 value of 8.27, calculated from seven cells; under the argument used in previous cases, this would imply 6 degrees of freedom for x^2. However, this does not take into account the fact that we have also used our data to estimate λ. We allow for this by deducting one further degree of freedom and look up Table A5 with *five degrees of freedom*. We find that a minimum value of 11.07 is needed for significance at the 5 per cent level.

Conclusion. There is insufficient evidence to reject the null hypothesis that the data is consistent with a Poisson distribution and an appropriate distribution is one with $\lambda = 3.64$.

Comments. Had our result been significant we should have concluded that the data were not consistent with *any* Poisson distribution. This would imply either that the errors were not random, or, if they were, that the rate was not constant but tended to vary from batch to batch of the typist's work.

*   *   *

One phenomenon that might at first glance be expected to follow a Poisson distribution is the accident rate associated with particular jobs – say those involving workers on an industrial production line. However, several studies have shown this not to be so. This may be explained in terms of 'accident proneness' or a tendency for some individuals to be involved in more accidents than others. What is observed can also be explained by a theory that once a person has sustained one accident, there is a changed probability that they have another. They may be more likely to have a further accident because they suffer a nervous reaction from the first that makes them less confident in future, which exposes them to further hazards; on the other hand, the effect of one unfortunate experience may make them more careful, leading to a reduction in the probability of their having a further accident.

Fields of Application

Here are some situations where a x^2 test of goodness of fit would be appropriate:

Genetics Genetic theories often specify the proportion of plants in a certain cross that are expected to have, say, blue or white flowers, round or crinkled seeds, etc. Given a sample in which we know the numbers of each combination of flower colour and seed shape, we may test if these are consistent with the theoretical proportions.

Sport It is often claimed that starting positions in horse-racing, athletic or rowing events may influence chances of winning. If we have starting positions and winners for a series of, say, rowing events in which there have always been six starters, we can test the hypothesis that there is no effect by testing whether the number of wins from each starting position is consistent with a uniform distribution. Siegel (1956) gives an example from horse racing in his book.

Horticulture Positions at which leaf-buds or flowers form on the stem of a plant are called nodes. Some theories suggest a certain statistical distribution for the node number (counted from the bottom of the stem) at which the first flower forms. These theories can be tested using a x^2 test.

Commerce A motor salesman may have doubts about the value of advertising. He might compare sales over a considerable period for weeks in which he advertised in 0, 1, 2, 3, or 4 newspapers. He would expect a uniform distribution if advertising were worthless. Note that in this example some consideration must be given to trends in time with sales; the effect of this should be minimized if the weeks are decided at random.

Queues The number of people entering a post office during one-minute intervals might be recorded over a long period. If the process is completely random the number of intervals in which 0, 1, 2, . . . people enter should be consistent with a Poisson distribution.

Chi-squared and Continuous Data

The chi-squared test of goodness of fit is particularly appropriate for discrete data such as counts of items falling into various categories, although there are sometimes better parametric alternatives for particular distributions, e.g. the Poisson.

It is also used sometimes in rather crude tests with continuous data. Though not to be recommended for this purpose, its use is so widespread that we describe it briefly and draw attention to a major difficulty.

Suppose we are given a sample of 2,000 light bulbs and wish to test a hypothesis that their lifetimes have a normal distribution with mean 1,000 hours and standard deviation 40 hours. We might group the lifetimes of our samples into *counts* of the number lasting, say, less than 900 hours, between 900 and 950 hours, between 950 and 1,000 hours, between 1,000 and 1,050 hours, between 1,050 and 1,100 hours, and over 1,100 hours.

Using tables of the standard normal variable (and methods we are not going to describe in detail) we can work out the expected number for each of the above time periods in a sample of 2,000, assuming the null hypothesis holds. We may then calculate a x^2 statistic in the usual way.

The test is fairly simple to perform, but it has the serious drawback that the result may be influenced by the way we choose our dividing points between the various groups. For example, if instead of putting the divisions at 900, 950, 1,000, 1,050, 1,100 hours we had put them at 880, 920, 960, 1,000, 1,040, 1,080 and 1,120 hours, we might find that we get a significant result with the first partitioning and not with the second, or vice versa.

The problem is that for grouping genuinely continuous data there is no natural grouping division as there is in counts of numbers of errors, children of a given sex, etc.

Whenever a significant result is reported using the x^2 test for goodness of fit to, say, a normal distribution, there is a lurking suspicion that somebody may have fudged the dividing lines to get the result they want. Fortunately, there are more appropriate tests for dealing with continuous data.

Before we move on to these, there is one situation where a x^2 test may be appropriate with data that are basically continuous. This is the situation when we have very limited information about the parent population and indeed no particular form is specified for the population.

A good example of this last situation is provided by a case arising in Chapter 5, Examples 23 and 26. There we considered examination marks for 17 candidates from Goldbeach College; our problems were, respectively, to see whether they were consistent with having come from a population with median 54 and whether they were consistent with having come from a population with first quartile 47. In Chapter 5 we tested these hypotheses separately. In Example 64 we consider both together.

Example 64

The Problem. Given the examination marks of 17 Goldbeach College students considered in Examples 23, i.e. 38, 29, 58, 41, 82, 51, 45, 39, 60, 42, 36, 55, 46, 61, 43, 52 and 64, are these consistent with their being a random sample from a population with first quartile 47 and median 54?

Statistical Formulation. In a sample of 17 from such a population the expected numbers below the first and between the first and second quartiles are each $17/4 = 4 \cdot 25$ and the expected number exceeding the median is $17/2 = 8 \cdot 5$. Although an expectation of $4 \cdot 25$ is a little small for the x^2 approximation according to our rule of thumb, it does not fall far short of five, so we proceed to a x^2 test of goodness of fit.

Procedure. From the marks for the Goldbeach College students we see the number below 47 is 9, the number between 47 and 54 is 2 and the number above 54 is 6. Thus

$$x^2 = \frac{(9 - 4 \cdot 25)^2}{4 \cdot 25} + \frac{(2 - 4 \cdot 25)^2}{4 \cdot 25} + \frac{(6 - 8 \cdot 5)^2}{8 \cdot 5} = 5 \cdot 31 + 1 \cdot 19 + 0 \cdot 74$$

$$= 7 \cdot 24$$

Since the sample size of 17 is fixed and there are three cells, x^2 has 2 degrees of freedom. Table A5 shows a value of $7 \cdot 24$ to be significant at the 5 per cent level.

Conclusion. We reject the hypothesis that the sample comes from a population with the given first quartile and median.

Comments. The result is consistent with the finding in Example 26, but it uses also the information about the median. While there may be grounds for hesitation about using x^2 with such small expected numbers, it is a valid approximation to a rather complicated exact test that covers this situation and which is based on a generalization of the binomial distribution.

The example illustrates rather nicely the non-parametric nature of the x^2 test. We assumed nothing about the population specified in the null hypothesis except that it had a known first quartile and median; we made no assumption of symmetry or any other property.

*   *   *

Kolmogorov–Smirnov Tests

In this section we describe a general class of tests appropriate for deciding whether data are consistent with a continuous distribution. The tests can be modified to deal with discrete variables too but have certain limitations in that case. These tests are usually associated with the name of A.N. Kolmogorov. A modification enables us to compare two samples with a view to deciding whether they may come from the same unspecified parent population; tests of this sort were first developed by N.V. Smirnov.

The theoretical basis of either type of test is very similar, so it is common practice to refer to them jointly as Kolmogorov–Smirnov tests.

To use them we need a new concept, the *cumulative distribution function* (often called just the *distribution function*). The notion is applied both to a population and to a sample.

Let us illustrate the concept for what is probably the simplest of all continuous distributions, the *continuous uniform distribution*, also sometimes called the *rectangular distribution*. It specifies the distribution of a random variable which is equally likely to take a value in any segment of a fixed length within a named interval. For example, suppose pieces of thread each exactly 6 inches in length are clamped at each end and a force applied until they break; if the thread always breaks at its weakest point and this is likely to be anywhere along its length, then the breaking point will be uniformly distributed over the interval from 0 to 6 – usually written (0, 6) – where the distance to the break is measured in inches (make it centimetres if you prefer to go metric) from the left-hand clamp.

In Chapter 4 we met the idea of a *probability density function* for the normal distribution; this had a characteristic bell shape. Its most important property was that the area 'under that curve' between any two X-values gave the probability that the random variable took a value in that range.

We may use an analogous representation for other distributions such as the continuous uniform distribution. In this case the probability density function reflects the fact that the probability associated with any subinterval of a given length within the range of possible values (0 to 6 in the thread example) must be the same. This implies that the area under the curve between 0 and 1 must equal that between 2 and 3 or between 3·59 and 4·59; similarly, the area under the curve between 0 and 0·5 must equal that between 2·57 and 3·07 or any other 'half-inch' interval. Further, the area under the curve for each half-inch interval must be half the area for each one-inch interval.

Now, since there is a probability of 1 that the thread will break somewhere in the range 0 to 6, we must have the total area under the probability density curve between 0 and 6 equal to 1; clearly, only one form of the density function satisfies both this condition and that of equal probability for segments of the same length wherever they lie in the interval. The function is graphed in Figure 21 and is essentially a line running from 0 to 6 at height (or Y-coordinate) 1/6 above the X-axis.

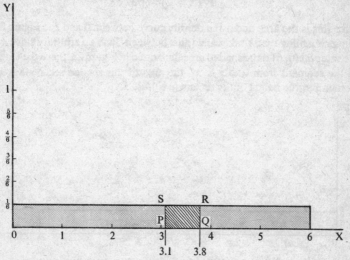

Figure 21 Probability density function for continuous uniform distribution

The 'rectangular' nature of the density function in Figure 21 explains the alternative name of rectangular distribution. The lightly shaded area represents the total probability of one for the whole distribution. The heavily shaded rectangle $PQRS$ between 3·1 and 3·8 on the X-axis represents the probability that X takes a value between 3·1 and 3·8 when it is uniformly distributed between 0 and 6. Since $PS = QR = 1/6$ and $PQ = RS = 3·8 - 3·1 = 0·7$ the probability, equal to the area of the rectangle $PQRS$, is clearly $0·7 \times (1/6) = 0·1167$ and this is the probability that the thread will break between 3·1 and 3·8 inches from the left-hand end, or indeed the probability that it will break in any segment of length 0·7 inches lying entirely within the interval (0, 6).

The tests we are about to describe do not make direct use of probability density functions, but of a related curve describing the *cumulative* distribution. For any given random variable X, the cumulative distribution function specifies for each possible value x that the random variable may take the probability that it takes *that value or some lesser value*. Remember here that our notation (c.f. p. 75) means that X is just a name or label given to a particular random variable and x (lower case or small letter) represents a particular value of X that interests us. In the thread example the probability that the break occurs in the first two inches of the thread is

$$Pr(X \leqq 2) = 1/3$$

since this is the area under the density curve between 0 and 2 in Figure 21. The probability that X takes any value between 0 and an arbitrary value x in the interval $(0, 6)$ is the shaded area illustrated in Figure 22. Since the length of the segment from 0 to x is 'x', the area of this shaded rectangle is $x/6$ (remember the height of the rectangle is $1/6$).

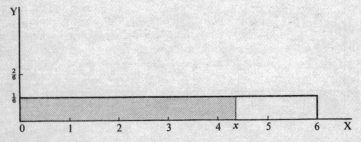

Figure 22 Probability that $X \leqq x$ for uniform distribution over $(0,6)$

We often denote $Pr(X \leqq x)$ by $F(x)$, which is a mathematician's way of saying that the probability is a function of x, i.e. it depends upon x in a known way. Do not be too alarmed if you are unfamiliar with this *functional notation*; just remember that $F(x)$ means the same as $Pr(X \leqq x)$.

Figure 22 tells us that

$$F(x) = Pr(X \leqq x) = x/6 \qquad \text{(Eq. 32)}$$

for a rectangular distribution over $(0, 6)$. This means that as x increases from 0 to 6, $F(x)$ increases in a straight line from 0 (at $x = 0$) to 1 (at $x = 6$). This is consistent with a probability of zero at 0, for X cannot take values less than 0, and a probability of 1 when $x = 6$, i.e. $Pr(X \leqq 6) = 1$, for X must take some value between 0 and 6. The graph of $F(x) = x/6$ for a uniform or rectangular distribution over the interval $(0, 6)$ is shown in Figure 23.

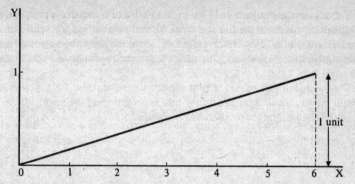

Figure 23 Cumulative distribution function for uniform distribution
over (0,6)

This idea can be extended to a uniform distribution over any interval from
a to *b* and the cumulative distribution function is then a straight line rising
from zero (when $x = a$) to 1 (when $x = b$). The graph is shown in Figure 24.

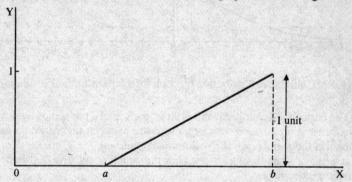

Figure 24 Cumulative distribution function for uniform distribution
over (*a,b*)

Just as the probability density functions for other continuous distributions such as, for example, the normal, are not quite so simple as that for the
uniform distribution, so too the cumulative distribution functions are more
complicated. However, for continuous distributions of the type usually met
with, they are always smooth curves starting at zero, moving upward from
left to right and finally reaching the value 1. Although we shall not go into
the mathematical derivation, Figure 25 shows the form of the cumulative
distribution function for the standard normal distribution.

Table 24 in the *Penguin Tables* is in fact a table of values of the cumulative distribution function for the standard normal distribution for values of X greater than zero. For lesser values of X we may get the values of the cumulative distribution function using the symmetry properties explained in Chapter 4 (p. 71).

We may use these values to plot the cumulative distribution function on graph paper. You might like to try this as an exercise; the result will be a curve of the general shape sketched in Figure 25.

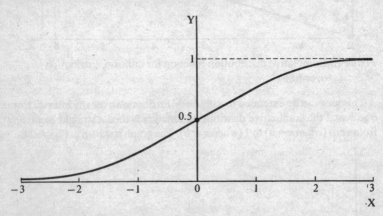

Figure 25 Cumulative distribution function for standard normal distribution

The basis of a Kolmogorov test is a comparison of a population cumulative distribution function with a related curve based on sample values and known as the *sample cumulative distribution function*.

If we have a sample of n observations the sample cumulative distribution function is defined as

$$S(x) = \frac{\text{number of sample values less than or equal to } x}{n} \quad \text{(Eq. 33)}$$

Example 65

The Problem. Given the distance from one end at which a sample of 20 threads (each 6 inches in length) break when subjected to a strain, form and graph the sample cumulative distribution function. The distances, arranged in ascending order for convenience, are given in Table 59.

Table 59   Distances of thread breaks from one end

0·6	0·8	1·1	1·2	1·4	1·7	1·8	1·9	2·2	2·4
2·5	2·9	3·1	3·4	3·4	3·9	4·4	4·9	5·2	5·9

Statistical Formulation. From (Eq. 33) it is clear that $S(x)$ changes in value every time x increases through a sample value and that it retains this new value until x reaches a further sample value. Thus, if we calculate $S(x)$ at each sample value, we get the value of the function at each change and this enables us to represent the function graphically.

Procedure. When $x = 0$, $S(x) = 0$ since no sample value can be less than 0. It maintains the value 0 until $x = 0·6$, the lowest value in Table 59. When $x = 0·6$ we see from (Eq. 33) that $S(0·6) = 1/20$, since $n = 20$. This value is maintained until $x = 0·8$, when $S(x)$ takes the value 2/20, since there are two sample values less than or equal to 0·8, viz. 0·6 and 0·8 itself.

Table 60 gives the values of $S(x)$ at each point where a change occurs. Such points are called step points; between such points $S(x)$ maintains the value it achieved at the previous step. Note that if two sample values coincide, as they do at 3·4, we get in accord with (Eq. 33) a double step of height 2/20; more generally if r steps coincide in a sample of n we get a step of height r/n.

The function $S(x)$ is called a step function for reasons that are obvious from the above description and the form of the graph in Figure 26.

Table 60   Values of S(x) at step points

x	0·6	0·8	1·1	1·2	1·4	1·7	1·8	1·9	2·2	2·4
$S(x)$	1/20	2/20	3/20	4/20	5/20	6/20	7/20	8/20	9/20	10/20

x	2·5	2·9	3·1	3·4*	3·9	4·4	4·9	5·2	5·9
$S(x)$	11/20	12/20	13/20	15/20	16/20	17/20	18/20	19/20	20/20

* Repeated sample value – double step.

Conclusion. For the given data $S(x)$ has the form given in Figure 26.

Comments. If a sample really does come from a distribution specified in a null hypothesis, it is reasonable to suppose that the step function $S(x)$ will not be too far away from the population cumulative distribution. In this example, if the breaks are uniformly distributed over (0, 6), one could

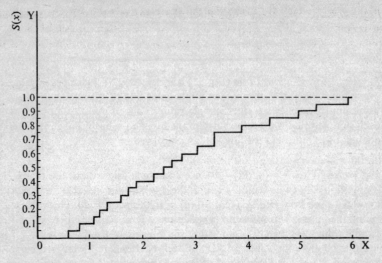

Figure 26 Sample cumulative distribution function for thread break data

reasonably expect about half of them to be in the interval $(0, 3)$ so that $S(3)$ should have a value not too far removed from one half, and so on.

*   *   *

The idea that $S(x)$ should never depart too violently from $F(x)$ if we have a sample from a population with cumulative distribution function $F(x)$ is the fundamental idea behind the Kolmogorov test. The test looks at the difference in magnitude between $F(x)$ and $S(x)$.

We illustrate our first Kolmogorov–Smirnov type of test with the thread break example.

Example 66

The Problem. Given the 20 breaking distances in Table 59, is it reasonable to suppose the breaking lengths are uniformly distributed over $(0, 6)$?

Statistical Formulation. The Kolmogorov test examines the maximum difference in magnitude between $F(x)$ and $S(x)$; this is then compared with a tabulated value to see if significance is indicated.

Procedure. In Table 61 we show values of $F(x)$ and $S(x)$ at each of the points at which we calculated $S(x)$ in Table 60. We also show at each of these points x_i the difference $F(x_i) - S(x_i)$. Unfortunately we cannot always guarantee that the *maximum* difference will occur among this set. Figure 27 shows what may happen. Here we suppose there are 8 step points (some of which may be multiple steps) and $F(x)$ is the straight line. Clearly the largest value of $F(x_i) - S(x_i)$ is that at $x = x_3$ and is represented by the dotted line AB; yet the biggest difference between the two functions occurs *just below* x_4 and is represented by CD in the figure. It will be clear that to be sure we have the maximum difference we must evaluate $F(x_i) - S(x_{i-1})$ in each case, for the maximum difference may occur just *before* or *at* a step.

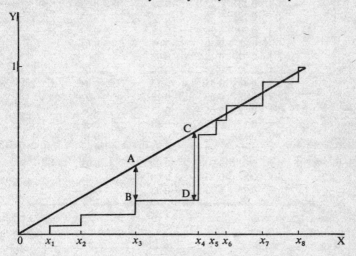

Figure 27 Locating a maximum difference between $F(x)$ and $S(x)$

For this reason we include an additional column of differences $F(x_i) - S(x_{i-1})$ in Table 61. The value of $F(x)$ at any step point is calculated from (Eq. 32), e.g. when $x = 1·2$, $F(x) = 1·2/6 = 0·20$. All values are given to 2 decimal places. To calculate a value of $F(x_i) - S(x_{i-1})$ in any row we subtract from the value of $F(x)$ in that row the value of $S(x)$ in the row above (remembering that $S(x) = 0$ until we get to the first sample point).

We shall assume our alternative to the null hypothesis is that the break lengths have some other unspecified distribution. A two-tail test is appropriate in this case; in the 'comments' we shall discuss situations where a one-tail test may be relevant.

The message in Table 61 is perhaps most clearly presented graphically by plotting $F(x)$ and $S(x)$. This is done in Figure 28.

Table 61 Comparison of F(x) and S(x) for thread breaks

x_i	$F(x_i)$	$S(x_i)$	$F(x_i) - S(x_i)$	$F(x_i) - S(x_{i-1})$
0·6	0·10	0·05	0·05	0·10
0·8	0·13	0·10	0·03	0·08
1·1	0·18	0·15	0·03	0·08
1·2	0·20	0·20	0·00	0·05
1·4	0·23	0·25	−0·02	0·03
1·7	0·28	0·30	−0·02	0·03
1·8	0·30	0·35	−0·05	0·00
1·9	0·32	0·40	−0·08	−0·03
2·2	0·37	0·45	−0·08	−0·03
2·4	0·40	0·50	−0·10	−0·05
2·5	0·42	0·55	−0·13	−0·08
2·9	0·48	0·60	−0·12	−0·07
3·1	0·52	0·65	−0·13	−0·08
3·4	0·57	0·75	−0·18	−0·08
3·9	0·65	0·80	−0·15	−0·10
4·4	0·73	0·85	−0·12	−0·07
4·9	0·82	0·90	−0·08	−0·03
5·2	0·87	0·95	−0·08	−0·03
5·9	0·98	1·00	−0·02	0·03

From Figure 28 we see that for much of the time the step function $S(x)$ lies above the straight line $F(x)$. From Table 61 (and it could be verified if the curves were drawn accurately on graph paper after the manner of Figure 28) we see that the entry of greatest magnitude in the last two columns is −0·18 corresponding to $x_i = 3·4$. Table A6 tells us that the *magnitude* of the largest difference (positive or negative) must exceed 0·294 for significance at the 5 per cent level.

Conclusion. Since the largest observed difference between sample and hypothesized population distribution function is only of *magnitude* 0·18, we have insufficient evidence to reject the hypothesis that the breaks may be uniformly distributed.

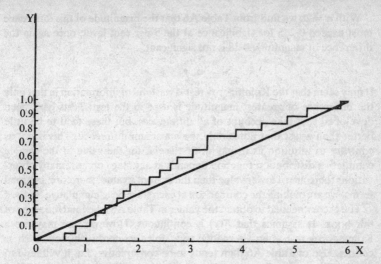

Figure 28 Graph of $F(x)$ and $S(x)$ for thread break lengths

Comments. The two-tail test is appropriate when our alternative hypothesis is that the observations may come from any other unspecified distribution. Practical situations may occur where the only possible alternative is one in which the cumulative distribution function must lie either *only* above or only below that specified by the null hypothesis. For example, in the thread problem it may be known that the machine used for the test places stresses on the string that, if not uniformly distributed, are higher at the left end of the string and decrease as we move along it. This would increase the tendency for breaks to occur close to the left end of the string. Reflection will show that, with a higher probability for breaks at low x and a steady decrease in this probability as x increases, the cumulative density function would everywhere lie above the straight line relevant to $F(x)$ for the uniform distribution. Thus, a maximum difference with $S(x)$ greater than $F(x)$ for the uniform distribution would favour the acceptable alternative whereas if the maximum occurred with $S(x)$ below $F(x)$ this would indicate a preference for the null hypothesis over any *acceptable* alternative. Thus, for a one-sided alternative hypothesis, we use a one-tail test and only reject the null hypothesis if the largest difference has the appropriate sign.

If, in this example, our one-sided alternative were that the population cumulative distribution function were always above that of the uniform distribution, a negative difference would be appropriate in Table 61.

With $n = 20$ we find from Table A6 that the magnitude of this difference must exceed 0.265 for significance at the 5 per cent level; once again the difference of magnitude 0.18 is not significant.

*   *   *

It may seem that the Kolmogorov test is wasteful of information in that only the difference of greatest magnitude is used in the test. Tests have been developed that take account of all differences, but these tend to be little better than a test that notes only the maximum difference. This is not as contrary to intuition as it may at first seem, for the value of the sample cumulative distribution function depends at any stage on how many observations there are of lower value than the current x value; therefore, in broad terms, we are making the comparison at each stage on a 'cumulative' basis.

The theory needed to obtain the values in Table A6 is beyond the scope of this book. It assumes that $F(x)$ is continuous. However, we may use a Kolmogorov test as an alternative to x^2 for discrete distributions such as counts. Use of Table A6 then tends to be conservative, i.e. it will tend to give too few rather than too many significant results; one advantage it has over x^2 is that it is valid for small expected or observed numbers in any cell. In the case of a discrete distribution such as a count we again define $F(x)$ as $Pr(X \leqq x)$, but since non-zero probabilities are only associated with discrete values, it follows that $F(x)$, like $S(x)$, is now a step function. The steps in each coincide (except in trivial cases where no sample value is observed for a permissible value of X, so $S(x)$ does not change in value). It therefore suffices to compare $F(x)$ and $S(x)$ at only those values of x associated with non-zero probabilities; in the case of counts this is commonly the values 0, 1, 2, 3, etc.

We illustrate the method by applying the test to the machine component data in Example 60.

Example 67

The Problem. We reconsider the problem on the life of a machine part discussed in Example 60 (see Table 51, p. 177 for the data) and use the Kolmogorov test with null hypothesis $p = 0.95$, $n = 4$.

Statistical Formulation. We calculate $F(x)$ and $S(x)$ at $x = 0, 1, 2, 3$ and 4 and obtain the difference between them having greatest magnitude.

Procedure. The values of $F(x)$ and $S(x)$ at each step point are given in Table 62. The entry for 0.185 for $F(x)$ at $x = 3$, for example, is obtained by adding the probabilities that $X = 0, 1, 2$ or 3 given on p. 178, i.e. $Pr\ (X \leqq 3) = 0\cdot0000 + 0\cdot0005 + 0\cdot0135 + 0\cdot1715 = 0\cdot1855$, working to 4 decimal places. The corresponding value of $S(x)$ is obtained from Table 51, remembering that the total sample size is 100. Thus $S(3) = (2 + 2 + 3 + 24)/100 = 31/100 = 0\cdot310$. The last line of Table 62 gives the differences $F(x) - S(x)$ at the step points.

Table 62   F(x) and S(x) for machine part data

x	$\cdot0$	1	2	3	4
$F(x)$	0·000	0·000	0·014	0·185	1·000
$S(x)$	0·002	0·004	0·100	0·310	1·000
$F(x) - S(x)$	−0·002	−0·004	−0·086	−0·125	−0·000

The largest difference in Table 62 has a magnitude of $0\cdot125$. The approximation for large-sample size given at the foot of Table A6 indicates that a value of $0\cdot122$ is required for significance in a one-tail test with sample size 100. If a two-tail test is appropriate a value of $0\cdot136$ would be required for significance.

Conclusion. Only if a one-tail test could be justified on *a priori* grounds would we reject the null hypothesis.

Comments. In this example the test has not done as well as the $\varkappa^2$ test. This is a somewhat extreme example and illustrates why the test is conservative for discrete distributions. Had we been dealing with a continuous $F(x)$ (and the same sample values as here), its value when x was very close to but just below 4 would almost be 1 and the corresponding $S(x)$ value would still be 0·310. As in Example 66 we could then validly have looked at the difference $F(4) - S(3) = 1 - 0\cdot310 = 0\cdot69$. However, we cannot do this in the discrete case because here when x is just below 4, $F(x)$ still has the value it acquired at the step at $x = 3$. Some work has been done on modification of critical values in situations such as this, but the subject is a complicated one, which, somewhat regretfully, we must leave at this stage. In many practical examples the effect of discontinuity will not be as extreme as in the above example.

*   *   *

A Confidence Region for a Cumulative Distribution Function

It is very easy to define with a certain degree of *confidence* – say, 95 per cent – a region in which the true $F(x)$ must lie by working from the significance test argument in the usual way. The idea is most easily described by means of an example.

Example 68

The Problem. Determine a region with 95 per cent confidence level for the true cumulative distribution function for the data on thread breaks used in Examples 65 and 66.

Statistical Formulation. Given $S(x)$ for the data, we endeavour to find a region about $S(x)$ for which we can in the usual 'confidence level' terminology be 95 per cent confident that it contains the population cumulative distribution function completely within its boundaries. We find the boundaries to such a region by placing them at appropriate distances vertically above and below the step function $S(x)$, subject only to constraints that the boundaries do not allow values of $F(x)$ outside the range 0 to 1, since a cumulative distribution function cannot take values outside that range.

Procedure. The values of $S(x)$ at the step points for this example have already been given in Table 60. This function is graphed as the dark line in Figure 29. From Table A6 we see that for a sample of 20 the minimum difference required for significance at the 5 per cent level is $0 \cdot 294$. If the difference $F(x) - S(x)$ exceeds this magnitude *anywhere* we would reject the hypothesized form of $F(x)$.

The two lighter lines in Figure 29 are at vertical distances $0 \cdot 294$ units above and below the step function, except where those limits lie below zero or above 1, when we replace them by zero and 1 respectively. So long as $F(x)$ lies entirely within these limits we would accept a hypothesis that specifies $F(x)$ as the population cumulative distribution function using a test (two-tailed) at the 5 per cent significance level; if $F(x)$ leaves this region anywhere, the hypothesis would be rejected as the maximum of $F(x) - S(x)$ would exceed the value needed for significance.

Conclusion. The region enclosed by the lighter step function lines in Figure 29 is a 95 per cent confidence region for $F(x)$.

Comments. The straight line joining AB in Figure 29 is the cumulative distribution function for the uniform distribution over $(0, 6)$. As expected, it lies entirely within the confidence region since we accepted the null hypothesis in Example 66.

The dotted curve in Figure 29 indicates another form of $F(x)$ that would

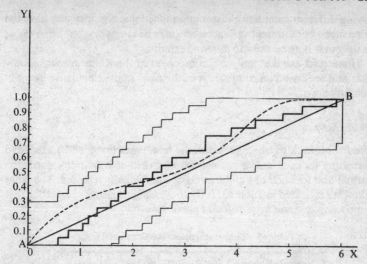

Figure 29 Confidence region for population cumulative distribution function

be acceptable; this is simply a free-hand curve with properties of a cumulative distribution function; it is not based on any mathematical model involving parameters and thus shows well the truly non-parametric nature of our procedure for getting a confidence region.

*   *   *

Confidence regions at other levels, e.g. 99 per cent, can be obtained using the appropriate entry from Table A6. As we would expect, a 99 per cent confidence region is larger than a 95 per cent region – the usual story of the additional price we pay for increased assurance that we are including the true $F(x)$ in our region.

The Comparison of Two Samples

So far in this chapter we have considered only single sample problems. In Chapter 7 we introduced Wilcoxon and Mann–Whitney tests to determine whether two samples could reasonably be supposed to come from identical populations or populations that differed only in median or mean.

We now describe tests for the null hypothesis of identical populations against the alternative of populations that differ merely in the sense of having different cumulative distribution functions, e.g. they may have the same mean but different variances; one may be symmetric, the other skew; or they may both be skew to differing extents.

These tests are the 'Smirnov' component of the Kolmogorov–Smirnov tests and are based on comparison of the two sample cumulative distribution functions.

Example 69

The Problem. A psychologist notes the total times (in seconds) needed to perform a series of simple manual tasks for each of 7 children regarded as normal and for each of 8 children classed as mentally retarded. The times taken are recorded in Table 63. Is there evidence to justify an assertion that these samples come from different populations?

Table 63 Times to complete simple manual tasks

Normal children	204	218	197	183	227	233	191	
Retarded children	243	228	261	202	343	242	220	239

Statistical Formulation. We calculate the respective sample cumulative distribution functions which we denote by $S_1(x)$ and $S_2(y)$ respectively. These are calculated at each observed value; unless there are ties there is only a step in one of the two at each given value. The maximum difference, or magnitude of the maximum difference, is the test statistic, critical values being given in Table A7. More extensive tables are given by Daniel (1978), pp. 463–5.

Procedure. To obtain the relevant values of $S_1(x)$ and $S_2(y)$ we order the obsevations for both samples as we did in the Wilcoxon rank sum test. We calculate $S_1(x) - S_2(y)$ at each step point. A convenient way to set out the complete calculation is shown in Table 64.

The difference in the first line of Table 64 is $1/7 - 0 = 1/7$, but we have written this as 8/56, so that all fractions are written with denominator 56 in the last column; this makes it easier to spot the largest difference, which is 35/56.

A prior decision should, of course, have been made by the psychologist as to whether a one- or two-tail test is appropriate. He may know from his past experience with retarded children in general, or from knowledge of the type of problem he is dealing with, that retarded children will certainly not perform better than normal children; at best they could be no worse. In such circumstances a one-tail test would be appropriate, with positive values of the statistic $S_1(x) - S_2(y)$ indicating significance if the maximum is sufficiently large. (Think carefully why it is *positive* values.)

Table 64   Calculations for Smirnov two-sample test

Ordered Samples		$S_1(x)$	$S_2(y)$	$S_1(x) - S_2(y)$
x	y			
183		1/7	0	8/56
191		2/7	0	16/56
197		3/7	0	24/56
	202	3/7	1/8	17/56
204		4/7	1/8	25/56
218		5/7	1/8	33/56
	220	5/7	2/8	26/56
227		6/7	2/8	34/56
	228	6/7	3/8	27/56
233		7/7	3/8	35/56
	239	7/7	4/8	28/56
	242	7/7	5/8	21/56
	243	7/7	6/8	14/56
	261	7/7	7/8	7/56
	343	7/7	8/8	0

As with the Kolmogorov test statistic, the appropriate test is based on the difference of greatest magnitude, here positive and equal to 35/56.

From Table A7 with $m_1 = 7$, $m_2 = 8$ we see that for significance at the 5 per cent level with a one-tail test, we require the maximum difference to be at least 33/56.

Conclusion. We reject the null hypothesis that the populations are identical, i.e. have the same cumulative distribution functions. Denoting these by $F_1(x)$, $F_2(x)$ our alternative which we accept is that for some x at least $F_1(x) > F_2(x)$.

Comments. Had the psychologist been unable to assert firmly that retarded children could in no circumstances do better than normal children, a two-tail test would have been appropriate, since our alternative hypothesis would then have been $F_1(x) \neq F_2(x)$ for some x at least. In this case Table A7 indicates a value of at least 35/36 for significance at the 5 per cent level, so we would class our result as just reaching significance in a two-tail test.

* * *

It is worth noting that we only require the rankings of x and y and not their actual values to carry out the test. If, for example, the x value of 191 had been 162 instead, all the calculated values of $S_1(x) - S_2(y)$ would have been the same. This feature makes it easier to indicate the theoretical basis of the test. Essentially, we consider the maximum differences $S_1(x) - S_2(y)$ for all possible arrangements of the ranks of which there are the same number as in the Wilcoxon rank sum test). Clearly, differences that are very large in magnitude will be associated with extreme cases; in particular, the largest possible difference of 1 will occur if all ranks for one sample are less than any for the other. Tables such as Table A7 may be formed by the laborious process of calculating for each possible configuration of ranks the value of $S_1(x) - S_2(y)$ of greatest magnitude; the largest among these maxima correspond to significant results.

Fields of Application

The Kolmogorov test can be used in many situations where we have single-sample data consisting of measurements of the type we considered in Chapter 5, providing that *in addition* we have the notion of some particular distribution of interest that *might* be appropriate to the population. The test is then capable of detecting a variety of possible departures from this hypothetical distribution. If we specify a normal distribution with designated mean and variance the test may indicate either a departure from the designated mean, or from the designated variance, or a lack of symmetry, or some mixture of such departures from hypothesis. We give two specific examples:

Biology Heart weights may be obtained for a number of rats used in a drug-testing experiment. We may want to test whether they are consistent with a normal distribution with a mean of 11 gm. and a standard deviation of 3 gm.

Forestry The volume of usable timber per tree may be obtained for 50 trees selected at random from a large forest. We may wish to know whether they are consistent with a specified normal distribution of volumes.

The Smirnov test can be used when we have measurements for two independent samples; it is useful for seeking population differences of *any* kind, as distinct from differences in median of the type considered in

Chapter 7. We might extend the forestry example given above and have data for another sample of trees from a different forest; the medians may be similar, but we may suspect the sample from the second forest has a more skew distribution of volume.

Exercises

1. When personal or highly emotive questions are asked in interviews, there is some evidence that answers may be influenced by factors such as the sex, age, social background and race of the interviewer. In an investigation into such influence a random sample of 500 women aged between 30 and 40 are further divided randomly into 5 groups of 100. Each group is allocated to one of the following five interviewers:

A. A 25-year-old white female with secretarial qualifications;
B. A middle-aged clergyman;
C. A retired army colonel;
D. A 30-year-old Pakistani female;
E. A non-white male University student.

Each interviewer asks each of the 100 women allocated to him or her:
Do you consider marriages between people of different ethnic groups socially desirable?
The numbers answering 'yes' in each group are given in Table 65. Assess the evidence that responses may be influenced by the background and type of person conducting the interview.

Table 65   Positive responses in 100 interviews

Interviewer	A	B	C	D	E
Number of 'yes' answers	32	41	18	57	36

2. Practical situations often arise in which we suspect we have a binomial population and we know n but not p. As in the case of the Poisson distribution where we estimated λ from the data (Example 63), we may estimate p in an obvious way from the sample. Think how you would then develop a x^2 test for consistency with a binomial distribution. In particular, how many degrees of freedom are there?

Table 66 gives the results on tests on the abrasive resistance of cloth. One hundred samples of a fabric are each subjected to wear for ten minutes under a series of 5 scourers, each of which may or may not make a hole. The number of holes (between 0 and 5) is recorded for each sample. Test whether these data are consistent with a binomial distribution with $n = 5$ and some p estimated from the data.

Table 66   Frequency of 0–5 holes in 100 tests

Number of holes	0	1	2	3	4	5
Number of samples	42	36	14	3	4	1

3. Table 67 gives the number of deaths recorded in each four-hour period of the day for one year in a large hospital. Test the hypothesis that deaths are spread uniformly throughout the day.

Table 67   Distribution of deaths by time of day

Period	Midn.– 4 a.m.	4 a.m.– 8 a.m.	8 a.m.– noon	noon– 4 p.m.	4 p.m.– 8 p.m.	8 p.m.– midn.
Number of deaths	89	63	29	36	39	42

4. A slightly more difficult problem, this one. First, given a normal distribution with mean 100 and standard deviation 5, how do we determine its cumulative distribution function? (Hint – note that if X is a random variable normally distributed with mean 100 and standard deviation 5, then $Z = (X - 100)/5$ is a standard normal variable (p. 75). Thus, for example, $Pr(X \leq 110) = Pr(Z \leq (110) - 100)/5) = Pr(Z \leq 2) = 0.9772$ from tables of the standard normal distribution (e.g. *Penguin Tables*, Table 24). Remembering $F(x) = Pr(X \leq x)$, this means that when $x = 110$, $F(x)$ has the value 0.9772. Other values can be worked out in similar fashion.)

Now, the data in Table 68 are the resistances measured for each of a sample of 11 resistors; test the hypothesis that these resistances may be supposed normally distributed with a mean of 100 ohms and a standard deviation of 5 ohms.

Table 68   Resistances in ohms of 11 resistors

89, 102, 93, 112, 91, 100, 117, 84, 112, 91, 114

5. Table 69 gives the scores of 10 pupils from Downtown High School and 10 from Uptown High School in an arithmetic test. Can the pupils reasonably be regarded as samples from the same population as far as arithmetic ability is concerned?

Table 69   Scores in arithmetic tests

Downtown High	42	39	51	63	54	58	61	72	49	57
Uptown High	29	83	57	17	75	33	91	77	11	90

6. In Examples 40 and 43 we gave some two-sample data on oven cooling times. Apply the Smirnov test to these data to determine whether it is reasonable to conclude that they come from the same population.

10. Related Measurements

Scope

When we measure two or more quantities on each individual we are often interested in any indication of association between them. Do students who perform well in French tend to do likewise in German? Do housewives generally agree on their order of preference for different varieties of apple? Do several judges agree in the ranking of performers in an ice skating competition? The relevant concept is *correlation*.

We may also be interested in the nature of relationships between variables; such problems are often termed *regression* problems. We shall discuss one relevant non-parametric method in this area, where non-parametric methods generally need further development to be of much practical use.

Correlation in General

Table 70 gives the marks for the same 10 students in French, German and Mathematics.

Table 70 Students' marks in three subjects

	A	B	C	D	E	F	G	H	I	J
French	83	27	42	51	53	44	47	55	61	33
German	74	22	49	54	48	47	55	61	59	29
Mathematics	64	11	66	65	59	52	50	91	83	55

A quick glance at Table 70 shows that student *B* is bottom of the class in all three subjects, while student *J*, who is second from the bottom in the two languages, has performed rather better in Mathematics. There are also differences in the mark allocations in the three subjects; in French the marks range from 27 to 83, in German from 22 to 74 and in Mathematics from 11 to 91. It is common to find a wider range of marks in Mathematics than in many other subjects because full marks are usually given for a correct answer and none or very few marks for a feeble attempt at a question; in subjects with a more qualitative element it is harder to gain full marks as there is a strong subjective factor in deciding what constitutes, say, the perfect essay; seldom does a candidate gain either full or zero marks for such a question.

Although Table 70 gives the impression that there is some sort of correlation between the marks in each subject, and that it is probably stronger between the two languages than it is between either language and Mathematics, the differences in the marking scales make it difficult to be very precise about the nature of the relationship.

In Table 71 we have ranked the students *separately* for each subject, ranking the best performer 1 each time.

Table 71 Ranks for students based on marks

	A	B	C	D	E	F	G	H	I	J
French	1	10	8	5	4	7	6	3	2	9
German	1	10	6	5	7	8	4	2	3	9
Mathematics	5	10	3	4	6	8	9	1	2	7

We would regard it as a perfect *rank* agreement if each student had the same rank in each subject. In that case the difference between the ranks in any two subjects would be zero for all students. If we look at the ranks for French and German in Table 71 we see that the difference between ranks is zero for students *A*, *B*, *D*, *J*; it is 1 for students *F*, *H*, *I*; it is 2 for students *C*, *G* and 3 for *E*.

We may work out rank differences for the other subjects and these are given in Table 72.

Table 72 Differences between rankings in pairs of subjects

	A	B	C	D	E	F	G	H	I	J
French and German	0	0	2	0	3	1	2	1	1	0
French and Maths	4	0	5	1	2	1	3	2	0	2
German and Maths	4	0	3	1	1	0	5	1	1	2

A crude measure of agreement would be given by the sums of these differences; these are 10 for the first line and 20 and 18, respectively, for the second and third, confirming our earlier visual impression that there are greater differences between performances in Mathematics and a language than there are between performances in the two languages.

Rank Correlation

A more sophisticated measure of agreement between ranks is given by a *rank correlation coefficient*. Readers of *Statistics in Action* will have met the *product moment correlation coefficient* (we just called it the 'correlation coefficient' in that book, because it was the only one we dealt with). That coefficient measured how close to a straight line paired observations x and y lie when plotted on graph paper. The coefficient, denoted by r, took the value $+1$ if there was a perfect straight line relationship with y increasing as x increased; it took the value -1 if there was a perfect straight line relationship with y decreasing as x increased. If there were no linear relationship at all (e.g. if the points were more or less randomly scattered in space) r took a value near zero. Examples of these situations are given in Figure 30 (a), (b) and (c).

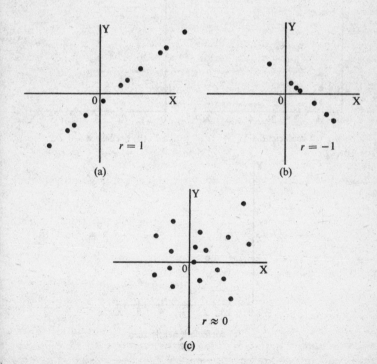

Figure 30 Special cases of the product moment correlation coefficient

It seems appropriate to ask that a rank correlation coefficient should have somewhat analogous properties with respect to ranks. For instance, if the rank orders coincide completely for two variables, we want the coefficient to take the value +1, for if we plot the ranks we get the situation depicted in Figure 31 (a), the analogue of Figure 30 (a). If there is a complete reversal of rankings between the two variables the situation is that depicted in Figure 31 (b), the analogue of Figure 30 (b) and we want our coefficient to take the value −1. If the ranks do not match up and, in particular, if the pairing seems completely haphazard we want the coefficient to take a value near zero; such a situation is depicted in Figure 31 (c).

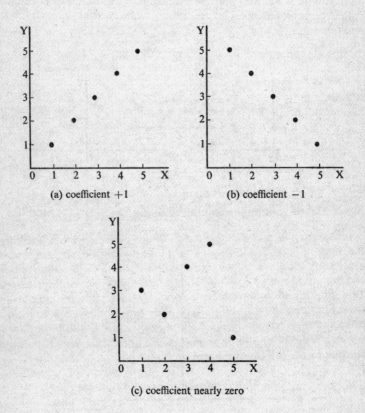

(a) coefficient +1

(b) coefficient −1

(c) coefficient nearly zero

Figure 31 Special cases of rank correlation

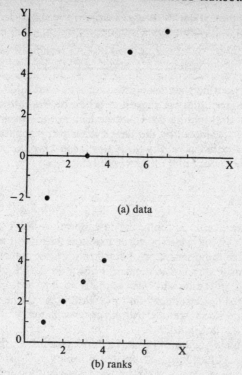

Figure 32 Data not on a straight line, ranks on a straight line

It is worth noting that if the product moment correlation coefficient has the value 1, then the observed x and y values will exhibit perfect *rank* agreement. However, we may have situations where the product moment correlation coefficient is less than 1, but there is perfect rank agreement. This is illustrated by the data in Tables 73 and 74, the latter table giving ranks (1 for lowest value) for the data in the former. It will be seen there is perfect rank agreement. Figure 32 (a) shows the plot for the Table 73 data and clearly these do not lie on a straight line. Figure 32 (b) shows the straight line plot for the corresponding ranks.

Table 73   Example of data not on a straight line

x	1	3	5	7
y	−2	0	5	6

Table 74   Ranks for data in Table 73

Rank x	1 2 3 4
Rank y	1 2 3 4

There are two widely used coefficients of rank correlation, each having the desirable properties we suggested. The first was introduced at the beginning of this century by C. Spearman and is usually known as *Spearman's rho*, denoted by the Greek letter ϱ (pronounced *rho*). The second was proposed in 1938 by M.G. Kendall and is called *Kendall's tau*, denoted by the Greek letter τ (pronounced *tau*).

Spearman's rho

Spearman introduced his coefficient in connection with experiments in psychology; it is still widely used in that context as well as others. Its numerical value is the same as that obtained if we use the formula for the product moment correlation coefficient given on p. 129 of *Statistics in Action* and apply it to the ranks instead of the original data.

However, to appreciate more fully its logical status as a measure of rank correlation and also to get a rather easier formula for its calculation, we usually look at it rather differently.

We may obtain Spearman's rho as a development from the concept of rank differences of the kind we tabulated in Table 72. In calculating rho we introduce the square of these differences. If we have n subjects or pairs, then ϱ is given by

$$\varrho = 1 - \frac{6\Sigma d_i^2}{n(n^2 - 1)} \qquad \text{(Eq. 34)}$$

where d_i represents the difference in ranks for the ith subject and Σ is the usual summation symbol (see *Statistics in Action*, pp. 75−6), meaning that we sum the squares of d_i *for all n* subjects.

Example 70

The Problem. Calculate Spearman's rho for the rankings in (i) French and German and (ii) French and Mathematics in Table 71.

Statistical Formulation. The differences must be calculated (Table 72) and inserted in (Eq. 34).

Procedure. Since there are data for 10 students, $n = 10$. The values of d_i for French and German are obtained from the appropriate line in Table 72, so

$$\Sigma d_i^2 = 0^2 + 0^2 + 2^2 + 0^2 + 3^2 + 1^2 + 2^2 + 1^2 + 1^2 + 0^2 = 20,$$

whence, from (Eq. 34)

$$\varrho = 1 - \frac{6 \times 20}{10 \times 99} = 1 - \frac{4}{33} = \frac{29}{33} = 0\cdot879.$$

Similarly, for French and Mathematics we find that $\Sigma d_i^2 = 64$ and $\varrho = 0\cdot612$.

Conclusion. The required values of Spearman's rho are $0\cdot879$ and $0\cdot612$ respectively, confirming our impression of a higher rank correlation between performances in the two languages than there is between French and Mathematics.

*   *   *

It is obvious from (Eq. 34) that if there is complete agreement between two rankings all the d_i are zero and $\varrho = 1$, since Σd_i^2 is then also zero.

If we have inverse rankings then we may show by some rather cumbersome algebra that $\varrho = -1$. We shall not give details, but for perfect inverse ranking we find that

$$\Sigma d_i^2 = \frac{n(n^2 - 1)}{3}$$

We shall not establish this algebraically, but it is easily verified for the case $n = 5$, where the above formula gives

$$\Sigma d_i^2 = \frac{5 \times 24}{3} = 40.$$

We verify this directly. The d_i for inverse ranking when $n = 5$ are given in Table 75; squaring and adding these we again get $\Sigma d_i^2 = 40$, whence

$$\varrho = 1 - \frac{6 \times 40}{5 \times 24} = 1 - 2 = -1.$$

Table 75   Inverse rankings and differences

Rank x	1	2	3	4	5
Rank y	5	4	3	2	1
Difference d	4	2	0	2	4

Kendall's tau

Kendall's tau is calculated from the basic idea of looking at units (students in Table 71) in pairs and for each ranking noting whether the order is the natural or the inverse order for that pair. A score of *plus one* is allocated to a natural ordering and a score of *minus one* to an inverse ordering. The procedure for obtaining these scores and then using them to calculate tau is best illustrated by an example. To bring out the principles we use a rather long method; in practical applications this is usually replaced by the method in Example 72.

Example 71

The Problem. Use the data for French and German in Table 71 to illustrate calculation of Kendall's tau.

Statistical Formulation. We allocate plus one and minus one scores to each comparison of subjects in the manner indicated above. For each pair we multiply the score for each subject (getting a product of $+1$ or -1). Tau is based on the sum of these products.

Procedure. Since there are 10 students in this example there are $^{10}C_2 = 45$ possible pairings. For each pair we allocate a score of $+1$ or -1 in each subject and record the product score for that pair. For the first pair of students (A, B in Table 71) the order of their ranks in French is 1, 10 (i.e. the natural order: 1 comes before 10) and so scores $+1$. The ranks are the same in German and so the score is again $+1$. The product is again $+1$. Consider now the pair D, E; for French the ranks are 5, 4 and score -1 as they are in inverse order; for German the ranks are in the correct order 5, 7 and so score $+1$. The product, $(-1) \times (+1) = -1$, is the contribution of this pair to tau.

Table 76 gives the product scores for all 45 pairs worked out in this way from the French and German ranks in Table 71.

Table 76   Product scores for student pairs in French and German

Pair	AB	AC	AD	AE	AF	AG	AH	AI	AJ	BC	BD	BE	BF	BG	BH
Score	+1	+1	+1	+1	+1	+1	+1	+1	+1	+1	+1	+1	+1	+1	+1

Pair	BI	BJ	CD	CE	CF	CG	CH	CI	CJ	DE	DF	DG	DH	DI	DJ
Score	+1	+1	+1	−1	−1	+1	+1	+1	+1	−1	+1	−1	+1	+1	+1

Pair	EF	EG	EH	EI	EJ	FG	FH	FI	FJ	GH	GI	GJ	HI	HJ	IJ
Score	+1	−1	+1	+1	+1	+1	+1	+1	+1	+1	+1	+1	−1	+1	+1

Clearly, if we had perfect direct correlation, all signs would be $+1$ in Table 76; a moment's reflection will show that perfect inverse correlation would give all negative signs in such a table. Thus, the maximum possible total product score is equal to the number of pairs, in our example $^nC_2$. Bearing in mind the desirable properties for a rank correlation coefficient given on p. 210, Kendall defined his coefficient as

$$\tau = \frac{\text{number of plus scores} - \text{number of minus scores}}{\text{maximum possible score}} \quad \text{(Eq. 35)}$$

Conclusion. For French and German (Eq. 35) gives

$$\tau = \frac{39 - 6}{45} = \frac{33}{45} = 0 \cdot 733$$

Comments. We note that for the same data $\varrho = 0 \cdot 879$ (p. 213). The two coefficients are not in general equal.

*   *   *

It is clear that when there is perfect agreement in the two rankings and all scores are positive τ takes the value $+1$; with perfect inverse ranking and all scores negative τ takes the value -1; with little agreement direct or inverse we would expect a fair mixture of positive and negative scores, giving values of τ near zero.

We now consider how we may arrive at the score totals in an easier way.

Example 72

The Problem. Using the same data as in Example 71, to streamline the calculation of τ.

Statistical Formulation. Essentially the same as in Example 71 but now we rearrange the ordering of students so that they are ranked in natural order for French. The 'procedure' shows how scoring is now simplified.

Procedure. Table 77 is a rearranging of Table 71 so that students appear in order of their ranking in French.

Table 77   Students ordered by ranking in French

	A	I	H	E	D	G	F	C	J	B
French Rank	1	2	3	4	5	6	7	8	9	10
German Rank	1	3	2	7	5	4	8	6	9	10

Clearly all pairs (working from left to right) are in their natural order for French so all score +1. If any pair has German in the natural order that will also score +1, so the product score is +1. If the German ranking is inverse for a pair it scores −1 and so the product is −1. Thus, to get the positive scores, all we have to do is examine each German rank and count how many students to the right of it have a higher score. Summing these for all students gives the number of positive scores. Since the first German rank is 1, all other 9 students have a higher rank, so we count 9 positive scores. The next student has rank 3 in German and 7, 5, 4, 8, 6, 9, 10 are all higher, so we count 7 positive scores. The next student with rank 2 counts 7. The fourth student has rank 7, so the only higher ranks to the right are 8, 9, 10 and he contributes a positive score of 3. Continuing in this way, we get a total positive score (which the reader should check) of

$$9 + 7 + 7 + 3 + 4 + 4 + 2 + 2 + 1 = 39,$$

the same value as we got from Table 76. Since any score that is not positive must be negative, we can get the negative score by subtracting the positive score from the maximum possible score (which occurs, remember, when *all* scores are positive). Since the maximum possible score equals the number of pairs, i.e. $^{10}C_2 = 45$, the number of negative scores is $45 - 39 = 6$. This can of course be checked by counting for each German student the number of students of *lower* rank to his right in Table 77. The total is 6.

Conclusion. Substituting in (Eq. 35) we again find that $\tau = 0.733$.

*   *   *

In general, if we rank n items for each of two characteristics the number of comparisons (taking the items in pairs) is $^nC_2 = n(n - 1)/2$. This is the maximum possible score. Since the number of negative scores equals the maximum score less the number of positive scores we may write τ in several forms, e.g.

$$\tau = \frac{\text{number of positive scores} - \text{number of negative scores}}{n(n - 1)/2}$$

$$= \frac{\text{number of positive scores} - \{n(n - 1)/2 - \text{number of positive scores}\}}{n(n - 1)/2}$$

$$= \frac{2 \times (\text{number of positive scores}) - n(n - 1)/2}{n(n - 1)/2}$$

$$= \frac{2 \times (\text{number of positive scores})}{n(n - 1)/2} - 1 \qquad \text{(Eq. 36)}$$

This last form is especially appropriate to the method used in Example 72, for putting $n = 10$ and noting that the number of positive scores is 39 we get

$$\tau = \frac{2 \times 39}{(10 \times 9)/2} - 1 = \frac{78}{45} - 1 = \frac{33}{45} = 0.733.$$

The *number of positive scores* minus *the number of negative scores* is often denoted by S, whence

$$\tau = \frac{S}{n(n-1)/2}.$$

It is left as an exercise to the reader to show that by analogy with (Eq. 36) we get

$$\tau = 1 - \frac{2 \times (\text{number of negative scores})}{n(n-1)/2}.$$

This latter form is useful for the graphical method illustrated in Example 73.

Example 73

The Problem. Using the same data as Examples 71 and 72 calculate tau graphically.

Statistical Formulation. Students are ranked in order of their ranking in French as in the previous example; see Table 77.

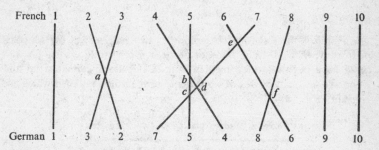

Figure 33 A graphical method for rank correlation

Procedure. The ranks are written down in parallel rows in the same order as in Table 77. Figure 33 illustrates this. Corresponding ranks in top and bottom rows are joined. The number of intersections of these joins equals the number of negative scores. Care should be taken in making the joins to avoid multiple intersections, this being easily done by slight repositioning of the lines. The intersections are labelled a, b, c, d, e, f in Figure 33 and are 6 in number.

Conclusion.

$$\tau = 1 - \frac{2 \times 6}{45} = 0 \cdot 733, \text{ as before.}$$

* * *

Ties

As in the case of nearly all procedures using ranks, to calculate *rho* and *tau*, it usually suffices, when ties occur, to assign the median value to them. We may then calculate rho using (Eq. 34); this presents no problems except the minor arithmetic one that some of the values of d_i may be fractional.

For Kendall's tau, ties present a counting difficulty if we try to evaluate positive scores directly. It is better to work from first principles, scoring zero for comparisons involving ties. When doing this, the counting is easier if we rank one of the variables in order. We illustrate the calculation of both coefficients in Example 74.

Example 74

The Problem. In a skating championship two judges rank the six competitors A, B, C, D, E, F in order of merit. Both produce some ties and these have been allocated median rank. Calculate Spearman's rho and Kendall's tau as measures of agreement between their rankings which are given in Table 78.

Table 78   Judges' placings in a skating contest

Entrant	A	B	C	D	E	F
First judge	1	2·5	2·5	4	5·5	5·5
Second judge	2	1	3·5	5	3·5	6

Statistical Formulation. In essence, we calculate rho and tau using (Eq. 34) and (Eq. 35) with appropriate modification for ties.

Procedure. Calculation of rho is straightforward. From Table 78 we find that the rank differences are 1, 1·5, 1, 1, 2 and 0·5, whence

$$\Sigma d_i^2 = 1^2 + 1\cdot5^2 + 1^2 + 1^2 + 2^2 + 0\cdot5^2 = 9\cdot50;$$

thus, with $n = 6$, (Eq. 34) gives

$$\varrho = 1 - \frac{6 \times 9\cdot5}{6 \times 35} = 0\cdot729.$$

To calculate tau we must add the scores for all $^6C_2 = 15$ pairs *AB, AC, AD, AE, AF, BC, BD, BE, BF, CD, CE, CF, DE, DF, EF*, remembering that if either judge awards a tie, a zero score is awarded, irrespective of the activity of the other judge. Thus, from Table 78 the scores are $AB = -1$, $AC = 1$, $AD = 1$, $AE = 1$, $AF = 1$, $BC = 0$ (since first judge ties them), $BD = 1$, $BE = 1$, $BF = 1$, $CD = 1$, $CE = 0$ (second judge ties them), $CF = 1$, $DE = 1$, $DF = 1$, $EF = 0$ (why?). We have 11 plus scores and 1 minus score. Since the maximum possible score is 15, by (Eq. 35)

$$\tau = \frac{11 - 1}{15} = \frac{2}{3}.$$

Conclusion. For the given data, $\varrho = 0\cdot729$ and $\tau = 0\cdot667$.

Comments. Kendall pointed out in 1948 – see Kendall (1970), Chapter 3, or Daniel (1978), Chapter 9 – that further modification of the formula for tau may be desirable with ties since the zero contribution associated with a tie makes it impossible to attain the same maximum possible score. He suggested how this might be taken into account and presented rather subtle arguments for and against any further adjustment.

*   *   *

Tests of Rank Correlation

One reason for calculating a rank correlation is to see whether sample data give any indication of association in their ranking. In the introduction to this chapter we indicated that a rank correlation near zero implies lack of association. However, variation from sample to sample means that even if there is no association in the population rank correlation, coefficients are not (except in very exceptional circumstances) exactly zero when calculated from samples. Clearly, however, values *near* zero are more likely than values near $+1$ or -1 if there is no association in the population.

To illustrate the basic concept of hypothesis testing, let us suppose we have rankings on two characteristics for 5 individuals. Under the null hypotheses all possible pairings are equally likely, How many pairings are there? We may think of the items for the first characteristic ranked in order: $X = 1, 2, 3, 4, 5$. With that ranked 1 we may have any of the ranks $Y = 1$ to 5 for the second characteristic; once that is chosen, there remain 4 rankings that can be matched with rank 2 for the first characteristic and so on, giving in all 5! ways of pairing an X-ranking with a Y-ranking. In theory we can work out rho and tau for each and it is the *tail* values of these coefficients, i.e. those near $+1$ or -1, that provide evidence against the null hypothesis. Let us consider the 'top' tail of values near 1. For Spearman's rho there is only one pairing that gives the value 1; this happens when both X and Y rankings occur in their natural order. If the matching is

$$1 \quad 2 \quad 3 \quad 4 \quad 5$$
$$2 \quad 1 \quad 3 \quad 4 \quad 5$$

we get the next highest value of rho. Here $\Sigma d_i^2 = 2$ and (Eq. 34) gives $\varrho = 0.9$. It is easily verified that if the ranking of Y corresponding to the natural order for X is $1, 3, 2, 4, 5$, *or* $1, 2, 4, 3, 5$, *or* $1, 2, 3, 5, 4$, then we still get $\varrho = 0.9$. Any other ordering will give a smaller value of ϱ. Thus, there is 1 case for which $\varrho = 1$ and 4 cases for which $\varrho = 0.9$, giving 5 cases out of 5! = 120 cases for which $\varrho \geqq 0.9$. Thus, under the null hypothesis of no association,

$$Pr(\varrho \geqq 0.9) = 5/120 \approx 0.042.$$

This provides a critical region of nominal size 0·05 (actual size 0·042) for a one-tail test at the 5 per cent significance level. That is, with a sample of 5, we reject the null hypothesis that $\varrho = 0$ for the population in favour of the hypothesis that there is some direct association between X and Y, if the sample value of rho is greater than or equal to 0·9. Similar arguments may be used to show that using Kendall's tau we should reject the null hypothesis in a one-tail test at the same level if $\tau \geqq 0.08$.

Fortunately tables are available that enable us in most practical cases to decide whether a value is significant without working from first principles in this way. Tables A8 and A9 in the Appendix are short tables for this purpose; fuller tables are given as Tables 29 and 30 in the *Penguin Tables*.

Example 75

The Problem. Using Tables A8 and A9, decide whether or not we should accept the hypothesis that there is no association between performance in French and performance in German on the basis of the rankings in Table 71. Test using both rho and tau. Assume a one-sided alternative that there is a direct association.

Statistical Formulation. We have to compare the calculated values of $\varrho = 0.879$ (Example 70) and $\tau = 0.733$ (Example 71) with the critical values provided by Tables A8 and A9.

Procedure. Table A8 is easy to use. Entering the table at $n = 10$, we find that a value of 0.564 is required for significance at the 5 per cent level and a value of 0.746 for significance at the 1 per cent level in a one-tail test, so our observed value clearly indicates significance at the 1 per cent level.

Table A9 is used in a rather different way. What is given is the value of the sum of scores (positive scores – negative scores) actually attained, i.e. the numerator in (Eq. 71), that just reaches significance at the indicated level in a one-tail test (the corresponding table in the *Penguin Tables* is in a rather different form). From Example 71 we see that the sum of the scores is 33; with $n = 10$ Table A9 tells us that this, being above 27, is significant at the 1 per cent level in a one-tail test.

Conclusion. Either coefficient indicates a highly significant departure from the null hypothesis, so there is strong evidence (hardly unexpected!) of association between performance in the languages.

Comments. Some modification for tests of significance are needed in the case of ties. This is discussed by Daniel (1978), p. 310, and, in more detail, by Kendall (1970).

*   *   *

For two-tail tests the significance levels are double those given in Tables A8 and A9 for one-tail tests and values of rho and tau equal or greater in *magnitude* than the critical values imply significance.

In most practical situations there will be little difference in conclusions drawn from hypothesis tests using rho or using tau. Spearman's rho is a little easier to calculate, but Kendall's tau has certain theoretical advantages in more advanced applications.

Large-sample Approximation

When n exceeds about 20, under the null hypothesis of no association

$$z_1 = \varrho\sqrt{(n-1)} \text{ and } z_2 = \frac{3\tau\sqrt{\{n(n-1)\}}}{\sqrt{\{2(2n+5)\}}}$$

are both approximately standard normal variables. For moderate values of n, the better approximation is given by z_2.

For sufficiently large values of n, critical values are those given in Table 13, e.g. at the 5 per cent level, 1·64 for a one-tail test and 1·96 for a two-tail test.

Example 76

The Problem. It has been noticed that with certain varieties of apple the trees that carry a good fruit crop in a particular year often put on very poor growth of a vegetative kind, i.e. new and longer shoots, etc. In an experimental orchard 25 trees are graded visually by experts and ranked 1 to 25 for growth vigour. These are the X rankings in Table 79. The crop from each tree is then weighed; the results are ranked as 'Crop Y' in Table 79. Calculate rho and tau for these data and test the hypothesis of no association between fruiting and vegetative growth against the alternative that there is an inverse relationship.

Table 79   Ranking of trees by growth vigour and crop

Vigour X	1	2	3	4	5	6	7	8	9	10	11	12	13
Crop Y	15	25	19	13	20	14	18	12	24	17	7	21	3

Vigour X	14	15	16	17	18	19	20	21	22	23	24	25
Crop Y	16	5	22	9	1	23	11	8	10	6	4	2

Statistical Formulation. The coefficients are calculated using (Eq. 34) and (Eq. 36), and since $n = 25$ the large-sample normal approximations are used in the test.

Procedure. It is left as an exercise for the reader to verify, using (Eq. 34), that $\Sigma d_i^2 = 4,080$ and $\varrho = -0.569$, that the sum of the positive scores for Kendall's tau is 88 and that the maximum possible score is 300, whence (Eq. 36) gives $\tau = -0.413$. To test significance we calculate

$$z_1 = -0.569 \times \sqrt{24} = -2.79$$

and

$$z_2 = \frac{3 \times (-0.413) \times \sqrt{(25 \times 24)}}{\sqrt{(2 \times 55)}}$$
$$= -2.89.$$

Since the sign of z_1 and z_2 leads us to the correct tail for the alternative hypothesis of an inverse relationship, we may determine the probability of this or a more extreme value under the null hypothesis from Table 24 in the *Penguin Tables.* The relevant probabilities will be found to be 0·0026 and 0·0019 for z_1 and z_2, respectively. Thus, for a one-tail test the result is significant at the 1 per cent level. This is a nominal level; note that the actual levels differ only slightly for the two coefficients.

Conclusion. We reject the hypothesis of no association in favour of the hypothesis of an inverse association.

*   *   *

Concordance

We are often interested in the overall agreement between several rankings. Indeed, Table 71 provides an example. While calculation of correlation coefficients gives some idea of the relative strength of relationships, it is obviously desirable to have an exact measure of agreement between rankings.

The case for such a measure becomes particularly strong when all three rankings have a common goal. Judges in a beauty contest, for example, are trying to rank contestants in order of merit, using criteria which are somewhat subjective; while there might be fairly wide agreement as to whether a particular girl is or is not beautiful, individuals will have different opinions as to which of two very beautiful girls is the worthier holder of the Miss World or Miss Universe title.

Kendall suggested the *coefficient of concordance* as a measure of agreement between rankings. If we have three rankings for each individual (those for ability in French, German and Mathematics in Table 71 provide a good example), we add them up. Now, if there is no agreement in the rankings, we would expect the totals to be rather similar for all individuals; there would be a good jumble of high, medium and low ranks. On the other hand, if one individual gets all low ranks, one or two all high ranks and in between a fair number of people get all moderate ranks, there will be a good deal of variation between the totals; so we see that variation between the totals is an indication of agreement in the rankings. Table 80 reproduces the rankings in Table 71 and gives in addition the sum of those ranks for each student.

Table 80   Sums of ranks as an indication of agreement

	A	B	C	D	E	F	G	H	I	J
French	1	10	8	5	4	7	6	3	2	9
German	1	10	6	5	7	8	4	2	3	9
Mathematics	5	10	3	4	6	8	9	1	2	7
Sum of ranks	7	30	17	14	17	23	19	6	7	25

We shall illustrate the rationale of Kendall's coefficient of concordance by reference to this data, before stating a more general formula for the coefficient.

Example 77

Problem. Given the rankings in Table 80, we seek an intuitively reasonable measure of the degree of agreement between the rankings. In particular we consider the null hypothesis of no agreement.

Statistical Formulation. Since the sum of the 'Sum of ranks' is 165 (check this), the *expected rank sum* for each pupil under the null hypothesis would be $165/10 = 16 \cdot 5$. If, on the other hand, there were perfect association, the sum of ranks for the student ranked 1 in each subject would be 3, for the student ranked 2 in each subject, 6, and so on – the student ranked 10 in each subject having a rank sum of 30.

As we remarked in the preliminary discussion, if there is little agreement in the rankings, all sums should be near the average. Now an obvious measure of deviation is the sum of squares of individual deviations (think of other places where we have used this or something like it in this book!). This sum of squares will have a maximum when there is perfect agreement. This suggests a reasonable measure of concordance might be

$$W = \frac{\text{sum of squares of actual deviations from } 16 \cdot 5}{\text{sum of squares of deviations when association perfect}}$$

This calculation gives us the value of Kendall's coefficient of concordance.

Procedure. For the ranks given in Table 80 the deviations (without regard to sign) from $16 \cdot 5$ are obtained from the last line of Table 80 as $9 \cdot 5$, $13 \cdot 5$, $0 \cdot 5$, $2 \cdot 5$, $0 \cdot 5$, $6 \cdot 5$, $2 \cdot 5$, $10 \cdot 5$, $9 \cdot 5$, $8 \cdot 5$; e.g. the second one is $30 - 16 \cdot 5 = 13 \cdot 5$. The sum of squares of these deviations is $600 \cdot 5$. Now if there were perfect agreement the sums of the ranks would be 3, 6, 9, 12, 15, 18, 21, 24, 27, 30 (see comments in the 'statistical formulation' above). Deviations from $16 \cdot 5$ (again ignoring signs) are $13 \cdot 5$, $10 \cdot 5$, $7 \cdot 5$, $4 \cdot 5$, $1 \cdot 5$, $1 \cdot 5$, $4 \cdot 5$, $7 \cdot 5$, $10 \cdot 5$, $13 \cdot 5$ and the sum of squares of these deviations is $742 \cdot 5$. Thus

$$W = \frac{600 \cdot 5}{742 \cdot 5} = 0 \cdot 809$$

Conclusion. An intuitively reasonable measure of concordance is $W = 0 \cdot 809$.

Comments. Since the denominator of W is the maximum for the sum of squares of the deviations, W cannot exceed 1. Also, since a sum of squares cannot be negative the numerator of W must always be positive or zero, so W can only take values between 0 and 1. Intuitively it is clear that values near 1 are an indication of definite associations in the rankings of a direct rather than an inverse nature.

*   *   *

We now consider a generalization of the results in Example 77. We shall quote a formula that gives the same arithmetic result but has been simplified by algebraic manipulation to a form that makes computation easier. Details of the algebraic manipulation will be found in Daniel (1978), pp. 327–9.

If we let v denote the number of rankings for each unit, n the number of units being ranked and R_i the sum of ranks for the ith unit, then in Example 77 $v = 3$, $n = 10$ and, e.g., $R_4 = 5 + 5 + 4 + = 14$, etc. We may write

$$W = \frac{12\Sigma R_i^2 - 3v^2 n(n + 1)^2}{v^2 n(n^2 - 1)} \quad \text{(Eq. 37)}$$

Table A10 is a brief table of values required for significance for a few values of n and v. More extensive tables are given by Daniel (1978) and by Kendall (1970).

Example 78

The Problem. Verify that (Eq. 37) leads to the value of W obtained by direct computation in Example 77 and use Table A10 to check if there is evidence of association.

Statistical Formulation. Obvious. A high value of W indicates association.

Procedure. The sums of the ranks R_i are given in Table 80. From these we find that $\Sigma R_i^2 = 3{,}323$, whence (Eq. 37) gives

$$W = \frac{12 \times 3{,}323 - 3 \times 9 \times 10 \times 11^2}{3^2 \times 10 \times (10^2 - 1)} = \frac{7{,}206}{8{,}910} = 0.809.$$

From Table A10 with $n = 10$ and $v = 3$ we find that a value of 0.48 or more indicates significance at the 1 per cent level.

Conclusion. There is strong evidence of a measure of agreement between the rankings in the three subjects.

*   *   *

Non-parametric Curve Fitting

This is a large and complicated topic and we shall only look very briefly at the simplest possible aspect, that of fitting the best straight line we can to a set of data.

The parametric approach to this problem was dealt with on pp. 133–49 of *Statistics in Action*. The method given there was that of *least squares*. For its strict validity it requires rather definite *parametric* assumptions about the nature of departures from the unknown 'true' straight line we are trying to estimate. It is strongly influenced by odd rogue points.

The non-parametric method we now describe is known at *Theil's incomplete method*. In *Statistics in Action* we pointed out that a straight line equation always has the form $y = a + bx$, where a and b are constants. The formula for estimating b (given a set of data lying approximately on a straight line) given in *Statistics in Action* was fairly complicated. Now, if we only have two points we can always draw a straight line through them. If the points are (x_1, y_1) and (x_2, y_2), then it can be shown that for the line joining these two points

$$b = \frac{y_2 - y_1}{x_2 - x_1}.$$

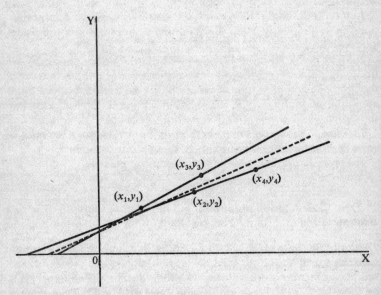

Figure 34 Points not quite on a straight line

Now, if we have 4 points (x_1, y_1), (x_2, y_2), (x_3, y_3) and (x_4, y_4) which do *not* lie on a single straight line, as in the case illustrated in Figure 34, the lines joining any two will be different and the values of b will be different. Writing b_{ij} for the value of b for the line joining the point (x_i, y_i) to (x_j, y_j), we can calculate b_{13} and b_{24} for the lines shown in Figure 34, where

$$b_{13} = \frac{y_3 - y_1}{x_3 - x_1} \text{ and } b_{24} = \frac{y_4 - y_2}{x_4 - x_2}$$

These constants, in fact, measure the slopes of the lines joining the respective points, where these are the tangents of the angles at which the lines meet the X axis – the greater the slope, the greater the inclination of the line to the axis. If we want to fit a line *as well as possible* to all four points in Figure 34, something like the dotted line would seem appropriate and this has a slope somewhere between b_{13} and b_{24}. If we took the mean or median of these slopes we might get a slope that would be about right. This is the sort of approach used in Theil's method. We shall describe it formally and then apply it to an example.

Suppose we are given n points (x_1, y_1), $i = 1, 2, \ldots, n$. We rank them in increasing order of the x values; for convenience we suppose that this has already been done. The steps then are:

1. If there are an odd number of points, delete the middle point corresponding to the median value of x. If there are an even number of points proceed straight to step 2.

2. Work out b_{ij} for the lines joining each of the following points: (a) the first to the point immediately after the median value of x, (b) the second to the point two above the median value of x, (c) the third to the point three above the median value of x, continuing in this way till the one just below the median value of x is joined to the nth or final point.

3. Arrange the b_{ij} so formed in ascending order and take the median value as the estimate of the slope of the line of best fit to the data.

The procedure is best followed with a numerical example.

Example 79

The Problem. To examine the toxic effect of inorganic bromine on carnations, an experimenter recorded the amount of inorganic bromine in the soil, x, on a number of soil plots and the average number of flowers per plant on these plots, y. The data are given in Table 81. Use Theil's method to estimate the slope of the line of best fit.

Table 81   Toxic effect of inorganic bromine

Bromine level x	3	4	6	7	8	10	12	15	16
Number of flowers y	3·2	2·9	3·7	2·2	1·8	2·3	1·7	0·8	0·3

Statistical Formulation. We follow the steps given on p. 227.

Procedure. The observations are arranged in ascending order of x. Since $n = 9$ we reject the point corresponding to $x = 8$, the median value of x. Labelling the points from 1 to 9 in the order given, we next calculate the slope of the line joining the first to the sixth, second to seventh points, etc., i.e. $b_{16}, b_{27}, b_{38}, b_{49}$. Thus

$$b_{16} = \frac{2 \cdot 3 - 3 \cdot 2}{10 - 3} = -0 \cdot 1286, \quad b_{27} = \frac{1 \cdot 7 - 2 \cdot 9}{12 - 4} = -0 \cdot 1500$$

$$b_{38} = \frac{0 \cdot 8 - 3 \cdot 7}{15 - 6} = -0 \cdot 3222, \quad b_{49} = \frac{0 \cdot 3 - 2 \cdot 2}{16 - 7} = -0 \cdot 2111$$

Arranging these four values of b_{ij} in ascending order we get $-0 \cdot 3222$, $-0 \cdot 2111$, $-0 \cdot 1500$, $-0 \cdot 1286$. The median of these four values is

$$b = \frac{-0 \cdot 2111 + (-0 \cdot 1500)}{2} = -0 \cdot 181$$

Conclusion. The slope of the appropriate line is $-0 \cdot 181$.

*   *   *

We have not yet considered an appropriate estimate for the other constant a in the equation $y = a + bx$. Geometrically, a is the co-ordinate of the point where the line cuts the Y axis. Theil proposed that a should be estimated by the following steps:

1. Using the estimate for b calculated by his method, calculate $a_i = y_i - bx_i$ for each of the given points (x_i, y_i).

2. Arrange the a_i in order and determine their median value. This gives the value of a for the line we fit.

Example 80

The Problem. Use Theil's method to calculate a for the problem considered in Example 79.

Statistical Formulation. In Example 79 we found that $b = -0 \cdot 181$. We use this value in the method just given to estimate a.

Procedure. Taking the points (x_i, y_i) in the order given in Table 81 we get

$$
\begin{aligned}
a_1 &= 3 \cdot 2 + 0 \cdot 181 \times\ \ 3 = 3 \cdot 743 \\
a_2 &= 2 \cdot 9 + 0 \cdot 181 \times\ \ 4 = 3 \cdot 624 \\
a_3 &= 3 \cdot 7 + 0 \cdot 181 \times\ \ 6 = 4 \cdot 786 \\
a_4 &= 2 \cdot 2 + 0 \cdot 181 \times\ \ 7 = 3 \cdot 467 \\
a_5 &= 1 \cdot 8 + 0 \cdot 181 \times\ \ 8 = 3 \cdot 248 \\
a_6 &= 2 \cdot 3 + 0 \cdot 181 \times 10 = 4 \cdot 110 \\
a_7 &= 1 \cdot 7 + 0 \cdot 181 \times 12 = 3 \cdot 872 \\
a_8 &= 0 \cdot 8 + 0 \cdot 181 \times 15 = 3 \cdot 515 \\
a_9 &= 0 \cdot 3 + 0 \cdot 181 \times 16 = 3 \cdot 196
\end{aligned}
$$

The median of these 9 values is the fifth when arranged in ascending order. This is easily seen to be $a_2 = 3 \cdot 624$.

Conclusion. The value of a for the line of best fit given by Theil's method is $3 \cdot 624$; combining this with the value of b obtained in Example 78 the equation of the line is

$$y = 3 \cdot 624 - 0 \cdot 181x.$$

Comments. The data used in this example were also used in *Statistics in Action*, where we used the method of least squares to fit a straight line and obtained as our solution

$$y = 4 \cdot 044 - 0 \cdot 216x.$$

It may be thought that these two equations look very different. In Figure 35 the points in Table 81 are plotted. The solid line is the line of best fit given by Theil's method and the broken line is the least squares fit. It will be seen that the difference is not great and that both give reasonable fits to the data.

However, the two lines are not quite on a par. A basic assumption in the regression fit is that the x's are measured without error and that departures from the line are all in the y direction. Although Theil's method requires some very general assumptions about the errors, it is valid even if the x values are not error-free, providing the errors are not so large as to alter the ranking we would obtain for them in the case of no errors. We shall not pursue the technicalities of these assumptions further here.

*   *   *

While the difference between the fits is not very great in the example we have considered, there is at least an indication in Figure 35 of a basic difference that can be of importance in practice. We often find situations where a number of our observations lie very close to a straight line but one observation is far removed, perhaps due to some peculiarity of the experimental material or because of an incorrect recording of data. The only observation that is suspect in this sense in Table 81 is that where $x = 6$ and $y = 3.7$; in view of the general downward trend in y as x increases, this is, perhaps, a surprisingly high value for y. The general impression in Figure 35 is that it is rather separate from the pattern of other points. Such observations have a much greater influence on least squares than on Theil's method. If we removed this point and recalculated both lines using only the remaining data, we should find the line given by Theil's method little altered, and the line given by least squares much closer to it. Methods that are little influenced by the odd rogue observation are said in statistical jargon to be *robust*.

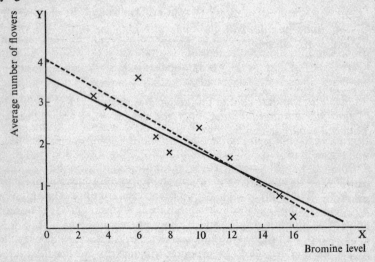

Figure 35 Theil line (continuous) and least squares line (broken)

Theil also developed another robust method of estimation – usually called his *complete method* – which has the disadvantage that it requires considerably more computation. There are other non-parametric methods of fitting straight lines; more important, there are methods of fitting curves other than straight lines, but regrettably we must leave the topic at this stage, since we are opening a veritable Pandora's box.

Fields of Application

We look especially in this section at a few possible situations where we may wish to calculate rank correlations or a coefficient of concordance.

Political science Leaders of political parties may be asked to rank certain problems facing their parliament in order of importance. If there are two leaders, rank correlations may be of interest; if more than two, a coefficient of concordance could be appropriate.

Psychology For ten twins (where we know the order of birth in each pair) we may record the times taken to perform a particular mental (or manual) assignment. We may rank the times for first-born and second-born and calculate a rank correlation. We could, of course, calculate a product moment correlation for the actual times.

Business A number of financial indices are used to indicate stock exchange fluctuations. A well-known one in the United Kingdom is the *Financial Times* shares index. If we had such an index for industrial shares and another for Government stocks, we could rank their observed values for a number of days and calculate the rank correlation or the coefficient of concordance for several such indices.

Medicine Blood counts may be ranked for a number of mothers and their newly born babies. Correlation of the ranks is of interest.

Personnel management A personnel officer may be interested in two methods of assessing the worth of a number of salesmen. He may rank them by turnover and by a score based on customers' comments as to how much they like each salesman. A rank correlation coefficient will indicate how well the methods agree.

Horticulture Leaf samples may be taken from each of 20 trees and the magnesium and calcium content determined by chemical analysis. We could see if the levels of these substances are related by using a product moment correlation coefficient, but this can be distorted if one tree has different levels of these chemicals from the others (something that quite often occurs in practice). A rank correlation coefficient may give a better picture of the correlation. If a third chemical, say cobalt, is also of interest, a coefficient of concordance would be appropriate.

232 QUICK STATISTICS

Exercises

1. A china manufacturer has seven designs for dinner sets that he is thinking about marketing. His main outlets are the British and the American markets. To get some idea of preferences on the two markets he asks random samples of 100 British housewives and 100 American housewives to rank the designs in order of preference from 1 for the favourite to 7 for the least desirable. In each country he adds up the ranks given by each member of the sample to give him total scores for each design. That with the lowest score he ranks 1 for that country, that with the next lowest 2 and so on. These overall rankings for each country are given in Table 82.

Table 82 British and American design preferences

Design	A	B	C	D	E	F	G
British ranking	1	2	3	4	5	6	7
American ranking	3	4	1	5	2	7	6

Calculate Spearman's rho and Kendall's tau for these data. Test whether there is adequate evidence for a direct association in the order of preference in the two countries.

2. The manufacturer in Question 1 later decides to assess the order of preference on the Canadian and Australian markets, using samples of 100 (as he did on the British and American markets) and adding their rankings to get the final rank order given in Table 82. The rankings for these countries are given in Table 83.

Table 83 Overseas ranking of designs

Design	A	B	C	D	E	F	G
Canadian ranking	5	3	2	4	1	6	7
Australian ranking	3	1	4	2	7	6	5

Using the data in Tables 82 and 83, obtain the coefficient of concordance between the rankings in all four countries. Is there evidence of agreement in the rankings?

3. Table 84 gives the number of rotten oranges, y, in ten boxes randomly selected from a large consignment after they have been kept in storage for a stated number of days, x. Use Theil's method to fit a straight line to these data. (These data were given in *Statistics in Action*, p. 148, for a least squares fit.)

Table 84   Rotten oranges in storage

Days in storage x	3	5	8	11	15	18	20	25	27	30
Number rotten y	6	10	20	22	31	33	39	51	54	63

If you would like to compare your line with the least squares fit on a graph like Figure 35, the least squares equation for the above data is

$$y = 0{\cdot}354 + 2{\cdot}009x.$$

11. Parametric or Non-parametric?

A Realistic Approach

A minority of statisticians argue that non-parametric statistics are the best to use in any circumstances; another minority argue that they are of little practical use. In between, the vast majority of practising statisticians find a use for both non-parametric and parametric methods. The latter usually imply an assumption of normality as a population property, but this is not always so, because there exists a celebrated theorem in statistics called the *central limit theorem* which 'justifies' many normal theory tests even when we are dealing with samples that are not from normal populations; it is indeed this theorem that provides the main justification for the use of the large sample normal approximations for various non-parametric tests.

On the other hand experience has shown us that there are also situations when there is no justification for assuming that normal theory parametric tests are appropriate; indeed, they may well lead to invalid conclusions.

Mathematical statisticians have devoted a lot of effort to comparing the performance of parametric and non-parametric tests. This work is highly technical and is mainly concerned with comparing the performance of non-parametric methods with their parametric counterparts *when the assumptions needed for the latter are valid*. In these circumstances the parametric tests usually do slightly better. This is not surprising, for even with non-parametric tests we have seen that the more assumptions we make and the more information we use, the better our tests become. If we can assume population symmetry, for example, smaller true differences may be detected as significant. The Wilcoxon signed rank test, for example, which requires an assumption of population symmetry, will often lead to rejection of a hypothesis about a median that would not be rejected by the sign test (which requires no symmetry assumption). It is not surprising then that if we can *validly* make a further assumption of, say, normality and build this into what is now a parametric test, it will be even better at picking up significance; similarly, procedures for confidence intervals tend to give shorter intervals the more sharply we define the population distribution.

The validity of the inference depends upon the validity of any assumptions; even when a normality assumption is justified, as we shall see in the next section, the gain over the parametric test is often small.

What is more important is that if we perform a parametric test when the assumptions are *not* justified it may be misleading, but even if it is not, it may not do as well as the appropriate non-parametric test. A very simple, if rather extreme, example is given in *Statistics in Action,* pp. 84–9, where we see that the sign test produces a significant result, whereas the corresponding parametric test (known as the *t-test*) does not, because the latter *assumes* what is clearly not the case, i.e. that we have a sample from a normal distribution.

Some Practical Considerations

It can fairly be claimed that the great majority of the test and estimation procedures described in this book require *at most* about the same amount of computation as their parametric counterparts, while in several instances (the sign test is perhaps the most notable example) they require *considerably* less.

This remark about ease of computation is particularly true with small samples; it is usually in these circumstances, too, that there is little evidence about the validity of any of the assumptions needed to justify parametric tests. So, for small samples, non-parametric methods often win on grounds of computational ease and avoidance of doubtful assumptions. For larger samples they perhaps involve equally complex calculation; it is also easier to assess the likely validity of parametric assumptions; but if the samples show evidence that casts doubt on such assumptions, non-parametric methods are the only alternative to a radically revised parametric test.

A past criticism of non-parametric methods has been that they emphasize hypothesis testing at the expense of estimation (e.g. confidence intervals). Modern developments have overcome this emphasis to a large extent; see, for example, the procedures for confidence intervals on pp. 90, 111, and 142.

The disadvantages of non-parametric methods become more pronounced in complicated problems with large amounts of data, especially if they involve large numbers of observations on each unit or large numbers of samples taken under varied conditions, and we want to make inferences about differences associated with changes in conditions. Non-parametric methods not only become computationally difficult in these circumstances, but, in our present state of knowledge, they lack the flexibility required to answer the wide range of questions that can be examined by parametric methods.

Bradley (1968), Chapter 2, gives a very good summary of the arguments for and against non-parametric methods, although sections of his presentation are rather technical.

We consider now an example which is fairly typical of the effect upon the estimation of confidence limits of moving from non-parametric to parametric by introducing a normality assumption.

In Example 39 we obtained 95 per cent confidence limits for the improvement in scores in an arithmetic test following extra tuition. Our method invoked the Wilcoxon signed rank procedure and the limits were 5 and 11·5. The corresponding limits based on the assumption that the population is normal can be calculated by methods given in Chapter 4 of *Statistics in Action* and turn out to be 5·26 and 11·24 – not a very marked difference and one that is slightly offset by the actual level for the Wilcoxon limits at 95·8 per cent being slightly higher (see p. 126).

Thinking Statistically

We have indicated that non-parametric methods are of practical importance. They are undoubtedly a very basic form of statistical inference in that they extract information from the data while making only a minimum of external assumptions. Thus, an understanding of the workings of non-parametric methods is perhaps the best way for the beginner to come to grips with statistical thinking.

In this book we have outlined the rationale of each method used; it has seldom been possible to do this in a fully rigorous way without introducing more advanced mathematics than we care to assume; sometimes, the intuitive reasonableness of a procedure is all we have been able to explain without going into too much technical detail.

Hopefully, the reader who regularly makes measurements and counts in his work will have found some methods he can use to solve the statistical problems facing him as a practical man; if he is a student meeting statistical ideas for the first time, coming to grips with the problems we have discussed should prove a useful introduction not only to further studies of non-parametric methods – but to the vast range of other methods of statistical inference from simple parametric analogues of the tests in this book to more sophisticated ones based on decision theory or Bayesian inference.

There are certain areas of application where non-parametric methods are more widely used at present than they are in others. If one were asked to rank in descending order the disciplines in which non-parametric methods have had the greatest impact a reasonable (but clearly very subjective) ranking might be: psychology, education, industry, medicine, sociology, business studies and agriculture. There are also examples in biology, politics, geography, etc., as we have indicated in the 'fields of application' sections in this book. Rather than thinking of their use as specific to particular fields, they are better regarded as safeguards against failure of unwarranted assumptions; in this sense they are categorized as a type of *robust* method – an area of statistics in which there is currently a rapidly increasing interest.

12. Looking at Exercises

This chapter contains solutions to and comments on the exercises at the ends of Chapters 1–10.

At the end there are some additional exercises.

Chapter 1, p. 20

1. (a) categorizing, ordinal.

(b) interval scale; note that this is not a ratio scale, as the choice of G.M.T. as a basis of measurement is arbitrary.

(c) ratio scale.

2. *A, C, B. B* scratches *C* and *C* scratches *A* is sufficient information to complete the ranking.

Chapter 2, p. 46

1. The first row of the table contains the ordered pairs AB, AC, AD, AE, AF, AG, AH, AI, BC, BD, BE, BF, BG, BH, BI, CD, CE, CF, CG, CH, CI, DE, DF, DG, DH, DI, EF, EG, EH, EI, FG, FH, FI, GH, GI, HI where individuals are denoted by the letters *A* to *I*. Second row is same 36 pairs with letters reversed. Total of 72 permutations and 36 combinations (given by first row).

2. Number of ways is $^{12}P_7 = 19,958,400$. With 10 meters this is reduced to $^{10}P_7 = 1,814,400$. Statement (iii) is therefore true; the number of ways is reduced by just over 90 per cent.

3. (i) 13/52 = 1/4; (ii) 26/52 = 1/2; (iii) 13/52 = 1/4; (iv) 4/52 = 1/13; (v) 12/52 = 3/13; (vi) 16/52 = 4/13 (note there are only 4 cards in each suit with a face value *less* than 5); (vii) 1/52. Sets of 3 mutually exclusive events are: (a) (i), (iii), (vii), (b) (v), (vi), (vii) and (c) (iv), (v), (vii). There are no sets of 4 such events.

4. $^5P_4 = 120$. Sum of digits is 20 if and only if digits are 1, 3, 7, 9. There are 4! = 24 such numbers, thus

$$Pr(\text{sum of digits is 20}) = 24/120 = 1/5.$$

We could also argue that we get a sum of 20 *only* if the digit 5 is *not* included, and since there is an equal likelihood of any of 5 digits beings left out of the number formed, then

$$Pr(5 \text{ not included}) = Pr(\text{sum of digits is 20}) = 1/5.$$

5. To satisfy conditions we want probability of event 'Jack's first shot misses *and* Jill's first shot misses *and* Jack's second shot misses *and* Jill's second shot hits'.

For any shot, Pr(Jack misses) $= 1 - Pr$(Jack hits) $= 2/3$, similarly Pr(Jill misses) $= 1/2$. Since hits and misses are independent, the multiplication rule gives required probability as $(2/3) \times (1/2) \times (2/3) \times (1/2) = 1/9$.

6. If first contains £1 second is drawn from 14 of which 4 contains £1; if first contains nothing second is drawn from 14 of which 5 contain £1. Thus,

$$Pr(\text{Second contains £1} \mid \text{First contains £1}) = 4/14;$$
$$Pr(\text{Second contains £1} \mid \text{First contains nothing}) = 5/14.$$

7. (i) $^{15}P_2$ choices of envelopes of which $^5P_2$ are favourable. Thus

$$Pr(\text{both contain £1}) = {}^5P_2/{}^{15}P_2 = 2/21.$$

(ii) If *first* contains £1 it may be chosen in 5 ways; then there are 10 choices of empty envelope for second; thus, Pr(£1 in first, nothing in second) $= 50/({}^{15}P_2) = 5/21$; similarly Pr(nothing in first, £1 in second) $= 5/21$; since these are mutually exclusive ways of getting exactly £1, Pr(total £1) $= 5/21 + 5/21 = 10/21$.

(iii) $^{10}P_2$ choices of empty envelopes, thus

$$Pr(\text{both empty}) = {}^{10}P_2/{}^{15}P_2 = 3/7.$$

Check: Three outcomes are mutually exclusive and exhaustive, so sum of probabilities is 1. Note that there are more sophisticated ways of solving this problem using an extension of the multiplication rule for events that are not independent.

8. By multiplication rule, $Pr(\text{4 bells}) = \dfrac{1}{24} \times \dfrac{1}{12} \times \dfrac{1}{24} \times \dfrac{1}{24} = \dfrac{1}{165,888}.$

As events are independent $Pr(\text{2 jackpots}) = \left(\dfrac{1}{165,888}\right)^2$

Pr(at least one jackpot) $= - Pr$(no jackpot in 2 shots), and Pr(no jackpot at any one shot) $= 165,887/165,888$. Since each shot independent,

$$Pr(\text{at least one jackpot}) = 1 - (165,887/165,888)^2$$
$$\approx 0{\cdot}000012.$$

9. *Assuming* a binomial distribution with $n = 5$, $p = 0{\cdot}4$, (Eq. 12) gives Pr(no win) $= 0{\cdot}07776$, $Pr(\text{1 win}) = 0{\cdot}25920$, $Pr(\text{2 wins}) = 0{\cdot}34560$, $Pr(\text{3 wins}) = 0{\cdot}23040$, $Pr(\text{4 wins}) = 0{\cdot}07680$, $Pr(\text{5 wins}) = 0{\cdot}01024$. Reject hypothesis only if 5 wins; this gives critical region of size $0{\cdot}01024$ and this is only possible region of size less than $0{\cdot}05$.

Assumption of same probability for England winning each match is very dubious; much will depend on weather, team changes, amount of practice between matches, etc. Before one jumps through statistical hoops, it is always worthwhile thinking whether one is being realistic.

10. Under null hypothesis, Pr(7 plus, 1 minus) $= 1/32$ by (Eq. 12). Equally or less likely outcomes are: (a) 8 plus, (b) 7 minus and 1 plus, (c) 8 minus. (Eq. 12) gives the *total* probability of all four outcomes as $18/256$. Since this exceeds $0{\cdot}05$, we do not reject null hypothesis. Two-tail test is appropriate. Why?

Chapter 3, p. 69

1. Mean $= 63 \cdot 28$, median $73 \cdot 5$. Five-number summary $(19, 61, 73 \cdot 5, 79, 80)$. Strong evidence of skewness. Probable reason is that on many days train virtually fully booked, but on Sundays and certain holidays only a very light demand.

2. Mean $= 1 \cdot 24$, median $= 1$, mode $= 0$. $Q_1 = 0$, $Q_3 = 2$, thus semi-interquartile range is 1. Although it is not demonstrated by the quartiles, which are symmetrically placed about the median, there is clearly some skewness in the data as is apparent from the minimum of 0 and maximum of 7 with a mean of $1 \cdot 24$ and a median of 1. The upper 'tail' may be due to one or two employees being more exposed to risk than others, or to their being more accident-prone.

3. Well, how did you get on?

Chapter 4, p. 82

1. $Z = \dfrac{X - 2 \cdot 05}{0 \cdot 02}$ is a standard normal variable.

(i) $Pr(X < 2) = Pr(Z < -2 \cdot 5) = Pr(Z > 2 \cdot 5) = 1 - Pr(Z < 2 \cdot 5)$
$= 1 - 0 \cdot 9938 = 0 \cdot 0062.$

(ii) $Pr(2 < X < 2 \cdot 08) = Pr(-2 \cdot 05 < Z < 1 \cdot 5) = Pr(Z < 1 \cdot 5) - Pr(Z < -2 \cdot 5)$
$= 0 \cdot 9332 - 0 \cdot 0062 = 0 \cdot 9270.$

(A diagram like Figure 13 may help.)

(iii) For any one bag (i) tells us $Pr(X < 2) = 0 \cdot 0062$. We now want the probability of 2 'successes' in a binomial distribution with $n = 3$ and $p = 0 \cdot 0062$, and (Eq. 12) gives
$$Pr(2 \text{ successes}) = {}^3C_2 (0 \cdot 0062)^2 (0 \cdot 9938) = 0 \cdot 0001146.$$

The implication of this last result is that if a bag weighing less than 2 kg. is underweight, there is only about 1 chance in 10,000 of exactly 2 bags from 3 being underweight.

2. $Z = \dfrac{X - 8{,}000}{180}$ is a standard normal variable.

(a) $Pr(X > 8{,}250) = Pr(Z > 25/18) = Pr(Z > 1 \cdot 3889) = 0 \cdot 0826.$

(b) $Pr(7{,}800 < X < 8{,}400) = Pr(-1 \cdot 1111 < Z < 2 \cdot 2222)$
$= 0 \cdot 9869 - 0 \cdot 1332 = 0 \cdot 8537.$

(c) $Pr(7{,}640 < X < 8{,}360) = Pr(-2 < Z < 2) = 2 \times Pr(0 < Z < 2)$
$= 2 \times 0 \cdot 4772 = 0 \cdot 9544.$

Tables indicate that $Pr(Z > 2 \cdot 327) = 0 \cdot 01$. Now
$$Z > 2 \cdot 327 \text{ implies } \frac{X - 8{,}000}{180} > 2 \cdot 327$$

or $X > 8{,}418 \cdot 86$; on this basis the official gave me the figure 8,419.

LOOKING AT THE EXERCISES 241

3. Since $np = 40·05$ and $npq = 4·05$ it follows that

$$Z = \frac{X - 40·5}{2·0125}$$

is approximately a standard normal variable. Remembering the continuity correction, to get the probability of 43 or more successes we set $X = 42·5$ (think carefully why it is 42·5 and not 43·5). Thus $Z = 2/2·0125 = 0·9938$. From tables $Pr(Z > 0·9938) = 0·1601$, so the approximation is reasonable.

Chapter 5, p. 117

1. Without symmetry, a sign test is appropriate. Assuming the median is 10, there are 11 minus signs, 3 plus signs and 1 zero. Using Table A1 with $n = 14$ we find the probability of 3 or less plus signs is 0·029. A two-tail test seems appropriate as we are not given *a priori* information that the loss might not exceed 10 kg., so we multiply this probability by 2, giving 0·058. This is very close to significance at the 5 per cent level, but does not quite attain it.

If we assume symmetry, we may use the Wilcoxon signed rank test. Ranking the deviations from 10 it will be found that $S_+ = 12$. Using Table A3 with $n = 14$, we find that for a two-tail test $S_+ = 12$ indicates significance at the 1 per cent level.

2. Assuming symmetry, we find from Table A3 that with $n = 15$ we have to eliminate the 25 largest and 25 smallest means from a tableau like Table 17. The entries we need to calculate to achieve this and get nominal 95 (actual 95·2) per cent confidence limits are given in Table 85.

Table 85   Extreme estimates of a median

	0	1	2	3	4	5	6	6	7	8	9	10	11	12	14
0	0	0·5	1	1·5	2	2·5	3	3	3·5	4					
1		1	1·5	2	2·5	3	3·5	3·5	4						
2			2	2·5	3	3·5	4	4							
3				3	3·5	4									
4					4										
5															
6														9	10
6														9	10
7													9	9·5	10·5
8												9	9·5	10	11
9											9	9·5	10	10·5	11·5
10												10	10·5	11	12
11													11	11·5	12·5
12														12	13
14															14

Note that there is no need to calculate the remaining entries in Table 85. Eliminating the 25 largest and 25 smallest entries gives the limits as 4 and 9.

If we cannot assume symmetry, we use a method based on the sign test. With 15 observations we see from Table A1 that we would reject a proposed value for the median at the 5 per cent level in a two-tail test (actual level 3·6 per cent) if we had 3 or fewer or 12 or more plus signs. We avoid this if the median is 3 or greater or 10 or less; thus the nominal 95 per cent confidence limits (actual level 96·4) are 3 and 10. These limits give a wider confidence interval than those given with the additional assumption of symmetry, reflecting the lower level of assumption about the form of the population.

3. Without a symmetry assumption, (Eq. 15) is appropriate with $n = 34$ (since there is one observation of 50 exactly). There are 21 minus signs and 13 plus signs when we consider deviations from 50. Thus from (Eq. 15)

$$z = \frac{21 - 17·5}{2·9155} = 1·2,$$

well below the value of 1·96 required for significance in a two-tail test.

If symmetry *can* be assumed, we use (Eq. 18). This requires the calculation of S and necessitates ranking the signed deviations from 50. This tedious but simple operation gives $S = S_+ = 280·5$ whence (Eq. 18) gives with $n = 34$

$$z = \frac{281 - 297·5}{58·49} = 0·28,$$

so again we accept the null hypothesis. There must be some doubt about the assumption of symmetry on pathological grounds. Disease in crops such as wheat is often rather patchy; we are likely to find many areas with light to moderate infestation and a few areas with very severe infestations. The data in this example give that impression. While a median level round about 50 seems not unreasonable (the sample median is 40), values observed range from 0 to 145, suggesting some lack of symmetry.

4. Making the usual allowance for ties, $S_- = 13$; using a two-tail test (do you think a one-tail test could be justified?), Table A3 shows that we fail to reach significance at the 5 per cent level. (A one-tail test would just attain significance.) In dealing with I.Q.s the idea of symmetry about a median of 100 is intuitively appealing, but even if we find a lack of symmetry it is likely to be slight and of far less consequence than in the previous exercise.

5. As we cannot assume symmetry, we must test for a median of 2 with a one-tail sign test. We have 2 minus signs, 8 plus signs and a zero. With $n = 10$ Table A1 tells us that the result just misses significance at the 5 per cent level; we have a probability of 0·055 of getting this or a less likely result in the relevant tail.

Chapter 6, p. 127

1. If we are prepared to assume symmetry we may use the Wilcoxon signed rank test. On the information given a one-tail test is appropriate. $S_- = 8·5$ and with $n = 11$

this is significant at the 5 per cent level but not quite at the 1 per cent level. If one were not prepared to assume symmetry (although symmetry seems a reasonable assumption here), a sign test would be needed; this does not give a significant result.

2. The arithmetic procedure follows much the pattern of the solution to Exercise 2 in Chapter 5. From Table A3 we find we have to eliminate the 8 largest and 8 smallest means. The limits turn out to be 0·05 and 0·85. Only the values in the top left and bottom right of the tableau need to be calculated if the differences are arranged in ascending order in rows and columns.

3. A two-tail test using the normal approximation is appropriate. (Eq. 18) gives $z = -2.25$ and since this exceeds 1·96 in magnitude, significance at the 5 per cent level is indicated; it would appear that the hormone increases growth rate.

4. With these non-numerical data the sign test is appropriate, counting W as minus and H as plus. A two-sided alternative is relevant. We have 4 minus and 13 plus. Table A1 indicates that this is just significant at the 5 per cent level, so there is acceptable evidence that husbands have a better appreciation of the problems.

Chapter 7, p. 150

1. Tukey's statistic has the value $T = 11$, which is significant at the 1 per cent level in a two-tail test.

2. A two-tail test is appropriate. The lower sum of ranks is that for the higher temperature and is $S = 41$. Thus $T = 13$. From Table A4 with $m_1 = 7$, $m_2 = 9$ we see that this almost reaches significance at the 5 per cent level. It would appear that the higher temperature produces the softer alloy, but this is not firmly established.

3. A tableau like Table 31 is required, except that only the entries in the bottom left and top right are required. We eliminate the 15 extreme entries in these corners. The entries needed are given in Table 86.

Table 86   Differences between oven cooling times

	13·9	14·2	14·8	14·9	15·3	15·7	16·1	17·2
12·9				2·0	2·4	2·8	3·2	4·3
13·7						2·0	2·4	3·5
14·0							2·1	3·2
14·1	-0·2						2·0	3·1
14·4	-0·5	-0·2						2·8
14·7	-0·8	-0·5						2·5
15·1	-1·2	-0·9	-0·3	-0·2				2·1
15·4	-1·5	-1·2	-0·6	-0·5				1·8
15·6	-1·7	-1·4	-0·8	-0·7	-0·3			

The confidence limits are thus -0·2 and 1·8.

4. Adding 12 to each group A reading, we rank the modified values and the original group B readings as in Table 87. The modified values are in italic.

Table 87 Ranks for testing a median difference of 12

Ordered data	24	27	27	28	28	29	30	31	32	33	
Ranks	1	2·5	2·5	4·5	4·5	6	7	8	9	10	
Ordered data	34	34	35	35	35	36	37	40	41	43	44
Ranks	11·5	11·5	14	14	14	16	17	18	19	20	21

$$S_2 = 1 + 2·5 + 2·5 + 4·5 + 4·5 + 9 + 10 + 11·5 + 14 + 14 + 19 = 92·5$$

whence $T_2 = 26·5$ since $m_2 = 11$. As this exceeds 26, it is not significant. Adding any number greater than 12 to the group A readings would give $T_2 < 26$.

5. Normal approximation is appropriate. If

$$S_1 = 428 \text{ and } m_1 = 17,$$
$$T_1 = 428 - (17 \times 18)/2 = 428 - 153 = 275, \text{ and}$$
$$T_2 = 17 \times 23 - 275 = 116.$$

From (Eq. 22) we then get $z = -2·19$, which is significant at the 5 per cent level using a two-tail test. As they have the higher T value the indication is that men show the greater anxiety.

Chapter 8, p. 173

1. $x^2 = 2·368$ without continuity correction and $1·813$ with continuity correction, both values well below that required for significance with 1 degree of freedom.

2. $x^2 = 80·83$ (6 degrees of freedom). This is significant at $0·1$ per cent level and indicates that the poor make less use of doctors. Over 80 per cent of those in the low-income group have either not seen a doctor at all or not seen one within the last 12 months, compared to about 73 per cent in the medium-income group and under 50 per cent in the high-income group. Of course this does not prove cause and effect – it could be that the poor are healthier and have less need of doctors!

3. $x^2 = 60·154$, which (with 3 degrees of freedom) is still significant at the $0·1$ per cent level, so the conclusion is unaltered.

4. McNemar's test is appropriate. When $n = 24$, we may use the normal approximation to the binomial with $p = \frac{1}{2}$, whence $np = 12$ and $\sqrt{npq} = \sqrt{6} = 2·449$.

With a continuity correction

$$z = \frac{8·5 - 12}{2·449} = -1·429$$

which is not significant, so we cannot reasonably conclude that the film and lecture have changed attitudes.

5. Writing tableaux as in Table 35 it will be clear on reflection that the only ones with the same or lower probabilities subject to the given marginal totals will be:

$$\begin{matrix} 0 & 6 \\ 5 & 1 \end{matrix} \quad \begin{matrix} 1 & 5 \\ 4 & 2 \end{matrix} \quad \begin{matrix} 5 & 1 \\ 0 & 6 \end{matrix} \text{ and perhaps } \begin{matrix} 4 & 2 \\ 1 & 5. \end{matrix}$$

(Eq. 26) gives the associated probabilities as, respectively, 0·007576, 0·1136, 0·007576, 0·1136. It is fairly obvious that the first and third and second and fourth probabilities must be the same. Why? Since the probability of the result we got or a less likely one is clearly well in excess of 0·05, there is insufficient evidence to claim association. Note that it is not a bad idea to work out the probability for the configuration actually obtained first; if this exceeds 0·05, there is little point in working out probabilities for other configurations.

Chapter 9, p. 205

1. If background of interviewers is irrelevant we would expect roughly the same number of 'yes' responses to be given to each. There are 184 'yes' responses, so the expected number for each is 184/5 = 36·8. Then x^2 = 21·82. There are 4 degrees of freedom and a value of 18·46 or greater implies significance at the 0·1 per cent level. There is very strong evidence that interviewers influence response.

2. An intuitively obvious estimate for p is the mean number of holes divided by n. The mean number is 0·94, so we estimate p as 0·94/5 = 0·188, and use our old friend (Eq. 12) to find the probability for each number of holes. To get the 'expected numbers' we multiply each probability by 100. The results are given in Table 88.

Table 88   Observed and expected numbers of holes

Number of holes	0	1	2	3	4	5
Observed numbers	42	36	14	3	4	1
Expected numbers	35·3	40·9	18·9	4·4	0·5	0·0

In view of the low 'expected numbers' we pool the results for 3, 4 and 5 holes, giving an observed and expected value for '3 or more holes'. These are 8 and 4·9 respectively. We find x^2 = 5·09. This is calculated from 4 cells after pooling. One degree of freedom is 'lost' for the fixed total and one more for calculation of p from the data. Thus, there are two degrees of freedom and our observed value falls short of the critical value of 5·99 needed for significance at the 5 per cent level. We would accept that the data may be consistent with a binomial distribution.

3. If uniformly distributed the expected number of deaths in any four-hour period is 49·67 (there being 298 deaths observed over the six periods). x^2 = 50·56. With 6 degrees of freedom this provides almost overwhelming evidence that times of death are *not* uniformly distributed.

4. We require the cumulative distribution function at values of X corresponding to sample points. Thus,

$$Pr(X \leqq 84) = Pr(Z \leqq \frac{84 - 100}{5}) = Pr(Z \leqq -3\cdot2) = 0\cdot0007.$$

A similar argument gives the value of $F(x) = Pr(X \leqq x)$ at the other sample points; these are recorded in Table 89, the layout being similar to that in Table 61.

Table 89   Comparison of F(x) and S(x) for resistor data

x_i	$F(x_i)$	$S(x_i)$	$F(x_i) - S(x_i)$	$F(x_i) - S(x_{i-1})$
84	0·0007	0·0909	−0·0902	0·0007
89	0·0139	0·1818	−0·1679	0·0770
91	0·0359	0·3636	−0·3277	0·1459
93	0·0808	0·4545	−0·3737	0·2828
100	0·5000	0·5455	−0·0455	0·0455
102	0·6554	0·6364	0·0190	0·1099
112	0·9918	0·8182	0·1736	0·3554
114	0·9974	0·9091	0·0883	0·1792
117	0·9997	1·0000	−0·0003	0·0906

The Kolmogorov test statistic is 0·3737. From Table A6 we see that this does not quite reach significance in a two-tail test (there is no logical reason for a one-tail test here). With $n = 11$ we require a value of 0·391. However, the probability is less than 0·1 of getting as high a value for the statistic, suggesting the need for caution in treating this as a sample from the specified normal population. An inspection of Table 89 suggests that the mean of the sample is fairly consistent with a population mean of 100, but the spread indicates the likelihood of a higher standard deviation.

5. Forming a table analogous to Table 64 we find that the maximum difference between the sample cumulative density functions is 0·5. From Table A7 with $m_1 = m_2 = 10$ we see the difference must exceed 0·5 for significance at the 5 per cent level. We cannot conclude that the samples come from different populations.

6. The test statistic value (found in similar manner to the previous example) is 10/24. From Table A7 with $m_1 = 8$, $m_2 = 9$ we find that this is not significant.

Chapter 10, p. 232

1. $\varrho = 4/7$, $\tau = 3/7$. Tables A8 and A9 indicate neither is significant. No firm evidence of association.

2. The sums of the ranks for all four markets for each type of set are 12, 10, 10, 15, 15, 25, 25. This gives $\Sigma R_i^2 = 2{,}044$. With $\nu = 4$ and $n = 7$, (Eq. 37) gives

$$W = 0\cdot5625.$$

Table A10 indicates that there is evidence of agreement in the markets. Inspection of the rank totals indicates that this is due in large measure to agreement in the allocation of the high ranks. Items F and G get a rank of 6 or 7 with a single exception where G gets 5. There is less unanimity about which sets get ranked 1 and 2.

3. We find that $b_{16} = 1 \cdot 8$, $b_{27} = 1 \cdot 933$, $b_{38} = 1 \cdot 824$, $b_{49} = 2 \cdot 0$ and $b_{5, 10} = 2 \cdot 133$. The median value is $1 \cdot 933$. The median value of a_i, *calculated as* $a_i = y_i - 1 \cdot 933 x_i$, is $1 \cdot 273$. Thus, Theil's method gives the line of best fit as

$$y = 1 \cdot 273 + 1 \cdot 933x.$$

The points and the line of least squares fit are shown together with this line in Figure 36.

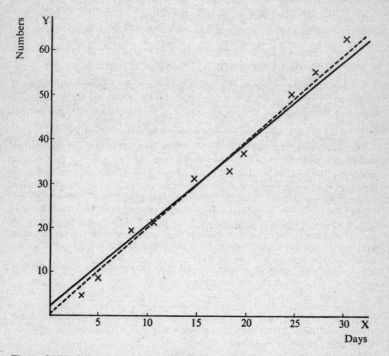

Figure 36 Theil line (continuous) and least squares line (broken) for orange storage data

Additional Examples

Here is a miscellaneous set of examples. They are in no particular order and no solutions are given.

1. *Cosmopolitan* magazine reported in December 1979 that doctors in the Midlands of England gave a cold sore treatment of paraffin ointment with weak boric acid to 14 patients; 11 of these thought it helped them. A further 11 patients were given paraffin ointment only and 3 of these thought it helped them. Concerning the usefulness of boric acid, the magazine reported: 'The doctors are sufficiently encouraged by the success of the tests to plan a more extensive trial.' Do you agree that they have grounds for encouragement?

2. In English 'O' level examinations, candidates are graded A, B, C, D, E; grade A is the most meritorious. For each of 15 students taking 'O' level mathematics, the grade predicted by the teacher one month before the examination is given below, followed by the grade actually obtained. Investigate the statements:

(i) the teacher underestimates his students' ability;
(ii) the teacher underestimates his students' ability by one grade.

(C, A) (C, C) (B, A) (E, C) (B, A) (C, A) (D, E) (B, A)

(B, B) (D, C) (B, A) (B, A) (C, A) (B, B) (B, A)

3. An hotel manager argues that men prefer their rooms warmer than women. He selects independent random samples of 8 visitors of each sex and asks them to adjust the thermostats on their room heating to their preferred setting in degrees centigrade.

The results are:

Men   18 22 19 17 20 25 18 21

Women   17 20 18 19 16 18 20 19

Do these results bear out the manager's claim? Would your analysis and conclusions be modified if the manager had asked couples staying in the same room to select their favourite temperature, the husband one night and the wife another, and the results had been as above, the first reading (18, 17) referring to the first couple and so on?

4. Records are kept of the lifetimes in days of a switching component in a machine for a random sample of 15 such components. The results are:

320, 318, 42, 11, 344, 276, 512, 402, 7, 829, 304, 317, 322, 874, 353.

Are these consistent with a normal distribution with mean 380 hours and standard deviation 100 hours? How would you obtain a 95 per cent confidence region for the population distribution function?

5. Trees in an orchard are ranked on the basis of the concentration of (a) calcium and (b) magnesium in their leaves. Is there evidence of a significant correlation between the ranks if we have the results below?

	A	B	C	D	E	F	G	H	I	J	K	L	M	N
Rank Ca	9	11	2	10	12	1	4	5	13	14	3	7	8	6
Rank Mg	8	12	4	11	14	7	1	6	10	13	3	2	5	9

6. A bakery requires its cake mixes to be of a certain consistency. The times in minutes to reach that consistency for a sample of 6 chocolate cakes are:

$$7\cdot2 \quad 6\cdot9 \quad 8\cdot4 \quad 7\cdot1 \quad 7\cdot3 \quad 8\cdot1$$

while for a random sample of 8 coffee cakes the times are:

$$8\cdot1 \quad 7\cdot4 \quad 9\cdot1 \quad 9\cdot2 \quad 9\cdot4 \quad 8\cdot7 \quad 8\cdot0 \quad 8\cdot5$$

Obtain 95 per cent confidence limits for the differences in median mixing times for chocolate cakes and coffee cakes.

Bibliography

Books

We give brief indications of the nature of various books referred to in the text.

BRADLEY, J.V., (1968), *Distribution-free Statistical Tests*, Prentice Hall, New Jersey.
> Emphasis on the rationale of non-parametric methods, with examples of applications; moderate level of mathematics.

CONOVER, W.J., (1971), *Practical Non-parametric Statistics*, Wiley, New York.
> Covers nearly everything in this book and other material as well at a mathematically more sophisticated level.

DANIEL, W.W., (1978), Applied Nonparametric Statistics, Houghton Mifflin, Boston.
> A wide-ranging reference book covering a much wider field than this one. Many worked examples and a good selection of tables. Description of rationale often rather terse. Assumes a little more mathematical and statistical background than we do. A good follow up to this book.

Facts in Focus (1980), 5th ed., Central Statistical Office/Penguin Books.
> An excellent digest of official statistics.

KENDALL, M.G., (1970), *Rank Correlation Methods*, 4th ed., Griffin, High Wycombe.
> The authoritative text on rank correlation. A fair mathematical knowledge needed for full appreciation.

LEHMANN, E.L., (1975), *Nonparametrics*, Holden-Day, San Francisco.
> A detailed discussion of the theory and practice of the main non-parametric methods. Requires a working knowledge of mathematics and statistics.

NELSON, R.D., (1980), *Penguin Book of Mathematical and Statistical Tables*, Penguin Books.
> A useful collection of tables, including some for non-parametric tests.

SIEGEL, S., (1956), *Nonparametric Statistics for the Behavioral Sciences*, McGraw-Hill, New York.
> Written at much the level of this book; particular emphasis is given to applications in the social sciences.

SPRENT, P., (1977), *Statistics in Action*, Penguin Books.
> A general introduction to the statistical approach to problems; assumes no previous statistical knowledge and a minimum of mathematics.

WETHERILL, G.B., (1972), *Elementary Statistical Methods*, Chapman and Hall, London.
> One of the more popular general introductory texts in statistics. More mathematical than this book.

Articles

We have not given references to the sources of procedures described in this book except in a few cases where the papers are of major general or historical interest.

ARBUTHNOT, J., (1710), 'An argument for Divine Providence, taken from the constant Regularity observ'd in the Births of Both Sexes', *Philos. Trans. Roy. Soc.*, vol. 27, pp. 186–90.

COX, D.R. and STUART, A.. (1955), 'Some Quick Tests for Trend in Location and Dispersion', *Biometrika*, vol. 42, pp. 80–95.

PLACKETT, R.L., (1979), 'John Arbuthnot', *Teaching Statistics*, vol. 1, no. 1, pp. 25–8.

TUKEY, J.W., (1959), 'A Quick, Compact, Two-Sample Test to Duckworth's Specifications', *Technometrics*, vol. 1, pp. 31–48.

WILCOXON, F., (1945), 'Individual Comparisons by Ranking Methods', *Biometrics*, vol. 1, pp. 80–83.

The reader wanting a fuller bibliography of articles on non-parametric methods should consult the books by Bradley, Conover, Daniel and Lehmann listed above; all abound in references. Some more recent references and examples in the social sciences are included in *Introduction to Statistics – A Nonparametric Approach for the Social Sciences* by C. Leach, published by Wiley in 1979.

Appendix: Abridged Tables for Non-parametric Methods

Table A1: The Sign Test

Binomial Distribution, p = 0·5. Probabilities of r or less successes for values of r from 0 to the integral part of n/2, for n from 6 to 20 (rounded to 3 decimal places).

r	0	1	2	3	4	5	6	7	8	9	10
n											
6	·016	·109	·344	·656							
7	·008	·062	·227	·500							
8	·004	·035	·145	·363	·637						
9	·002	·020	·090	·254	·500						
10	·001	·011	·055	·172	·377	·623					
11	·000	·006	·033	·113	·274	·500					
12	·000	·003	·019	·073	·194	·387	·613				
13	·000	·002	·011	·046	·133	·291	·500				
14	·000	·001	·006	·029	·090	·212	·395	·605			
15	·000	·000	·004	·018	·059	·151	·304	·500			
16	·000	·000	·002	·011	·038	·105	·227	·402	·598		
17	·000	·000	·001	·006	·025	·072	·166	·315	·500		
18	·000	·000	·001	·004	·015	·048	·119	·240	·407	·593	
19	·000	·000	·000	·002	·010	·032	·084	·180	·324	·500	
20	·000	·000	·000	·001	·006	·021	·058	·132	·252	·412	·588

Note: For $r > n/2$, $Pr(X \leq r) = 1 - Pr(X \leq n - r - 1)$, e.g. if $n = 9$ and $r = 6$, $Pr(X \leq 6) = 1 - Pr(X \leq 2) = 1 - 0·090 = 0·910$.

Table A2: Testing Quartiles

Binomial distribution, p = 0·75. Probabilities of r successes in upper and lower tails for all r such that $Pr(X = r) < 0·05$ together with smallest tail probability exceeding 0·05. An entry 0 implies corresponding probability less than 0·00005; other entries to 4 decimal places. $10 \leqq n \leqq 20$. In the lower tail for r = 0, 1 the entry is always zero.

					Lower Tail				
r	2	3	4	5	6	7	8	9	10
n									
10	·0004	·0031	·0162	·0584					
11	·0001	·0011	·0064	·0268	·0803				
12	0	·0004	·0024	·0115	·0401	·1032			
13	0	·0001	·0009	·0047	·0186	·0559			
14	0	0	·0003	·0018	·0082	·0280	·0734		
15	0	0	·0001	·0007	·0034	·0131	·0393	·0917	
16	0	0	0	·0002	·0014	·0058	·0197	·0524	
17	0	0	0	·0001	·0005	·0025	·0093	·0279	·0668

r	5	6	7	8	9	10	11	12
18	0	·0002	·0010	·0042	·0139	·0376	·0820	
19	0	·0001	·0004	·0018	·0066	·0198	·0487	·0974
20	0	0	·0002	·0007	·0030	·0099	·0271	·0609

					Upper Tail				
r	10	11	12	13	14	15	16	17	18
n									
10	·0563								
11	·1549	·0422							
12		·1267	·0317						
13			·1029	·0237					
14				·0832	·0178				
15					·0668	·0133			
16						·0535	·0100		
17						·1136	·0426	·0075	
18							·0958	·0338	·0056

r		17	18	19	20
19		·0803	·0268	·0042	
20			·0669	·0211	·0032

Table A3: Wilcoxon Signed Rank Test

For n from 5 to 15 we give the value of S, the lower of S_+ and S_-, together with the probability of obtaining that or a lower value of S in a one-tail test. Corresponding to nominal one-tail significance levels at the top of each column we give for each n the maximum value of S for significance and its corresponding actual associated one-tail probability.

One-tail level	5%		2·5%		1%		0·5%	
Two-tail level	10%		5%		2%		1%	
	S	p	S	p	S	p	S	p
n								
5	0	·031						
6	2	·047	0	·016				
7	3	·039	2	·023	0	·008		
8	5	·039	3	·020	1	·008	0	·004
9	8	·049	5	·020	3	·010	1	·004
10	10	·042	8	·024	5	·010	3	·005
11	13	·042	10	·021	7	·009	5	·005
12	17	·046	13	·021	9	·008	7	·005
13	21	·047	17	·024	12	·009	9	·004
14	25	·045	21	·025	15	·008	12	·004
15	30	·047	25	·024	19	·009	15	·004
16	35	·047	29	·022	23	·009	19	·005
17	41	·049	34	·022	27	·009	23	·005
18	47	·049	40	·024	32	·009	27	·005
19	53	·048	46	·025	37	·009	32	·005
20	60	·049	52	·024	43	·010	37	·005

Based on a table by F. Wilcoxon, S. Katti and R.A. Wilcox, published by the American Cyanamid Company (1963), by permission of the publishers.

Table A4: Wilcoxon Rank Sum Test
Mann–Whitney Test

Maximum value of T, the lower of T_1 and T_2, for significance at the 2·5 per cent and 5 per cent levels in a one-tail test (5 per cent and 10 per cent in a two-tail test) for sample sizes 5 to 15. Where sample sizes are unequal, we use m_1 for the smaller of the two.

m_1	%	m_2 5	6	7	8	9	10	11	12	13	14	15
5	2·5	2	3	5	6	7	8	9	11	12	13	14
	5	4	5	6	8	9	11	12	13	15	16	18
6	2·5		5	6	8	10	11	13	14	16	17	19
	5		7	8	10	12	14	16	17	19	21	23
7	2·5			8	10	12	14	16	18	20	22	24
	5			11	13	15	17	19	21	24	26	28
8	2·5				13	15	17	19	22	24	26	29
	5				15	18	20	23	26	28	31	33
9	2·5					17	20	23	26	28	31	34
	5					21	24	27	30	33	36	39
10	2·5						23	26	29	33	36	39
	5						27	31	34	37	41	44
11	2·5							30	33	37	40	44
	5							34	38	42	46	50
12	2·5								37	41	45	49
	5								42	47	51	55
13	2·5									45	50	54
	5									51	56	61
14	2·5										55	59
	5										61	66
15	2·5											64
	5											72

Adapted from tables by L.R. Verdooren in *Biometrika* (1963), by permission of the *Biometrika* trustees.

Table A5: Chi-Squared Test

Minimal values for significance at the 5 per cent, 1 per cent and 0·1 per cent levels, 1 to 10 degrees of freedom.

Degrees of freedom	5%	1%	0·1%
1	3·84	6·64	10·83
2	5·99	9·21	13·82
3	7·82	11·34	16·27
4	9·49	13·28	18·46
5	11·07	15·09	20·52
6	12·59	16·81	22·46
7	14·07	18·48	24·32
8	15·51	20·09	26·12
9	16·92	21·67	27·88
10	18·31	23·21	29·59

Adapted from a table by R.A. Fisher and F. Yates in *Statistical Tables for Biological, Agricultural and Medical Research* (1974), by permission of the publishers, Messrs Oliver and Boyd.

Table A6: The Kolmogorov Test Statistic

Minimum values of the magnitude of F(x) − S(x) maximum for significance at given levels. Sample sizes 5 to 30, 35, 40.

One-tail level	5%	2·5%	1%	0·5%
Two-tail level	10%	5%	2%	1%
Sample size				
5	·509	·563	·627	·669
6	·468	·519	·577	·617
7	·436	·483	·538	·576
8	·410	·454	·507	·542
9	·387	·430	·480	·513
10	·369	·409	·457	·489
11	·352	·391	·437	·468
12	·338	·375	·419	·449
13	·325	·361	·404	·432
14	·314	·349	·390	·418
15	·304	·338	·377	·404
16	·295	·327	·366	·392
17	·286	·318	·355	·381
18	·279	·309	·346	·371
19	·271	·301	·337	·361
20	·265	·294	·329	·352
21	·259	·287	·321	·344
22	·253	·281	·314	·337
23	·247	·275	·307	·330
24	·242	·269	·301	·323
25	·238	·264	·295	·317
26	·233	·259	·290	·311
27	·229	·254	·284	·305
28	·225	·250	·279	·300
29	·221	·246	·275	·295
30	·218	·242	·270	·290
35	·202	·224	·251	·269
40	·189	·210	·235	·252
$n > 40$	$\dfrac{1 \cdot 22}{\sqrt{n}}$	$\dfrac{1 \cdot 36}{\sqrt{n}}$	$\dfrac{1 \cdot 52}{\sqrt{n}}$	$\dfrac{1 \cdot 63}{\sqrt{n}}$

Based on a table by L.H. Miller in *Journal of the American Statistical Association* (1956), by permission of the publishers.

Table A7: The Smirnov Two-sample Test

Values of magnitude of $S_1(x) - S_2(x)$ maximum which must be attained for significance at the given levels. Where sample sizes are unequal, we use m_1 for the smaller of the two.

One-tail level		5%	2·5%	1%	0·5%
Two-tail level		10%	5%	2%	1%
Sample sizes					
m_1	m_2				
5	5	3/5	4/5	4/5	4/5
	6	4/6	4/6	5/6	5/6
	7	23/35	25/35	29/35	30/35
	8	25/40	27/40	32/40	32/40
	9	27/45	31/45	35/45	36/45
	10	6/10	7/10	7/10	8/10
6	6	4/6	4/6	5/6	5/6
	7	24/42	29/42	30/42	35/42
	8	7/12	8/12	9/12	9/12
	9	10/18	12/18	13/18	14/18
	10	17/30	19/30	21/30	22/30
7	7	4/7	5/7	5/7	5/7
	8	33/56	35/56	41/56	42/56
	9	35/63	40/63	45/63	47/63
	10	39/70	43/70	49/70	50/70
8	8	4/8	5/8	5/8	6/8
	9	13/24	15/24	16/24	18/24
	10	21/40	23/40	27/40	28/40
9	9	5/9	5/9	6/9	6/9
	10	45/90	52/90	60/90	62/90
10	10	5/10	6/10	6/10	7/10

Based on tables by F.J. Massey (1952) and Z.W. Birnbaum and R.A. Hall (1960) in *Annals of Mathematical Statistics*, by permission of the publishers.

Table A8: Spearman's rho

Minimum value of ϱ for significance at levels indicated for sample sizes 5 to 20.

One-tail level	5%	2·5%	1%	0·5%
Two-tail level	10%	5%	2%	1%
n				
5	0·900	1·000	1·000	
6	·829	·886	·943	1·000
7	·714	·786	·893	·929
8	·643	·714	·833	·881
9	·600	·700	·783	·833
10	·564	·648	·746	·794
11	·536	·618	·709	·764
12	·503	·587	·678	·734
13	·484	·560	·648	·703
14	·464	·538	·626	·679
15	·446	·521	·604	·657
16	·429	·503	·585	·635
17	·414	·488	·566	·618
18	·401	·474	·550	·600
19	·391	·460	·535	·584
20	·380	·447	·522	·570

Adapted from tables by G.J. Glasser and R.F. Winter in *Biometrika* (1961), by permission of the *Biometrika* trustees.

Table A9: Kendall's tau

The table gives the minimum value of S (number of positive scores − number of negative scores) for significance at the levels indicated, when using Kendall's tau as a measure of association.

One-tail level	5%	2·5%	1%	0·5%
Two-tail level	10%	5%	2%	1%
n				
4	6	8	8	8
5	8	10	10	12
6	11	13	13	15
7	13	15	17	19
8	16	18	20	22
9	18	20	24	26
10	21	23	27	29
11	23	27	31	33
12	26	30	36	38
13	28	34	40	44
14	33	37	43	47
15	35	41	49	53
16	38	46	52	58
17	42	50	58	64
18	45	53	63	69
19	49	57	67	75
20	52	62	72	80

Adapted from tables by Kaarsemaker and van Wijngaarden in *Statistics Neerlandica* (1953), by permission of the publishers.

Table A10: Kendall's Coefficient of Concordance

Minimum values of W for significance at the 5 per cent and 1 per cent levels for certain values of n and v.

	v = 3			v = 4	
n	5%	1%	n	5%	1%
5	·640	·840	5	·520	·664
6	·583	·750	6	·422	·578
7	·510	·633	7	·371	·494
8	·391	·578	8	·319	·438
9	·346	·531			
10	·310	·480			
11	·298	·430			
12	·271	·396			

Modified from tables by M.G. Kendall in *Rank Correlation Methods* (1970), by permission of the publishers, Messrs Charles Griffin and Co. Ltd.

Index

More about Penguins and Pelicans

For further information about books available from Penguins please write to Dept EP, Penguin Books Ltd, Harmondsworth, Middlesex UB7 0DA.

In the U.S.A.: For a complete list of books available from Penguins in the United States write to Dept CS, Penguin Books, 625 Madison Avenue, New York, New York 10022.

In Canada: For a complete list of books available from Penguins in Canada write to Penguin Books Canada Ltd, 2801 John Street, Markham, Ontario L3R 1B4.

In Australia: For a complete list of books available from Penguins in Australia write to the Marketing Department, Penguin Books Australia Ltd, PO Box 257, Ringwood, Victoria 3134.

STATISTICS FOR THE SOCIAL SCIENTIST:

VOL 1 – INTRODUCING STATISTICS
VOL 2 – APPLIED STATISTICS
K. A. Yeomans

Two important works for the student or professional who needs to be informed of up-to-date statistical methods and applications. Volume 1 is aimed at the non-mathematician and is an ideal introductory text. Volume 2 extends the field of study to sampling and multiple regression and correlation, and includes an introduction to non-parametric methods.

STATISTICS IN ACTION
Peter Sprent

By working from useful concrete examples Professor Sprent provides a lucid introduction to the professional work of a statistician at a level that anyone who has taken 'O' level maths can cope with.

STATISTICS WITHOUT TEARS:
A PRIMER FOR NON-MATHEMATICIANS
Derek Rowntree

A clear, straightforward introduction to the basic concepts of statistics. Particularly suited to non-mathematical readers taking an introductory course in statistics, this book covers the normal distribution sampling and correlation.

USE AND ABUSE OF STATISTICS
W. J. Reichman

A long-established classic of which the *Financial Times* said, 'the really important part of the book – and at this level it is the best I have read on the subject – is his discussion of what statistics is and does . . . the book will prove a boon.'

General Mathematics

CATASTROPHE THEORY
Alexander Woodcock and Monte Davis

'A superbly written non-technical exposition of elementary catastrophe theory: its geometry, its significance, its applications and its controversy. Written jointly by one of the leading practitioners of catastrophe theory and a professional science writer, this brief gem communicates an immense amount of information without using a single formula!' – *American Mathematical Monthly*

CONCEPTS OF MODERN MATHEMATICS
Ian Stewart

Aimed particularly at the general reader, this book provides a clear and comprehensive introduction to the aims, methods, problems and applications of modern mathematics. Topics include sets, groups, topology and logic.

GÖDEL, ESCHER, BACH:
AN ETERNAL GOLDEN BRAID
Douglas R. Hofstader

'A *tour de force* of scholarly and playful metaphor, linking the diverse mirror with which art and science reflect reality . . . a brilliant creative and very personal synthesis without precedent or peer in modern literature.' – *American Mathematical Monthly*

This extraordinary and fascinating book uses the musical structures of Bach and the paradoxical illustrations of M. C. Escher to explore the relationships between a wide variety of artistic and mathematical imaginations, to illuminate, and be illuminated by, the ideas underlying Gödel's Theorem and its proofs.

MATHEMATICIAN'S DELIGHT
W. W. Sawyer

'Recommended for the light it throws upon the discovery and application of many common mathematical operations.' – *The Times Literary Supplement*

This book was first published in Penguin in 1943 and has been a source of inspiration and delight to mathematicians ever since.

MATHEMATICS AND LOGIC
Marc Kac and Stanislaw Ulam

Two eminent mathematicians explain to the layman how the mathematician thinks and what he is thinking about. 'Books which succeed in explaining the aims and scope of mathematics to the layman are as rare as hens' teeth ... this is a very worthwhile book.' – *New Scientist*

MATHEMATICS IN WESTERN CULTURE
Morris Kline

'He is unfalteringly clear in explaining mathematical ideas ... an exciting and provocative book.' – *Scientific American*

A masterly survey of the history of mathematical thought and the relationship between the nature of a society and its mathematics.

NEWER USES OF MATHEMATICS
Edited by James Lighthill

Six mathematicians examine the modern applications of mathematics to problems and situations that affect the general public to whom the book is addressed. The weather, animal migration, decision theory, formation of telephone networks, ruin theory and global planning are all now grist to the mathematician's mill.

THE PENGUIN BOOK OF MATHEMATICAL AND STATISTICAL TABLES
R. D. Nelson

A collection of tables that is not superseded by the pocket calculator. Besides providing all the tables necessary for examination purposes in schools, particular attention has been paid to the needs of those who are learning or using statistics. Besides the standard tables there are prime numbers, random numbers, binomial, poisson, correlation and non-parametric tables.

THE PSYCHOLOGY OF LEARNING MATHEMATICS
Richard R. Skemp

A book of interest both to those who are studying mathematics and to those who teach it. Professor Skemp is convinced that to teach mathematics effectively, one has to understand how one learns, and he suggests, with many mathematical examples, how numeracy can be acquired by anyone.

REASON BY NUMBERS
Peter G. Moore

Written specifically for managers and businessmen wishing to improve their numeracy in direct and practical ways, this book sets out to develop the personal skills of managers so that they can appreciate the power of analytical techniques, ask the right questions of the relevant experts and be able to interpret the results provided. The examples and exercises at the end of each chapter are based on typical problems encountered in industry, commerce, medicine, agriculture and in the many areas of public administration.

ADVENTURES WITH YOUR POCKET CALCULATOR
Lennart Rade and Burt A. Kaufman

An amusing but non-trivial selection of mathematical problems and recreations, with solutions and explanations, in the areas of arithmetic, probability and geometry. The book only requires a basic knowledge of mathematics. It is designed to be fun and stimulating and to enable the owner of a calculator to learn something about mathematics.

THE CREATIVE USE OF CALCULATORS
J. P. Killingbeck

Dr. Killingbeck believes that by thoroughly exploring the possibilities of an ordinary calculator a reader can familiarize himself with many of the key areas of elementary mathematical thought. His book presents a wide and original survey of the field from an original viewpoint. It covers the principles of the calculator, everyday calculations and more advanced areas such as trigonometric functions, exponentials, calculus and matrices.

ELECTRONIC COMPUTERS
S. H. Hollingdale and G. C. Toothill

A comprehensive survey of the development of the electronic computer, how it works and what sort of problems it can tackle. This book provides a particularly good survey of the history of the electronic computer.

THE PENGUIN DICTIONARY OF COMPUTERS
Anthony Chandor, with John Graham and Robin Williamson

A glossary of some 300 words, phrases and acronyms used in connection with computers. It has been designed to assist both technical readers and the increasing number of non-specialists whose work is to some extent affected by the computer.

A DICTIONARY OF MICRO-PROCESSORS
Anthony Chandor

A companion volume to the DICTIONARY OF COMPUTERS extending his coverage into this rapidly growing field.